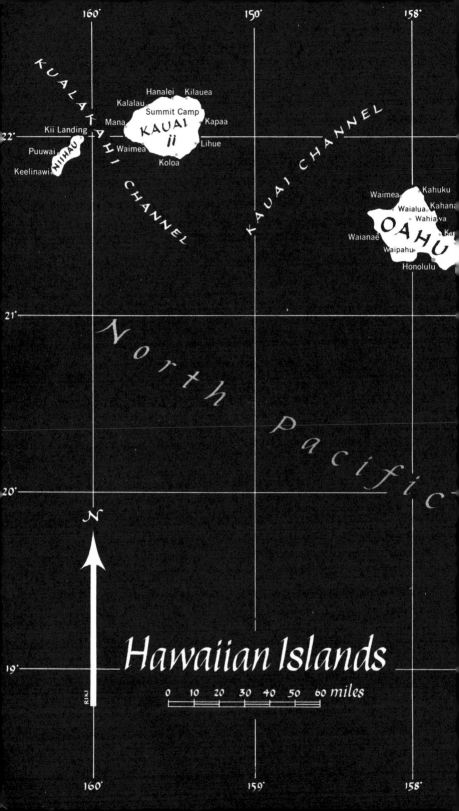

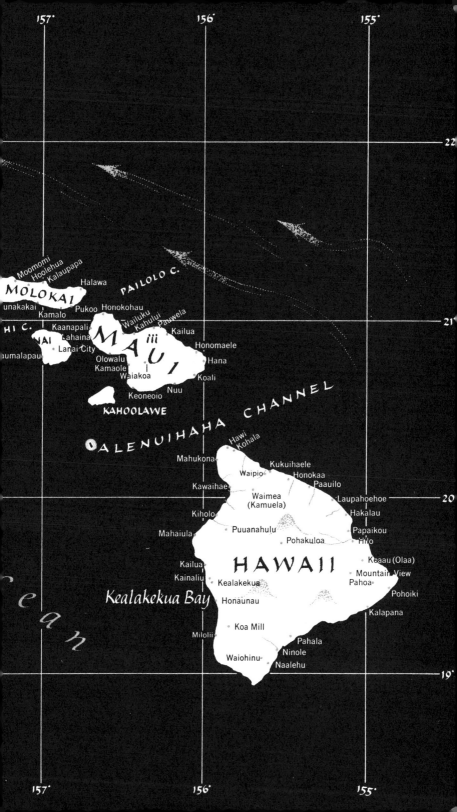

THE WARRIOR KING
HAWAII'S KAMEHAMEHA THE GREAT

THE WARRIOR
KAMEHAMEHA

Richard Tregaskis

KING ⋈ HAWAII'S THE GREAT

FALMOUTH PRESS

Honolulu, Hawaii

The Macmillan Publishing Co., Inc.
866 Third Avenue, New York, N.Y. 10022
Collier-Macmillan Canada Ltd., Toronto, Ontario

Library of Congress Catalogue Card Number: 73-2329

First Printing 1973

Printed in the United States of America

Soft Cover Edition
Published by Falmouth Press
581 Kamoku Street, Suite 1202
Honolulu, Hawaii 96826

Printed in Canada 1984

To the mana *of Kamehameha,*
the Napoleon of the Pacific,
that gave me the power to write this book.

Acknowledgments

To Moana Tregaskis; Maude Tregaskis-Hanford; Lisa Schon Grieshaber; Pattie and John Burgess; Paul Seaman; MeiMei Burke; Professor Marjorie Sinclair of the University of Hawaii; Dr. Roland Force, Director of the Bishop Museum; Johanna Cluny, the leading practitioner of the featherwork art; Agnes Conrad, Director of the Archives of the State of Hawaii; Loy McCandliss Marks; and hundreds of other Hawaiians who smilingly taught me the meaning of Aloha.

Contents

FAMILY CHART OF KAHEKILI, PROBABLY KAMEHAMEHA'S REAL FATHER

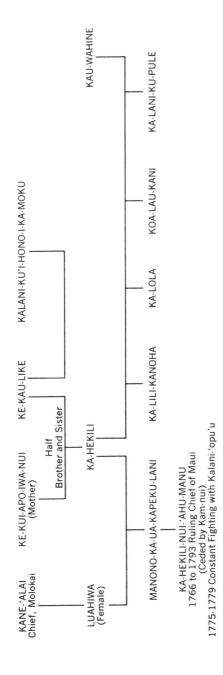

KANE-'ALAI
Chief, Molokai

KE-KUI-APO-IWA-NUI
(Mother)

KE-KAU-LIKE

KALANI-KU'I-HONO-I-KA-MOKU

KAU-WAHINE

LUAHIWA
(Female)

KA-HEKILI

Half
Brother and Sister

MANONO-KA-UA-KAPEKU-LANI

KA-LILI-KANOHA

KA-LOLA

KOA-LAU-KANI

KA-LANI-KU-PULE

KA-HEKILI-NUI-'AHU-MANU
1766 to 1793 Ruling Chief of Maui
(Ceded by Kam-nui)
1775-1779 Constant Fighting with Kalani-'opu'u

Kahekili was the King of Maui, ruthless, clever, unscrupulous, and Kamehameha's archenemy and nearly lifelong opponent.

This chart shows Kahekili's antecedents and acknowledged children by two of his wives, Kau-wahini and Luahiwa. In 1802, the late Kahekili passed word to Kamehameha by Kahekili's half brother, Kameeiamoku, that Kahekili was his father. Kahekili sired Kamehameha by Kekui-apo-iwa.

The men and women Alii, or nobles, were the freest of all nobility. Both men and women could have as many mates—husbands, wives or lovers—as they chose, or their other mates would permit. Thus Kamehameha had twenty-one official wives and a much larger number of lovers, and probably as many as sixty children. Kekui-apo-iwa, Kamehameha's mother, had four official husbands and, of course, many lovers besides.

In view of the sexual freedom of the Hawaiians, family trees grow extremely complicated. They are more complicated than the genealogies of the most marriage-prone of modern actors and actresses. The reason is simple: Lovemaking, in wedlock or not, was acceptable and desirable.

In this Polynesian paradise, the hospitable Hawaiian environment and social system welcomed children, in or out of marriage. This book, however, details some of the circumstances in which an offspring can suffer, even in the Polynesian free-wheeling marriage system. For example, Kamehameha's son Pauli, his first, who was his child by his aunt, Queen Kane-kapo-lei. Kamehameha's dissatisfaction with the circumstances of Pauli's birth and up-bringing led to his marriage with Keopuolani, his "sacred wife." By her, he had children of the high Niau-pio caste.

Credit: Lisa Schön Grieshaber

MOTHER'S SIDE

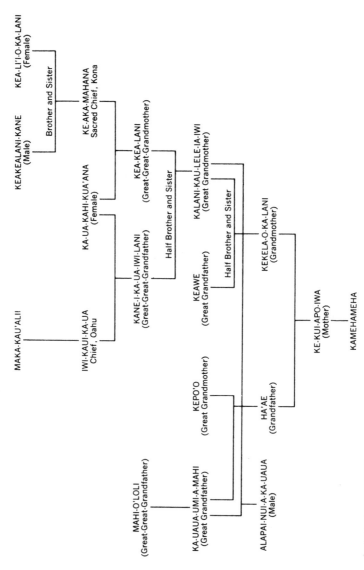

Credit: Lisa Schön Grieshaber

FATHER'S SIDE

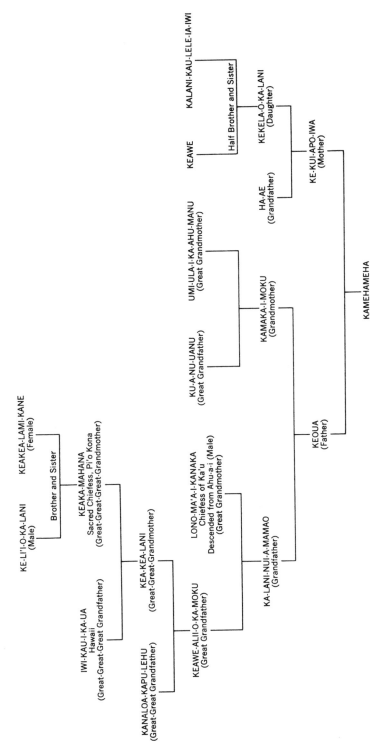

Credit: Lisa Schön Grieshaber

◖◗◖ *Preface*

THE recorded history of Hawaii began with the arrival of Captain James Cook on the island of Kauai, January 18, 1778,
when the United States was not quite two years old. Before that
time, the Hawaiians had used a lunar calendar, with twelve
months, and a few days at the end of each year for celebration.
But there was no system of numbering the years like those of the
Christians or Muslims, from the date of birth of their respective
prophets. In the beautiful Hawaiian world, one year followed
another with no particular count or reason to count. The best
reference to past history was that a certain event happened in the
Day of Ulu, who was the father of Nanai, who was the father of
Nanailani, who was the father of Waikulani, who was the father
of Keheleimona, etc., all of these worthies being early founders of
the genealogy of Ulu which is officially credited with being the
ancestry of Kamehameha. But there were no dates like 68 B.C. or
A.D. 74, or 1020 A.H. None at all.

So there was no rigidity in the dates of Hawaiian history before Captain Cook took his ships to the Islands. After that, the white man's calendar made events more measurable, and easier to record—as it helped to formalize and give proportion and emphasis to Hawaiian history.

Since Kamehameha was first chronicled as a young warrior in the court of the moi or king of the largest part of the island of Hawaii when Cook came, his pre-Cook history is shrouded in myth and legend.

Further, there was no written language in the Hawaiian Islands until the white man came to render it into something like phonetic sounds in the English alphabet. So the early chroniclers of Hawaiian history depended altogether on the memories of old warriors and priests or kahunas whose recollections were sometimes tinged by flights of imagination, wishful thinking or self-aggrandizement. The early historians, Malo, Kamakau, Ii and Fornander, worked from complicated networks of the reminiscences of fallible old men.

For this reason, Kamehameha's birth date has been variously estimated at many figures between 1736 and 1759, resulting in some surprising historical errata such as Gowan's startling statement that he had "fleshed his virgin sword" on the interisland civil wars conducted by King Alapai of the island of Hawaii against the rulers of Maui, Molokai and Oahu. Since the early historians believe these campaigns occurred between 1730 and 1740, Kamehameha must have been wielding that virgin sword at a precocious age—since Gowan contends that Kamehameha was born between 1736 and 1740. His military strength must have been considerable at the age of two or younger.

In the same way, Kamakau and Fornander assign the birth date 1736 to Kamehameha, which would make him eighty-three at the time of his death in 1819, and forty when Cook's third captain or assistant met him and described him as a young man, in 1779. Two men who knew him at the time of his death, John Young and Fernando Marin, said that he was, respectively, seventy-one and sixty and a half. This latter would make his birth date 1758, and that age would fit into some of his known life accomplishments—but not all of them. He would simply be too young to be a warrior with Kalaniopuu when Kalaniopuu seized power in Hawaii. And too young to have sired his first (illegitimate) child, Kao-lei-oku, by the wife of Kalaniopuu, Kane-kapo-lei. Also six years too young to have been born of his alleged father, Keoua, if one accepts Mellen's Kamehameha birth date, 1758, and Fornander's and Kamakau's death date for Keoua, 1752. However, these two classic Hawaiian historians seem to have been five to fifteen years too early with some of their dates.

John Young's estimate of Kamehameha's birth date, 1748 or 1749, allows gearing with all of Kamehameha's legendary exploits —and still allows him to be a "young man" in appearance on Captain Cook's arrival in 1779—thirty or thirty-one years old. Even though it seems improbable that he could have been thirty-nine to forty-three, which is provided by Fornander and Kamakau's birth date of 1736 to 1740.

The man who is probably Hawaii's best historian, R. K. Kuykendall, cautiously estimates that the date of 1753 would be an average drawn from the estimates of Young and Marin. He also points out that historian John F. G. Stokes concluded Kamehameha "was born between 1750 and 1760, probably after 1755." In my opinion somewhere around 1750 would be closest to the truth because it would provide the proper age for the accomplishments which legend has assigned to him, before the advent of the Christian calendar with Cook's arrival in Hawaii, and still allow him to be a "young man" (twenty-eight or twenty-nine) for Cook's arrival in Maui in 1779.

So in the absence of better sources, one has to thread one's way through the conflicting stories and legends of the early Hawaiians, and the somewhat better documented reminiscences of European and American traders, missionaries and adventurers. The latchstring of Hawaii, the tropical string of Pacific islands which offer the world's closest approach to paradise in climate and terrain, is long and always out to ill-assorted travelers and seekers after Elysium and worldly fulfillment, and even some of the later Christian chronicles therefore grow somewhat fanciful and imaginative.

I have threaded my way through these sources of various kinds and attempted to fathom a life story of Kamehameha which is credible and as realistic as I can make it, and as close as possible to what seems to be probable about him. Especially in the earlier stories of his life, I have had to extrapolate—as the space scientists say—many events from extremely collapsible sources. If I have done an interesting, credible and dramatic story of the giant of a man who first united the Hawaiian Islands and became their first and greatest king, then I have succeeded.

Kamehameha the Great was a glorious warrior, a very constructive and bright administrator and diplomat who brought these warring island tribes together in their first long years of peace and plenty. He was also a great surfer and swimmer, a mighty warrior and artful dodger of spears and the wrath of females, a prestigious lover of women, as Polynesians think a male should be. And he was also the Hawaiian king who met the first Europeans and Americans and cleverly used their technology, their muskets and cannon, to conquer and bring peace and unity to the Hawaiian Islands.

Consider the startling differences between this Napoleon of the Pacific and the European (Corsican-French) model. Napoleon Bonaparte was barely five feet tall, pale and sickly compared with Kamehameha, who stood six feet six inches tall and at his thinnest weighed twice as much as Napoleon at his fattest.

Bonaparte was frail, a Faustian man haunted by Western man's sense of shame, sin and combativeness, and his concomitant penchant for cynicism and self-criticism.

Kamehameha was a natural athlete and a powerful warrior to his last days, when he still detailed expert spear-throwers to lie in wait along the path of his afternoon walk, so they could surprise him with long pololu javelins, which he would skillfully dodge or catch.

He learned language and skills from the white man, but to his death he remained true to the Hawaiian-Polynesian ways, true to the Hawaiian gods and the hospitable and warmhearted ways of life of the Hawaiians. He was also true to the Hawaiian fondness for the good things of life like feats of athletics and strength and grace: swimming and surfing and tropical seas and shores, pursuing beautiful women and voluptuousness, living among palms and flowers, mountains, rainbows, volcanoes and white surf and tropical lagoons, and the trade winds—nature's air-conditioning—which have made Hawaii and Polynesia world famous. I am sure that Kamehameha, if he were alive today, would be anxious to find the spirit of these things in print, as well as the story of his own illustrious life. For the Hawaiians of Kamehameha's day were in many ways ahead of us today in their enjoyment of many of the things in life which we are evaluating anew these days; also, the Hawaiian morality, like that of Kamehameha, is generally well beyond what we might consider our most advanced level. We might say we could learn much from this fierce heathen, about both good and bad.

How to Pronounce Hawaiian

Ideally, every vowel in this twelve-letter language should be sounded. As a practical procedure, the long, heavily voweled Hawaiian names should be broken into short syllables, at the vowels; for example, Ka-la-ka-ua-a, the name of Waikiki's main street, which in ordinary fast pronunciation slips into Kala-kau-a.

The language is strong and vivid, especially when broken into syllables: pi-i ka-u-la, to blush, or "go up the color of a cooked lobster." Or the name of Waikiki: Wai, water, and kiki, spurting.

THE WARRIOR KING
HAWAII'S KAMEHAMEHA THE GREAT

CHAPTER 1
Perilous Passport to Status

IT WAS A rainy day, as most days are on this side of the Big Island, where the rich green slopes begin their climb to the summits of Mauna Loa and Mauna Kea. In addition, it was the rainy part of the year, the Maka-hiki time. Maka-Iii, the Hawaiian name for the stars called Pleiades, had been hazy this year, indicating there might be too much rain, even floods, on this lush green Hilo side of the island of Hawaii.

The Maka-hiki or New Year time was a time for celebration, and at the big heiau or temple at Kona, despite fitful rains, hundreds of people had gathered for sports and feasting. Today, unless the rain began to fall too heavily, there would be the games of Noa, Puhemeheme, Ume, Kilu and Konane, and everyone would be having fun.

Everyone, that is, except the fourteen-year-old dark-skinned big boy named Kamehameha, the Lonely One. Kamehameha had come to the Maka-hiki festivities with a grim resolve to test his strength in a feat which might cost him his life if he failed.

Kamehameha was already tall and long and powerful of limb. At fourteen, he was taller than most warriors, more than six feet tall by the European scale. With his kahu or tutor Naeole, he had come across the mountain this week from the Kona side of the island in the Court of the Moi, Alapai the Great, where he was a minor retainer, nephew and a person of mysterious standing in the Court of the King.

Today, as the mist drifted across Hilo Bay and the mob of at least four hundred celebrants huddled around the thatched roof shelters and the heiaus on the plain overlooking the bay, Kamehameha knew that this could be a day of death, or great fame. If he failed in what he proposed to do, then the kahuna of the Hilo king might drown him, strangle him or beat him to death this very afternoon for violation of a mortal kapu.

The test in the minds of both Kamehameha and his tutor was whether this sturdy, brown-skinned youth with the solemn face and the dignified bearing of the Alii was going to be able to move the giant black lava boulder called the Naha Stone. The Naha Stone rested like a miniature fort near the largest heiau of King Keawe-mauhili of Hilo.

That giant boulder of pitted puka-puka or "hole-hole" cooled lava flow was as heavy as the King's giant, forty-man dugout canoe. It was as long as the olo, the favorite fast surfboard of the Alii, a full six strides of a grown man.

This, the Naha Stone, was as mammoth an object as any one man might conceivably dream of moving by himself. Even the most imaginative kahuna would have to admit that to budge it would take more strength than any single known man in the islands could summon—except, perhaps, if he could be inspired by some magical spell invoked by a skillful kahuna.

Of all the sturdy young men that day at the heiau, only a few would be rivals to Kamehameha in stature. The tall ones were always nobles or Alii, half a foot to a foot taller than the commoners or kanaka or Makaaina, the common people, or the masses of darker and still shorter people, the Kauwa, the slave class.

Kamehameha had always been a distinguished athlete. He was a rapid student of spear-throwing and the concomitant art of spear-dodging. He was vastly skilled and strong and quick at wrestling, as good at it as any full-grown man; and he was fearsome at the sport of mokomoko, stiff-armed boxing. He could stand and knock down challengers with unwearying power, apparently ad infinitum; and yet his smooth, long muscles were also marked with the grace of the habitual and powerful swimmer. And from his many months and years in the surf, paddling his long olo board which weighed as much as a fat pig, his back was a broad, smooth wedge of the round and dorsal muscles, a rising fort of muscle.

Kamehameha knew his strength. He had been reared almost always alone, at first with his general kahu, Naeole, and later with his military tutor, Kekuhaupio.

While Kamehameha was being trained at the school for warriors in Alapai's court, at first some of the other Alii boys chided him about his dark skin. Partly, his dark-brownness came from the years he had spent in the surf at Kawaihae, or Kealakekua Bay, in the usual costume of the surfers, male and female, which was nothing—nudity. The surfers, incidentally, were glad to be nude in the water, for the simple reason that it felt good. In fact, compared to being strapped in folds of clothes, it felt glorious.

Kamehameha had been deeply and violently angered one day at the green playing ground above Kawaihae when an exceptionally tall Alii boy with especially light skin, Keauluholu, taunted him with the idea that he must have some Kauwa blood in him to be so dark. Kamehameha was always sensitive to the rumors that his birth was uncertain and that Keoua was not even his true father.

Kamehameha fell into a cold, calculating fury and contrived a mock contest with spears, the long ihe variety. He was phenomenally adept at dodging these big spears and had the strength to keep on throwing them. Kamehameha caught two of Keaulu-holu's, dodged the next two and then flung three of his own so fast that Keaulu fell badly wounded in the side. In the heat of his battle lust, Kamehameha enjoyed the triumph and the blood. But in the dark of that midnight he wondered if his anger had been just. Others in this Alii school for warriors had made cruder jests about his possible illegitimacy and his dark color.

However, Kamehameha had been twelve then, and from then on the Alii boys were careful not to irritate him with remarks about his color. And they knew he would be deadly in his reaction to any jests that he might not be the son of Keoua.

Naeole, the tutor, knew very well the chance that Kamehameha was taking this day at Maka-hiki time. He had tried to dissuade Kamehameha from taking the gamble. But Kamehameha had always had a will of his own, Naeole knew. It was no good trying to dissuade the boy from any purpose he had settled on. Naeole had learned that the hard way.

The great hazard was that, according to tradition, the Naha Stone could be touched, and possibly moved, only by a nobleman or Alii of the Naha caste, and Kamehameha simply did not qualify to be a member of that caste.

The qualification, any Hawaiian knew, was one of birth. A Naha of course had to be born to a noble or Alii family, but much more than that, he had to be the child of a chief who was married to his own half sister.

There were two castes higher than Naha: the Pio and Niau-pio. The Pio was the highest: the child of a chief and his sister, with the further requirement that the grandfather or grandmother be also the child of a brother-sister marriage.

Kamehameha was of the fourth noble caste, the Wohi, because his father and mother, while they were certainly Alii and members of the ruling clique on the Big Island of Hawaii, were only cousins.

The three top castes, the Pio, Niau-pio and Naha, all had the supreme or burning kapu: All were protected from death by burning. The next step down, to the Wohi and Kuhaulua, was a long one. To the burning kapu castes, the Wohi were dirt, although they were Alii.

It was not known which fearsome kahuna in Hawaii's long history had made the original prophecy that the man who moved the Naha Stone would be the greatest king of Hawaii and bring all of the scattered mois, or major chiefs, under his control.

But Naeole, the aged and wise tutor, knowing Kamehameha and his singular willfulness, knew well in advance of Kamehameha's intent. So he had worked subtly to pass the word among the people at Hilo that on this day, his ward and student Kamehameha was going to summon the magic and trickery of the gods, and his own brute strength, and move the Naha Stone. Already, as Naeole and Kamehameha hovered in the lee of the thatch hut where the game of Konane, a kind of checker contest, was being held, a group of curious Makaainas, ordinary people but not quite as low as the Kauwa, the slave caste, had gathered and were eyeing the tall lad and waiting for him to attempt his feat.

Naeole always said—and Kamehameha tended to remember nearly everything he did say—"Everyone knows what the elepaio bird does, because he lets it be known he is there, wherever he goes, by announcing: 'Elepaio! Elepaio!,' the sound which gives him his name. So let us be elepaio birds at the right time."

Naeole had not only spread the word among the Makaainas, but he had managed to get the word into the principal heiau of the moi of Hilo, Kaumana. The night before, as Naeole and Kamehameha camped in the Kaumana caves on the slope above Hilo, Naeole had come back from a hike down to Hilo to tell his ward the preparations for the big day. And the grizzled old man, who must have been four times Kamehameha's age, had assumed that the Makaainas would certainly be looking out for the mysterious prince from the sunset side of the island who would be trying brave and audacious feats at the Naha Stone.

Now, as he and Naeole waited for the rain to slacken a little, Kamehameha noted two tall, thin kahunas from the Hilo heiau standing among the crowd of curious onlookers.

Suddenly, a kanaka boy, probably the same age as Kamehameha

but the size of a tiny lauepala fish by comparison, rushed out and felt the upper arm muscle of the stalwart, dark-skinned youth.

Kamehameha's reactions were swift, and in the split second when the boy's hand touched his biceps, he had to make a conscious effort to restrain himself, to avoid lashing out with a stiff-armed mokomoko. Naeole had cautioned him that if he insisted on having a try at moving the Naha Stone, he would have to be among the Makaainas and he had to be very careful not to do injury to anyone, or to be easily offended by some violation of his own kapus. As an Alii of the fourth or Wohi rank, he would not have to be worried about the embarrassment of kapu moi, the obligation of anyone of lower caste to prostrate himself before the Alii.

But he would have to be careful that some kanaka or especially someone of the Kauwa class didn't by mistake touch his clothes. Kamehameha, having been reared by an independent-thinking man, Naeole, at first in the country district of Awini to the north, did not care about some of the kapus which so exercised many of the Alii. But if a righteous kahuna saw such a violation, there could be plenty of pilikia, or trouble. And essentially, the single-minded Kamehameha wanted only one thing to happen on this day: He was going to move the Naha Stone.

One reason Kamehameha was willing to take such great chances with violation of a mortal kapu was that he, until recently, had been living in a kind of banishment in Awini, with his own status as a member of the Alii in some doubt. But then Alapai-nui, moi of Kona, had recognized him as son of Keoua and his own grand-nephew and had brought him to the court at Kawaihae.

The gossip had been that when Kamehameha had been born a few days more than fourteen years before, in a cave near Honoipu on the northern coast of the island, King Alapai had sent out raiding parties to find the newborn infant. And at the same time, Kahekili, a prince of the nearby island of Maui, had also sent ashore parties of troops to find and kill the newborn infant. Each had sinister reasons. Principally, there was the kahuna prophecy that this infant would become a killer of kings. And there were other partly concealed rumors concerning Kahekili, the dreadful, black-tattooed, bloodthirsty warrior of Maui. Certainly, Kamehameha's mother had been at the court of the moi or king of Maui and known the king's younger brother, Kahekili.

All that was shrouded in mystery, and Naeole, his kahu, spoke very little of it. Kamehameha knew that five years before, he and Naeole had been taken to the court of King Alapai at Kailua. He had been welcomed as a true Alii and then, in a way, he assumed some of the status of Nalani, or heaven-born. It was hard to believe that, until that time, he had seen his parents only a few times: his father Keoua, Alapai's nephew, and his mother, that woman of mystery, Kekui-apo-iwa. Kekui-apo-iwa had lived for several years at the court of the king of Maui, Kamehameha Nui. And Kahekili, it was no secret, had been a lover of the passionate Kekui-apo-iwa.

And even now, here on the island of Hawaii, in the rather gay and rank-conscious court of King Alapai-nui, or Alapai the Great, the king's nephew, Kamehameha, was treated with a certain reserve which did not stem wholly from respect.

This was true especially because his mother Kekui-apo-iwa and his father Keoua spent most of their time away from the court, and as the gossips would have it, in different directions. Both had many other mates. The Alii could have as many as they liked. Of course, since the social life in the court was dedicated principally to enjoyment, most of the young Alii, male and female alike, had numerous affairs, and mates, and the gossips were kept busy with whisperings of this or that romantic attachment.

Kamehameha, with his precocious mentality and early maturity of judgment, would have to admit that Kekui-apo-iwa did spend much less time with him than most mothers would have; his noble-born father, Keoua, did have more wives than most of the chiefs. Closer, and more affectionate by far, was another of Keoua's wives, Kalola. Kalola was much younger, and infinitely more beautiful, in Kamehameha's mind. Kalola, as he grew to manhood, was lavish in her attentions to him.

Kamehameha wasn't sure, but there were probably twenty-six

or twenty-seven of Keoua's other wives, and they were well distributed throughout the sunny side of the Big Island, so that Keoua came to his son very rarely.

All this background, of course, was important in Kamehameha's designs upon the Naha Stone, and his driving eagerness to follow through on Naeole's plans to make the most of the occasion.

The occasion for the try was well chosen. It was the day after Hilo. That is the name of the village on the Big Island, but it is also the first day of the month, when the moon is new. On the day before the night of Hilo, the kahunas had chanted the kapus for that night, mainly that there be no puaa, or pig, cooked after sunset. This kapu would be strenuously enforced. But the next day, the stone ovens, or pits, would be stoked practically at first light, and the day would be one of general rejoicing, feasting, dancing and games.

Actually, Kamehameha had planned to make his try at moving the rock a month earlier, in the month of Ikuwa. But Ikuwa is a stern time, because the collectors of the Konohiki, the district chief, go about the land calling for taxes, and it is a hard month climatically, when the weather is full of thunder and the surf runs high.

Kamehameha would have to grant that the fertile mind of Naeole had been very wise in fixing his effort to move the Naha Stone in the month of Welehu. In general, Welehu is the month of fun and relaxation, and even the stern-minded kahunas are apt to unbend some of their rigorous discipline with the kapus at this time. Most important of all, Kamehameha knew, Naeole was thinking of the priestly prohibition, during this month, of sacrifices to Ku-kaili-moku, Kane and Kanaloa, the most feared gods in the Hawaiian religion. Instead, the good-natured god Lono is worshiped, and only his temples are open during the Maka-hiki season. The general temper of good nature is so pronounced in the Maka-hiki season that the kahunas enforce an absolute suspension of all war operations during this month. It is for this reason that the temples of Ku-kaili-moku, Kane and Kanaloa are briefly closed.

Kamehameha was aware of these considerations in Naeole's

mind, and aware too that his kahu was fearful of the consequences to Kamehameha in case he should fail to budge the Naha Stone. Kamehameha had no such fears. He had not yet had a chance to measure his strength against the task. The kahunas in the heiau, which was only a few steps from the Naha Stone, made sure that no one could try the Naha feat without declaring himself by approaching it in the sight of all and sundry. At night, they kept burning torches and kukui-nut lamps all around the Naha Stone so that it could always be watched. And it was under surveillance during the daylight.

But it was not in Kamehameha at this age to be afraid of the consequences in any case. At this point in his life, while he was genuinely respectful of the power of the sea, the Halemaumau firepit at the volcano, the unexpected wrath and might of the gods, nevertheless he felt little fear of the bodily harm another individual could do to him. Years of training under first the guidance of Naeole, and later his military tutor in the court of King Alapai, Kekuhaupio, had taught him confidence in the manly arts: the arts of throwing and dodging spears, the rugged fisticuffs of mokomoko, wrestling, and the skills of swimming and riding big surfboards in tall waves. All these had given him strength, confidence and agility.

Now, Kamehameha knew, the time was coming for his test, and he came the closest he would be to fear. But a strange natural omen seemed to be occurring. The scudding clouds overhead had suddenly grown less menacing and dark. These opua, or cluster clouds, only a few minutes before had been turning down at the edges. Now they appeared to be turning up suddenly; that was a sign of a lessening of the wind and an expected period of calm. However, the clouds were still dark, so dark they had to be called hoo-weli-weli or threatening.

Now the clouds were thinning overhead and the showers of rain had stopped. The sun was shining in the last fading sheet of rain that swept from the sky. He knew this would be his time.

He measured the distance to the Naha Stone. A squarish-built kahuna wearing the tall headgear and white powder of Lono stood idly by it. Even Lono, he knew, could demand a human sacrifice if the kahuna interpreted the situation that way. Usually the sacrifices to Lono were pigs or fish, but if the violation of the kapu was severe enough, if in fact he failed in his daring of the burning kapu, he might well end up a charred body on the makaiwa. There, a human victim could be demanded in the hole which would be filled eventually with the image of Lono, the wicked image with the towering red headcloth. Especially at this time of year, when the god figure of Lono was taken around the countryside and set up as a recipient of taxes, the kahunas were apt to be stern in their demand for human sacrifices to this essentially good-natured god. This was Lono's time.

Quickly and urgently, Kamehameha measured the bulk which he was to move. Fortunately, in the month of delay which Naeole had insisted upon before his assault upon the Naha Stone, Kamehameha had worked almost every day with lifting exceptionally heavy objects, deliberately building his strength.

Several times, when the canoe races were being conducted in the bay at Kailua-Kona, after he had done his stint as one of twelve paddlers, he had managed to find himself alone with the large and heavy dugout canoe. There, beside the heiau at the northern end of the harbor, he had lifted nearly half of the bulk of the canoe with one mighty heave. Many times that week he had repeated the exercise.

And in surfing he had always taken the biggest and heaviest board, the biggest olo board of heavy koa wood, when they went to ride the breakers at Kawaihae.

Now was the time. He studied Naeole's face, the dark eyes with some strangely purple shades fixing on him with a mixture of apprehension and a very visible concern. The concern he saw in the purplish eyes was that he, Naeole, might not have planned everything as well as it could be planned. Clearly, he was checking through in his mind the list of steps he had followed in preparation for the bold attempt by his protégé to fly in the face of tradition, to make a giant step toward the heritage which Kamehameha had known from the beginnings of his memory were to be his. Beneath Naeole's spiky silver eyebrows, mane of silvery hair, and in the sharp, purple black eyes as dark as Moana, the deep ocean water, Kamehameha read the message for him: "Go!"

Kamehameha began to move, in the fluid, smooth, poised gait which was always taught to the Alii by their kahus as an obligation of nobility and a mark of special grace. But Kamehameha's gait was especially distinctive in that he moved his large-boned body with all the speed of a small man. Mirrored in his movements were hundreds of hours of practicing the dodging of thrown spears, and assiduous practice in the balancing arts of riding the surfboard and the ti leaf slide. And, as with most Hawaiians, commoners or Alii or even the unprivileged slave caste, the Kauwa, most moves showed the totally relaxed and resilient manner of the swimmer. That was the graceful mark of the Pacific island people who live with Mother Ocean day and night. Naeole followed slowly while Kamehameha passed the squarish-bodied kahuna and reached the smaller end of the Naha Stone. He had calculated it this way, that this end of the stone was slimmer, lighter and probably therefore much more tractable for his heaving effort.

A quick glance backward showed Kamehameha that at least sixty or seventy of the crowd who had stood by him curiously outside the Onane hut had followed and were spread across the distance in a hesitant echelon. Foremost among them, the none-too-bright boy who had felt his muscle. And full-breasted women, bare bosomed, pale brown-color, clad only in small malos of tapa, with fresh lilikoi blossoms in their hair, some giggling and pressing forward, some hanging back shyly—but all curious about the big-bodied, graceful, muscular youth. Though curious, they all seemed uncertain about how far to venture into what was clearly going to be a man's (or even a god's) enterprise. And at just about the middle distance, Naeole was carefully watching the kahuna to read hostility or friendliness in his move as far in advance as possible.

Seen close up, the blackish surface of the puka-puka stone looked surprisingly dense, smooth and solid. He was struck with the realization that this end, while less cumbersome than the other, was still very deep and heavy. It was going to be a *big* job. He remembered, as his eye searched hurriedly for a purchase, to mouth a last-minute prayer to Ku-kaili-moku. It was the god Ku upon whom he would depend, since Ku, the war god and mightiest and most formidable of all, was the one he feared and respected most, not good-natured Lono who was most frequently addressed with pleas for help in these days of Maka-hiki and celebration. "E Kailimoku" was his imprecation, or "Kaili has risen over the islands." Kaili was the war god of his and Alapai's ancestor Ulu from the misty days of the past. A fierce, conquering, fearsome deity with ripping, huge, sharp teeth perpetually bared in a menacing snarl, Ku-kaili-moku was a fit deity to be feared, and to lead the chiefs of Ulu in war. He was the principal deity around the court of Alapai and for all his sons and nephews.

Now, Kamehameha could see Ku-kaili-moku clearly in his mind: a square-headed figure with especially long, bared lower fangs, and a tall headdress of yellow E'e feathers; and short muscular legs ready, like all the god figures, to spring into action at the blink of an eye.

As a hasty, last-minute thought he added a salutation as well for the god Lono. A figure of Lono, the Long-God which had been taken throughout Kona for the Maka-hiki festival of the tax-gathering, was easily visible at the top of the Anuu tower of the heiau, above the semicircle of other god images. He directed his gaze at this lofty height and also cried out, "Hail to Lono!"

In that second, he noted a sweet, broad smile suffusing the wide face of the kahuna as he heard the name, and he knew the reason. In the Maka-hiki season, the priests of Lono became the god himself, and the stalwart kahuna felt that *he* was being saluted. Kamehameha had started the salutation with the idea of asking divine help for his effort, but the Lono kahuna threw all that off when he responded, happily:

"Friend of Lono, you come to do honor to Lono at the Akua,

the very holy site of the Naha omen. I will give you a reading of the omens now, when the New Year is being born."

This was the moment Kamehameha chose to make his effort. The stone was smooth under his hands. His sturdy, long arms twined around the end of the great whale-shaped black wedge, and he bent his back to the tremendous task. And in that moment, while air hissed from his nostrils with the size of the effort, he felt the stone stir under his grasp. At least, he was moving the end of it!

But Kamehameha was made of stern stuff, and he was not about to be satisfied with a slight movement. He ground his okole or bottom, the human being's natural center of gravity, down toward the earth.

Kamehameha gave a mighty heave, and he expected that, like the dugout canoe, the big boulder would break loose under his concerted pressure. But the dreadful realization struck him that it was *not* moving.

He braced his legs deeper under him in the stance of Ku-kaili-moku. Desperately, he tried to get all the power of his broad back into the lift. Under his brown skin the smooth contours of his wedge-shaped knots of muscles below the shoulder, the teres complex, heaved and strained. In his broad forehead, the temporal vein knotted as if it were about to burst. And yet, the Naha Stone still did not move more than a few inches.

In the agony of that moment, he looked back and saw the priest of Lono coming closer, his smile now replaced by a puzzled frown. He saw Naeole hurrying toward him, and his gray-haired tutor showed in his face that he suspected a great catastrophe might be happening.

In the same glance, while he felt his head must break with the effort of heaving, Kamehameha saw a tall and angular kahuna approaching, carrying a god image of Ku-kaili-moku, the wooden image atop a long pole. Even from this distance, the pearl-shell eyes gleamed fiercely, and the protruding lower fangs shone white, probably the teeth of a large dog before they were magically changed to Ku's. Next to the god image towered the tall feather hat of the kahuna, and Kamehameha wondered now if this could be Laka, the chief kahuna for the Papalane or high chief of Hilo, Keawe-mauhili.

When he saw the fierce god descending upon him, in defiance of the Maka-hiki kapu, an extra spurt of energy seemed to run through Kamehameha's veins. Perhaps the kahuna had decided this was the time to end the seasonal kapu and put the fear of the fiercest god into the brash young man who assaulted the Naha kapu. Kamehameha decided now was the time to shift his grip once more, to make the great final effort—and he would win! It seemed as if the god Ku had appeared from nowhere, admittedly carried by a kahuna, to give him the final strength he needed.

With a quick, dexterous effort he shifted his grip a little closer toward the outer tip of the Naha Stone, the end closer toward the god Ku. And now, suddenly, the mass of the stone seemed to give in his grasp. Still, he had moved the stone only from the ground, had not turned it anywhere else. His driving leg muscles pistoned downward as he strained to move the mass toward his left. And strangely, the great boulder broke loose, progressed steadily under his pressure, with his legs driving under it, and it came to rest a good five feet from where it had been.

Kamehameha stepped back panting for breath. He saw Naeole stop, riveted with what happened—a sudden, surprising victory. He remembered that Naeole had said several times: "A warrior whose family god is Kaili will be satisfied with nothing less than total victory." Kamehameha was panting for air, sweat ran down the ripples of his belly, but he had succeeded.

Now, he had moved the stone, but not in the tradition worthy of the tribe of Ulu. Now he breathed deeply, braced himself as if he were catching a wave in the big surf at Kawaihae, and set himself for another charge at the rock. For his ancestor, the king Ulu, and Ku-kaili-moku!

This time, he would not only lift the end, but bring the whole end of the rock straight up, and heave it onto the other side. This time he lifted his end of the rock higher, with the leverage of his own weight, and with all the adroitness of a surfer scrambling into the curl of a big booming wave, he began to force his way up the slope of the rock until it stood almost upended. His strength seemed to have reached an apex and to have exhausted itself, but now he came through with the extra, superhuman effort which had already made him a champion in many sports. From somewhere deep in the springs of his will, he summoned the extra muscular effort from the depths of exhaustion and fatigue and with one final heave pushed the boulder over the top of the arc so that it fell with a crunching thud, and a splashing of groundwater on the far side.

He turned to face Laka, the priest of Lono, the other kahunas, Naeole and the miscellaneous mob of kanakas and Kauwas.

He saw in a glance the startled wonderment in the face of Naeole, and the priests of Ku and Lono frozen in their tracks, staring. And in that moment he saw an amazing thing: The malo-clad men and women of the crowd were beginning to prostrate themselves before him, in the kapu moi reserved for the highest Alii castes. They fell now like blocks in a game of Kilu when the gourds hit them—and the triumph was as satisfying, Kamehameha thought happily, as the kisses with a favorite wahine which were the prizes of the Kilu game.

In a few eyeblinks, it seemed, almost all of the members of the crowd were bowed before him in the kapu moi, and he was savoring the triumph, the object of the whole effort, but not without reserve. He kept a weather eye on the two nearest priests, and he glimpsed Naeole hurrying toward him.

The kahuna of Lono still stood rooted in his tracks, fascinated with the strange spectacle he was witnessing. But now the towering, hideous pole image of Ku was moving toward Kamehameha, the mother-of-pearl eyes flashing with the movement, the long, upcurved fangs gleaming. And below, the face of Laka, the priest of Ku-kaili-moku, seemed set with a matching purpose Kamehameha could not read.

But Naeole had hurried and now stood directly beside him. Evidently in his planning he had prepared for this eventuality, the complete triumph for Kamehameha over the challenge of the Naha Stone. He had evolved a definite course for the young prince, calculated as the first responsibility to keep the boy alive.

Now the purplish black old eyes beneath spiky white brows were alive with purpose. "You have done it, Kameha," he said, biting off the words more as if they were order of battle than simple congratulation. "But we had better move quickly, now. Before we tempt the gods too far." Kamehameha looked levelly out at the crowd, most of them prostrate, still, in the kapu moi. Evidently, the display of spontaneous respect was having its effect upon Laka, the priest of Ku-kaili-moku. Now, apparently given pause by the vast wave of kapu mois which had swept the crowd to the ground in front of Kamehameha, he had stopped, the pole image of Ku-kaili-moku standing motionless above him. Behind him, the priest of Lono was also motionless. Naeole was speaking fast: "Kameha, we must move wiki-wiki, and leave no trail for a while. The story of what you have done will grow mightily, by itself."

But Kamehameha, who was taller than Naeole and most of the crowd, was not content with this kind of unofficial retreat. He stepped forward to face the crowd and the priests, and said in a firm, loud voice that seemed suddenly hoarse with earnestness:

"I dedicate this feat of strength to you, Ku-kaili-moku, God of the tribe of Ulu and all of the rightfully noble-born chiefs of Hawaii."

He glanced at Naeole's face as he said it, because he wanted to see if the kahu would show extra alarm. The old man did, because Kamehameha's remark was a sly reference to the fact that King Alapai had killed Kamehameha's supposed grandfather and taken the throne of the true moi of west Hawaii. If one accepted the story that Kamehameha was the son of Keoua, as people commonly said, then Kamehameha should be the heir apparent and Keoua should have been moi or king in Alapai's place. Alapai was a usurper.

But the moment he had uttered it, Kamehameha was sorry for his slur on old Alapai. While it was probably true that Alapai had sent soldiers to try to kill Kamehameha when he was first born, there at the cave in Honoipu, nevertheless Alapai had befriended him later on and taken him into the court and treated him as a prince and a regal nephew.

It had been a spiteful streak that led him to make this remark in the feat of the Naha Stone, a kind of persisting soreness of temper about the matter of his inheritance. And he knew, without Naeole's telling him, that it had been a mistake. His remark, really quite innocent by itself, would be distorted in the telling by one of the brash, overproud Alii to sound as if he were starting a campaign against Alapai. That was wrong. Alapai was essentially a kind and forgiving old man. Furthermore, he had taken both Kamehameha's father Keoua and his uncle, his father's brother, Kalaniopuu, under his wing in his courts at Kawaihae and Kealakekua Bay.

Stop regrets, he told himself; it was time for action to get Naeole and himself clear. He started moving away, with the lithe, swift gait of the Alii but with even more than usual speed, and as he led the way he said in an aside to Naeole: "Naeole, follow me. I will head for the cave of Kaumana. And if we lose each other, then back at Kawaihae, on the sunny side of the island."

Soon, he had disappeared among the trees of the slopes rising toward the volcano, and Naeole, who could not walk as fast because of an old spear wound in his right leg, trailed behind. But on the playing field beside the heiau, the gossip was spreading like wildfire, and rather than follow the young conqueror into the forest, the crowd was content to ruminate on the marvelous event of the afternoon. They would spend the time swapping stories about the wonder of the new Naha, the young man who, according to legend, would rule the islands, soon. Kamehameha's star was beginning to rise, but the heavens around it were far from clear.

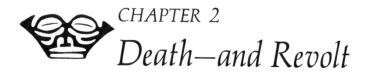

CHAPTER 2
Death—and Revolt

K AMEHAMEHA'S triumph of the lifting of the Naha Stone at Hilo attracted the notice he sought, and without too many innuendos in the telling and retelling. He escaped without having to flee to one of the Cities of Refuge for pardon in violating the kapu of the Nahas. It was all right, because he had been successful! And as the gossip, the calabash rumor, filtered back to King Alapai's court at Kawaihae, the young prince noted that Kalaniopuu, half-brother of his father, Keoua, suddenly seemed to be paying special attention to him.

He spoke about this to Naeole and that sage kahu remarked that Kalaniopuu was anxious to find warriors of the more formidable sort, including young ones with promise.

The old kahu explained enigmatically that when an old warrior dies, his heirs begin to squabble and scheme. Clearly he meant that Kalaniopuu was building strength for a takeover when Alapai died.

Also, on the rare occasions when he saw his father at Keoua's favorite spot in Waiolama, near Hilo, sometimes Kalaniopuu would be visiting with his father, and they always seemed to be extremely friendly. Actually, Kalaniopuu was the most likely heir to the domains of King Alapai, since he was older than Keoua. But Alapai also had a young and favored son, Keawe-opala. And court gossips had it that Keawe would certainly inherit the throne. Both Keoua and Kalaniopuu had served valiantly with Alapai when Alapai fought his great battles fifteen years before in Oahu, Molokai and Maui. Thus the two half-brothers enjoyed the additional brotherhood of comrades-in-arms.

Kamehameha knew that in the battles of those three islands, King Alapai had suffered dreadful losses among his warriors and he had won the battles less than half the time, as at Kawela on Molokai. The half-brothers frequently reminisced about Kawela, where the waters ran red with blood of the enemy. And, sometimes, if they were deep in their awa cups, they joked or wailed in proper Polynesian fashion over fallen comrades from the battles near Kaneohe on Oahu, and the dreadful slaughter of Puuene, near Lahaina on Maui.

Yet old Alapai, unsteady with age and heavy consumption of awa, remained kind and considerate of young Kamehameha, and if anything, Kamehameha, the Lonely One, was treated with even more than his former deference. Only once, when deep in his awa, his eyes rheumy with that indulgence, did Alapai mention the Naha Stone. That one time, when the chiefs had been chewing the awa and the noise and bustle of the hula filled the king's meeting hale, he summoned Kamehameha and asked unsteadily: "Grandnephew, was it true that you overthrew the great Naha Stone at Hilo?"

The hula girls, a line of six of them, were dancing vehemently to a noisy collection of pahus in the flickering light of kukui oil. Their bare brown breasts and wide hips bobbed and rolled wildly with the rapid rhythms of sex, as they chanted a salacious rhyme about the "small worm" and his adventures.

But the courtiers were paying little attention. Their ears were sharply tuned to any possible savoring of court gossip, and they crowded forward to hear the answer of the tall, strong, dark prince. Kamehameha sensed all this and chose his words carefully. He had already learned that when a king asks a question, he must be answered vigorously and with dispatch and point, even if the king is drunk with awa and his face scaling with the ravages of the intoxicant.

"Hanohano nui," he said, "Your Majesty, I moved the Naha Stone and dared the kapu!"

Alapai's watery old eyes tried to focus on the lithe, muscular bulk of the youth: "Did you dedicate your feat of strength to me?"

Kamehameha saw that the gossips had done their work and distorted what he had said at the Naha Stone. He was ready. "I dedicated it your great war god and mine, Ku-kaili-moku, and to Ulu and his kingly descendents."

Alapai looked up into the firm black eyes. He hesitated, then he touched Kamehameha's shoulder: "You are Lawa, a chief of great strength. You should have Ku-kaili-moku to keep for me."

"Mahalo. Thank you, Hanohano nui," said Kamehameha. And the old king had already turned his attention back to the hula girls. But Kameha was aglow with the compliment of the old king that the young prince should sometime become the guardian of Ku; that was the highest tribute Alapai could give, except the inheritance of the throne.

Kamehameha was struck also with the sudden attention paid to him by Kaumana, the high-chief of Hilo or Papa, who was a cousin and vassal of Alapai. It was because of the interest which the Hilo high-chief showed in Kamehameha that Keoua found a happy home in that vicinity. At Piopio (later called by its present name, Pepeekeo), Keoua seemed content to live peaceably with his six latest wives, and he did not seem vitally interested in the trouble shaping up between Kalaniopuu and his other full brother, the older Ke-e-au-moku.

The political struggle to decide who was going to succeed the ailing Alapai was accelerating. The next year, when Kamehameha was fifteen, and he had grown to massive size so that he was a full head taller than the biggest warriors, his father Keoua fell sick in his hale, or house, at Waiolama, near Piopio. His father's illness, and eventual death, were going to signal the start of the war of succession to Alapai's throne. Keoua sent a runner to summon his brother Kalaniopuu to his sickbed.

Kalaniopuu was now high chief of Ka'u, in the southern part of the rainy side of the island. And since Alapai by this time had taken a great fancy to living on the rainy side, at Hilo, Kamehameha also was there, and heard the news.

Kamehameha was a rapt student of the military arts at this time, and he had been learning rapidly from Kekuhaupio. But when he heard the ominous report, Kamehameha hurried north of Hilo toward the hale of Keoua. Before he could see the tapa-covered hut where he knew Keoua had been lying ill, he heard the wailing of the mourners, the male and female voices. As he came closer he could see the bodies of the men swaying in formal grief, and his heart sank momentarily until he saw Kamakoahua, Keoua's favorite wife, who answered his questioning look:

"Keoua lives still. But Kalaniopuu is with him now and the kahuna."

He walked closer to the hut with her, and heard the deep voice of his father, the sounds coming with difficulty now as if he were struggling for breath. And he heard an amazing diatribe delivered in that halting, hoarse voice, evidently addressing Kalaniopuu: "Kalani, you must know that Alapai has plans to install Kiwalao on the throne when he dies. You must beware of Kiwalao, the first-born son of Alapai. He has plans to cheat you of your inheritance."

Next, Kamehameha heard the voices of Kalaniopuu and Puna, the formidable warrior who was Kalaniopuu's tutor in martial arts. They were warning that Alapai had been praying for Keoua's death with the aid of a kahuna—since any good Hawaiian knew that this was possible; the process of projection of death through prayers toward some chosen object was called ana-ana. And then, Puna said, since Alapai was anxious to hang onto his reign in the face of any threats, it would be wise also to do away with young Kamehameha.

"You remember," Puna said, "that when Kekui-apo-iwa [Kamehameha's mother] was with child with Kamehameha, she had a midnight craving, a hunger craving for the eye of a chief—and you remember how Alapai viewed this as a threat, because a kahuna said that it augured that Alapai would be overthrown by Kekui-apo-iwa's offspring. I am sure you haven't forgotten that Alapai sent troops, soldiers, out to the Kohala north point to look for that baby."

There was only a hoarse, acknowledging grunt from his father. Kalaniopuu said: "Fortunately, Naeole had spirited the child away from the cave where Kekui-apo-iwa gave birth."

"But," said Keoua, "you must not forget that Alapai took Kamehameha into his court, and reared him as a prince, with privileges nearly equal to his own son, Keawe."

"Nevertheless," the clear voice of Puna went on, "to protect him, we should take Kamehameha away. You know, Kalaniopuu, that Keawe intends to move against you, and we should take the boy away from him. It could be that he might even hold him as a hostage."

Kamehameha hesitated about confronting the conspirators at this point, and was vacillating when suddenly he heard the cries of "Auwe, Auwe," as his father had evidently breathed his last. He burst into the hut, bowed to Puna and Kalaniopuu; a signal passed between them, and the Ka'u Chief Puna seized the opportunity: "Kamehameha is here! There is a war canoe at Piopio. Let us all go together!"

Kalaniopuu and Puna were swaying violently and crying in the prescribed loud wails over the dead, but there was no doubt about Puna's intentions for Kamehameha.

Kamehameha decided rapidly as the giant Puna, even taller than Kamehameha, led the way from the hale. They heard the women crying out with wails of grief over Keoua's death near the kaukau hut where the cooking was done. Puna looked back apprehensively: "Alapai's chiefs may be coming. They may have already heard of Keoua's death. They will know we are here."

In the flickering torchlight of the courtyard they saw that he was right. Inside the wall of the hale, they saw the glistening brown bodies of four men, hurrying toward Keoua's deathbed. Kamehameha recognized the younger son of Alapai, Keawe, in the lead, his plump, squarish body a distinctive shape even in the faint light.

Kalaniopuu acted fast. He spoke to the new arrivals, apparently feeling that they would find out that he and Puna had come to the house. Kalaniopuu stepped forward in the shadowy torchlight. "Auwe—brothers, my brother has left for the spirit world, to join Kane and Ku-kaili-moku."

Fat Keawe squinted at them, and recognized the bulk of Puna and Kamehameha and the comparatively slight structure of Kalaniopuu.

"Kalaniopuu, is that Kamehameha with you, and Puna?" His tone grew soft and conciliatory. "Auwe! We grieve for your brother—our brother. And for his son, Kamehameha. Come closer and let us see you, that we may cry out together over our loss."

The two groups of men came together in the light of a torch on the wall. He recognized chiefs who were "children of Alapai." His tutor Naeole had also marked them as possible enemies in the court intrigue: Kameeiamoku, and Ke-e-au-moku, a young, dashing chief from Ka'u who had been cool and distant to him. Naeole had warned him that Ke-e-au-moku was the young chief whom he might have to contend with when Alapai died, or even before.

The two groups stood in the torchlight, the new arrivals swaying their bodies and moaning. But he was watching Kamehameha very carefully, and while he swayed and between groans, he said to Puna and Kalaniopuu:

"Let us all go in together to the bed and bemoan the dead, Kamehameha too."

Kalaniopuu seized Kamehameha by the arm, the bony hand firm

on his biceps, and Kamehameha felt his vehemence as he answered, decisively:

"No! We have paid our respects. We must leave now—and Kamehameha with us! A war canoe waits for us."

Keawe's face broke uncertainly, a hypocritical attempt at beneficence. "Would it not be advisable for the son to stay and wail over the father?" he said tentatively.

Puna felt the menace and moved toward Keawe and Ke-e-au-moku. Now he was scowling.

"A guard of trusted warriors waits for him outside. A strong force."

In the tension of the moment, Ke-e-au-moku moved forward, too, his size dwarfed by the towering Puna. Now his face, too, wore a conciliatory expression. "It is better for the bereaved son to feel the grief of his father's death, is it not?"

Now Kalaniopuu's wiry body was tense, but he managed a half-smile. "Kamehameha has suffered enough for tonight with the death of the valiant Keoua," he said. "It is better that we give him some rest in his grief." He looked at the faces of the others now revealed as enemies, and his face grew stony. "My guards are waiting for him, and for us, outside!"

"But," sputtered Keawe, "the kahunas have not come yet. You must wait until they arrive. You must be here for the propitiation of the spirits." Kalaniopuu was moving Kamehameha toward the only exit from the walled enclosure.

"No! We must go, now."

Puna had no war club, spear or any other arms, but he was determined to spirit Kamehameha out of the enclosure despite any opposition. And Kalaniopuu was also ready for the effort: "My troops are waiting for him," he said evenly.

Ke-e-au-moku inserted his squarish bulk in the path and from somewhere, a gnarled war club had appeared in his hand. "This time, it is I who say no," he said. His three henchmen formed a wedge behind him, each of them now carrying a club. As if by magic, the whole walled enclosure behind them was filled with warriors, fierce, tattooed fighters, some with a warlike paste of white ashes also on their faces. "Kamehameha had better stay with us, the better to grieve for his father."

At the moment, there seemed to be nothing for Puna and Kalaniopuu to do except to bow to the superior force. Kalaniopuu directed a stern look at Ke-e-au-moku. "Watch how you handle him, for he is the legitimate successor to me, for the throne of the moi of Hawaii, as I am before him."

Suddenly his face broke into a smile: "Alapai-nui knows this, and it is for this reason that he has treated him as a true son, equal to you, Keawe-opala."

Kamehameha wondered: Why did he back away from Puna's stand? Perhaps, he isn't ready for a break with Alapai, and Keawe, yet.

Kalaniopuu stepped back, still smiling, to survey the threatening echelon of his court opponents. He laughed, the white teeth flashing in the torchlight. "After all," he said, "Alapai the Great is not dead. We must stop acting as if he were. Is that not right, Keawe? Of all people, you should know that."

He started from the enclosure, with the towering Puna following. But he halted to say to Kamehameha:

"You will be safe, Kamehameha. Alapai has pledged it. We will come back at Kihi time, when the sun is setting, and mourn the great Keoua."

Kamehameha remembered that night for the rest of his life—because it had been a forcible demonstration of court power-maneuvering, not because he had lost his father. Keoua had been very little more than a stranger to him throughout his life. From this time on, Kamehameha was caught up in the struggle for mastery of this island, the scheming evocation of force and the naked struggle like two mokomoko boxers fighting to the death. Naeole had taught him about the struggle for power and the intrigues of the court, but until this night it had not hit him with such vehement realization that the realities beneath were as real as death, the deathly earnestness of the battle for power.

But in the days and weeks of mourning after his father's death,

Keawe-opala, the son of Alapai, and his friends and supporters remained considerate and gracious to him. Kalaniopuu's words of reminder about the protection of Alapai for Kamehameha were not lost upon them. They helped him with the numerous chores of preparations for the burial of Keoua. Kalaniopuu and Puna came back in a few days after the death with a dozen of their leading chiefs, and 200 troops from Ka'u beating the deep-toned pahus in the grove of palms on the point of land at Piopio. Then the aging Alapai and his sons, true and adopted, offered the height of deference to Kamehameha, Kalaniopuu and his chief leader in arms, Puna.

Two days after the death, the kahunas came to prepare the body. With the help of Keoua's most recent wives, they washed the body with a jellylike embalming fluid made from the root of the ti plant. Many of the children of Keoua were there to help, but Kamehameha, being the oldest, had the lion's share of the responsibility. And Kiha, the kahuna nui, came to advise Kamehameha, and to counsel him on seeking out a secret cave, somewhere within the lands of Keoua, where he would deposit the highly esteemed long bones of the body in a sitting position.

The next day, King Alapai himself came. The little, stooped shell of a man, with a group of his courtiers, swayed and moaned over the loss of the departed. Kamehameha remembered how frail he seemed, and he was reminded again of the dusty mortal winds which blew as soon as a ruling monarch began to totter with age: the heirs, and those who were not heirs, planning for the division of the spoils when any great moi began to falter.

A group of kahunas came with the king and they began the long series of chants and prayers while the kahuna nui prepared the body.

Alapai, doing honor to a brave warrior who had fought well for him in many campaigns, was determined that Keoua should have the death ceremony of a high chief, almost a king.

To guarantee his innocence against the rumors of ana-ana, the necromantic process by which a powerful kahuna might pray a victim to death, Alapai asked the kahuna nui to perform the ceremony of kuni. In kuni a curse is delivered upon any kahuna or other person who might have prayed the deceased to death. The kuni prayer was delivered in the usual awesome tones of the deep-toned kahuna chant:

> Heaven speed the death of the kahuna ana-ana
> And of the one who got the mauuna for him,
> O Kane.

The next day, Kiha, the kahuna nui, found Kamehameha as he sat in the room with his father's body, while the wives raised a storm of tears and auwes that never ended. And cousins from all parts of the islands began to arrive. But in the mid-afternoon, while a chorus of kahunas were chanting the praises of the line of Umi, and reciting tales of Keoua's long genealogy, Kiha took him aside. He was a tall, straight and forbearing man, with a solemn mien.

"Kamehameha, you know the custom of pule hui. We will bury the body in a shallow fire pit and burn it for ten days. You may help me carry the unclean parts, the insides, the pela, at a kapu time of night and cast them into the ocean. I will save the long bones, the hands and skull for you and you know you must hide them well, so that no enemy may humiliate mighty Keoua by making fish hooks of the bones or shape a refuse pot from the skull."

So it was that after all the chants, visitors and lamentations, Kamehameha began his pilgrimage. In the time of the breaking of the shadows, in the afternoon, the Kakahi-aka time of day, he and the kahuna Kiha started up the slope above the bay, Kamehameha carrying the ball-like package of bones. The two men were heading toward the koa trees, near the Rainbow Falls, and a cave behind the falls.

Amid the misty sheets of iridescence that marked the Rainbow Falls with beauty, Kiha took his leave of Kamehameha. He stood at a kind of attention before the tall young warrior. "I leave you now, Kamehameha. Go deep into the caves and find a secret spot for the bones of Kalani-kupua-pai Kalani-nui Keoua," he said, using the formal name of Keoua. The lengthy name meant only "strong offspring of Kalani, the descendent of the great Kalani line." Thus, of course, Kamehameha was supposed to be one of the late descendents of the Kalani line. Kalani, in turn, meant "heavenly," from Ka, "from," and Lani, "heaven," or "descended from the sky."

Kamehameha had laid the remains down before entering the caves behind the falls. Kiha knelt beside the fallen warrior and looked up toward the clouds which by this time had grown gray and puffed with rain. "O great Ku-kaili-moku, we send a brave spirit to join you. One of the great heros of Alapai's army. At Kawela, where the bones of his dead enemies are as thick as the sand, at Kahului on Maui, and the many battlegrounds of Kaneohe on Oahu, he fought like Ulu himself. And came back to rest at home, acclaimed by Alapai-nui moi and all of his bravest soldiers."

The sky had grown darker, and a few drops of rain were falling. Kamehameha had heard these same lamentations for his father during the last few days. And Kamehameha was perceptive enough to realize that much of this so far had been "mouth honor" intended for the large audience of mourners. But now, when there were just the two of them, Kiha and he, and the remains of his dead father, there seemed to be a ringing sincerity in the priest's words.

Kamehameha knelt beside Kiha and a wave of loneliness and grief swept over him, really for the first time since he had come to his father's house and seen him on his deathbed. Like a succession of waves of surf, undulations of grief swept up his back and into his shoulders, and into the upper part of his head. It seemed as if sobs would seize him, and melt the powdery paste of ashes with which he had covered his face, in mourning. But he was determined not to give in to grief, and to withstand it as Naeole had told him many times he must. Naeole had said, "It is easy to give in to grief, or any other emotion. That does not even take wanting. But to resist emotion is the mark of a man."

He was afraid his shoulders would begin to shake, and he stood up abruptly. "Kiha, I take the mortal remains now to a secret cave, safe from any of Keoua's enemies. His mana of war strength and fortitude will be safe from the mischief and magic of his foes now."

Saying this seemed to steady him; he saluted the kahuna with a wave, and then shouldered the sacred package again and trudged toward the glistening rainbow of the falls.

But the kahuna was not leaving. Instead, he hurried after Kamehameha, overtook him—which was easy in view of the young man's burden—and said into his ear: "Kamehameha, one word of caution. When you return from this rite of Mua, and are back in the court of Alapai-nui, take heed of your enemies. There are many, since the day when your mother, Kekui-apo-iwa, had her dream about her birth appetite for the eye of a king."

Kamehameha stopped, and Kiha watched him solemnly. Suddenly, his voice seemed to take on an otherworldly role. "There are many mysteries about your birth, Kamehameha. And certain kings from afar want your death. Aside from your enemies in the court of Alapai."

"What kings do you speak of, Kiha?" Kamehameha had heard these rumors before, but he had never been able to pin them down.

Kiha seemed to shake himself back into his being, and his face was covered with a mask of impenetrability. Without a word, he turned to go.

Kamehameha smiled wryly. "Thank you anyway for the word of caution about my enemies in the court," he said.

"Recently, I have seen much to convince me that you are right, and that death lurks behind every bush for me in the court of Alapai."

He shouldered his tapa package again, and without looking back, trudged toward the falls. It was beginning to rain faster, the big soft warm drops of the Hilo cloud splattering him and his sad burden.

It was not long before the threads of revolt which Kamehameha had glimpsed in Kalaniopuu broke into the open against King Alapai. Within three months, Kalaniopuu declared that the provinces of Ka'u and Puna, about one-third of the area of the island of Hawaii, were independent of Alapai and that he, Kalaniopuu, was their moi. The most remarkable development at this time to Kamehameha was the singular calm with which Alapai reacted to the news.

Kamehameha went back to the eastern capital of Alapai on the heights above Hilo with a heavy heart.

He was also saddened by the departure of his beloved kahu Naeole on a mission of state to the district of Ka'u for Alapai. Alapai, in a sober moment, had ordered Naeole to northern Ka'u to feel out the mood of the chiefs, and cement their friendship.

Alapai had heard that Kalaniopuu was mobilizing the chiefs of the southern Ka'u district for a bid of force, an open revolt.

Leaving for his diplomatic mission to raise strength in Ka'u, Naeole took his leave of Kamehameha in a sad scene. He commended his powerful young charge to the care of the military tutor, Kekuhaupio.

The wise, purplish brown eyes were brimming with tears, as he rubbed noses in farewell with his almost-son. "Keku is a fitting guardian for you, Kameha," he said. "He is a much more skillful warrior than I. And at this age, you need the best as your mentor and companion."

Kamehameha said proudly: "*You* are the best, Naeole."

And when Naeole's canoe shoved off for the trip down the coast, Kameha had the sad conviction that it would be a long while before they would meet again. His depression was heightened during the succeeding weeks when his military tutor told him the rumors that flashed through the court, about Kalaniopuu.

Kalaniopuu, his kahu told Kamehameha, had broken into a death struggle against Alapai. Several battles had been fought along the Hamakua coast, at Puaaloa, Kualoa, and at Mahinaakaka. Kamehameha saw that Kekuhaupio was deeply disturbed.

Kameha had a continuing son's affection for Naeole, but his attachment for Keku deepened rapidly. This military kahu was in truth, as Naeole had said, the best, most skillful practitioner of the warlike arts. And with his quick, tight smile and ironic sense of humor, he rapidly had won Kamehameha's admiration and affection. Today, as Keku told Kameha the news, he seemed singularly depressed.

"Keku, honored chief," Kamehameha said, "Why does the heavy film of unhappiness lie so deeply over your eyes? Would you be homesick for a fight; to be on the battlefields again?"

"Partly that, Kameha," the chief said. "But it is more than that." His golden eyes looked straight at Kamehameha. "It is that I am not sure whether Kalaniopuu is right. Perhaps the right is on the side of the rebel rather than the king."

Then he smiled that tight, bright grin. "Any bright warrior has doubts about the rightness of his cause. Sometimes even in the midst of throwing a spear—and that can be unfortunate.

"I have my doubts about the rightness of supporting young Keawe as Alapai's successor."

Kamehameha knew that Kekuhaupio was being brave, because to utter this kind of disloyalty to the king was to risk execution as a traitor. Kamehameha waited for the rest. Kekuhaupio was a thorough and logical man, and always thought things through.

"It is true because your grandfather was the rightful moi of this island. Your dead father and your uncle Kalaniopuu were the true heirs, not Alapai. And certainly not that dubious warrior, Keawe."

Kamehameha knew this was true. But during his memory, Alapai had always treated him as a son and equal to his own true son, Keawe-opala.

The time of the mourning for his father, Keoua, when Alapai had been drunk with the chewing of the awa root, had been illuminating, and it had signalled that Keawe-opala might indeed be planning to dispose of Kamehameha and Kalaniopuu.

Yet when the first rumors of Kalaniopuu's revolt broke out, Alapai had remained kind and considerate to Kamehameha.

Nor did the old warrior chief, now that Kalaniopuu had made raids along the northern or Hamakua coast, launch any expedition against Kalaniopuu's home base at Ka'u. He seemed singularly disinclined toward war, and preferred awa and the dancing girls.

When Kamehameha saw Alapai these days, the king looked frail and sick, shunned his food, and too often he chose to spend the nights in long noisy awa-chewing sessions with his chieftains. And the mornings-after, Kamehameha knew he was more dead than alive, like a man with ague.

With a calculating eye upon those who had been revealed to be hostile in their intentions toward him, Kameha lost himself in warlike exercises prescribed by Kekuhaupio. And it was not long before he was finally to leave the court of King Alapai, not because of Alapai himself but thanks to the schemers of the court.

Meanwhile his kahu surprised him with two splendid marks of his adult chiefhood and warriorhood: his first ahuula, a flowing silky smooth yellow-and-black feather cloak, and his tall rigid helmet plumed with a comb of yellow. The cloak, painstakingly wrought by the magic of Hinaloa, the honored artisan of the feather cloak at the court of King Alapai, was one sleek expanse of yellow and black, its E'e feathers wrought like a rich cloth of gold. And his helmet, or mahiole, another Hinaloa creation, was so tall that if he wore it and stood next to a long olo surfboard, the board would seem as small and inconsiderable as the shorter alaia kind. Without the helmet, he was still nearly as tall as an ordinary alaia board, which would be six and a half feet in length.

Alapai, the king, came to visit him, and to marvel at the handiwork of yellow E'e feathers from the roots of the wings and tail of the black O'o bird. A strained mood of mellowness seemed to have taken over Alapai when he came with a train of courtiers to visit the thatch hut where Kamehameha stayed with his kahu Kekuhaupio. The king insisted that Kamehameha should don the warrior costume, and also that his military kahu should be on hand for the occasion.

Alapai and his closest supporters sat while Kamehameha stood before them. Kamehameha could see that their movements were growing erratic, their speech uncertain, and he knew that they must have been chewing and drinking the awa for some hours before. "The cloak is very long, Kamehameha," said Alapai, "but so are you. Here you are in your first warrior's garb, and you have not yet drawn the blood of an enemy." He turned to his son, Keawe-opala: "Is that not so, Keawe?"

"Yes, father." Keawe-opala seemed uneasy, and Kamehameha wondered if these awa-drunk Alii had been talking previously about him as a rebel.

Kamehameha knew a speech was expected: "My spear, my war club and my sling are ready to do battle against the enemies of King Alapai," Kamehameha said, and the move was deliberate, because he thought it might bring out Alapai's attitude further.

But Alapai was genuinely friendly in his disposition toward Kamehameha, even though tipsy with the awa cup. "Spoken with the vehemence and bravery of Keoua, foremost warrior of the House of Kalani," said Alapai gallantly.

And Kamehameha nodded, but there was something in Alapai's tone which galled him. The conversation he had overheard between Kalaniopuu and his dying father had reminded him that the Kalani family were the true kings of the island of Hawaii, and certainly not Keawe, the son of a half-grand-uncle. He could feel prickles of rage dancing through the back of his neck.

But Alapai, essentially a man of great kindness, sensed Kamehameha's reaction, even though the awa scene had filled him with the usual extra supply of warmth and recklessness. He backed away from his essay into wit, and spoke seriously. "Kamehameha, you are a handsome warrior in your ahuula and mahiole. Your appearance alone is a credit to my court." He turned to his Alii followers, and said: "Let us go and leave Kamehameha with his bright war garb. We old warriors, to whom war is tarnished, will chew the awa, and forget."

The old chief did not have long to live. His death came in the palace of Kawaihae, the scene of so many Polynesian revels in Alapai's later years.

Kamehameha had heard rumors about the invasion fleet of Kalaniopuu, but in indefinite terms, immediately after Alapai died.

Even at age fifteen, Kamehameha had been diplomatic and tactful enough to be off on a trip to Hilo when Keawe mounted his first canoe fleet and an army to do battle with Kalaniopuu and his new ally, the changeable Ke-e-au-moku.

At first, Ke-e-au-moku had been unsuccessful in his attempts to unseat Keawe. There had been a sea battle off the south Kona coast, with Keawe's canoes engaging with stones tossed by slings, and closer in with spears, eventually in hand-to-hand combat among the war canoes. It had gone badly for Ke-e-au-moku, and the remnants of his fleet had been forced to flee seaward after having failed to land on the rocky shore which Keawe-opala's men were defending. Ke-e-au-moku had sent the remnant of his forces to join with Kalaniopuu for the large assault on the authority of Keawe-opala.

About that time a runner from Kalaniopuu came in the night with a critically important message for Kamehameha. Kipu, the runner, reached Kamehameha's hut without difficulty.

Kipu's body gleamed with sweat, and Kamehameha guessed that he must have run all the way up from Honaunau. It was a good two-day paddle, and about one-tenth of the way around the island. But Kipu had several times run all the way around. He was lean as a spear, except for his mighty calf and thigh muscles.

Kamehameha called for Kamae, his body servant, and commanded a drink of water and food for Kipu. Kamehameha knew before Kipu could talk that Kalaniopuu was sending him word of a further rebellion against Alapai's kingdom, now about to be taken over by Keawe. Kameha called for Keku, and he came to hear the message.

"The moi, Kalaniopuu, is on the waves with a fleet of war canoes," said Kipu. He looked around the room and lowered his voice. "He has a large camp at Honaunau. And he asks that you join him there. He will send canoes to pick you up at Hapuna, tomorrow night."

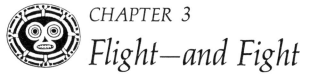

CHAPTER 3
Flight—and Fight

KAMEHAMEHA had no time to think about it. Since the death of Alapai, it had been clear to him that Alapai's son Keawe-opala had plans for him. And they were not exactly pleasant.

On that night, with Kekuhaupio, Kamehameha followed a secluded path to the outer wall of the compound, and managed to get through to Hapuna Bay. In the Pilipuka section of the night, about half way between midnight and the sunrise at 6 A.M., from the shelter of a keawe or mesquite bush, Kamehameha saw a long, rakish war canoe slipping through the night. The sharp prow curled waves, making a glitter visible in the light of the night sky, and the chunking of the paddles was distinctly audible. Two other canoes followed.

When Kamehameha had seen the canoes close to the point, he called out: "Kalaniopuu?"

The noise of the paddles stopped, and from the dark came a voice he did not recognize: "Who is that?"

"Kamehameha."

Again, another pause, and the same voice from the dark. "Good. We will meet you at the middle of Hapuna Beach."

At the appointed spot, a short distance south of the natural rock jetty in the middle of the sand of Hapuna, Kamehameha saw the glittering movement of a war canoe in the heave of the waves, just before they broke in a line of phosphorescence. Then the canoe scooted up on the sand, sturdy warriors strained to slide it further up, and the same voice called him again: "Is that Kamehameha?"

Kamehameha grunted assent. He noted, as he hurried down the beach to the canoe, that the man speaking was at the head of the canoe, a man taller than he—which would make him exceptionally large.

"Kalaniopuu sends for you," the warrior said with relief in his voice. "We have come from Honaunau, where Kalaniopuu has assembled his forces with those of Ke-e-au-moku for the battle with Keawe."

His informant went on: "We have more war canoes than Keawe has even seen. And our soldiers from Ka'u and Puna are as thick as a school of golden malolo."

According to the Hawaiian traditions of warfare, any large-scale war engagements were announced in advance, and several days of preparation were allowed so that the war gods could be propitiated with sacrifices and the kahunas could read the entrails for prophecies and omens.

So when Kamehameha and his military kahu came to the cove where the canoes and the crew of warriors were awaiting them, no one challenged them. However, Kekuhaupio was concerned about court informers, braves who might be on the beach with their sweethearts, or any other courtiers trying to get secret information which might win them the attention of Keawe, the new king.

Neither of the escapers noted any signs of discovery. But they both started when that voice spoke to them out of the darkness near the point of rocks that marked the northern end of the cove. He stood forward of the group. Clearly he was the leader. He was a tall, imposingly large man. Kamehameha could not make out his features in the faint light.

As the tall warrior came closer, however, Kamehameha recognized the battered, animated face of Ke-e-au-moku.

Kamehameha knew instantly how Ke-e-au-moku happened to be here. Since that scene by his father's deathbed, Kamehameha had felt good reason to distrust Ke-e-au-moku as unreliable, a man apt to shift from friend to enemy. But now, temporarily at least, he was an ally.

Kekuhaupio, Ke-e-au-moku and Kamehameha saluted each other with the customary tributes to each other's lineage and their eminence as warriors. Kamehameha knew it was only "mouth honor": There was only one real warrior of the three and that was Kekuhaupio, his military kahu, the son of the high kahuna Holoae. Kamehameha and Ke-e-au-moku were both young and Kamehameha had not yet been involved in his first war fight.

Kamehameha looked to Kekuhaupio for guidance. His kahu didn't seem to question Ke-e-au-moku's presence on this expedition. The kahu said softly, "Ono," meaning "good," and he added in a whisper: "I will tell you why it is ono, later on."

The three long canoes started along the coast under sail toward Puako and Honaunau—that was in the Lalo or south direction (the direction toward which the wind generally blew). The stars outlining the shape of Mano, the shark, were low on the southern horizon. It was also the direction of Kalaniopuu and his insurgent armies. Now in the nose of the canoe, Keku explained to Kameha: "Ke-e-au-moku is wild and impulsive, yet on your side he is useful—until he changes next month, or next week!"

Later on, as the three long canoes were moving south, Kekuhaupio and Kamehameha still sat in the prow, where they could hear the pleasant, soft gurgle of the waves and feel the fresh salt breeze. Keku continued:

"Ke-e-au-moku is wild and impulsive, but his father and his two brothers command wide support in the southern districts."

"Are they good warriors?" asked Kamehameha.

His tutor smiled. Now that they were away from the land, and farther from the darker masses of woods and hills, the light seemed brighter. The light-colored waves in this shallower water close to shore reflected more of the illumination of the stars and the crescent moon, and every whitecap glowed with phosphorescence. South of them, low on the horizon, lay the long undulant star-shape of Mano, the sharklike constellation which the Western world calls Hydra, the serpent.

The wind was strong, and it took them only a day and a half to reach Honaunau.

When the canoes reached Honaunau at twilight the second evening, Kalaniopuu was there to meet them. On the narrow beach in Honaunau Bay, standing next to the chunky, warlike figure of Kalaniopuu, stood a slightly stooped man with a large shock of white hair. It was Holoae, the father of Kekuhaupio. The face of Kamehameha's tutor was bright with a smile.

"Sometimes seeing a man can be more pleasure than going to meet one's beautiful ipo."

Ke-e-au-moku said: "He is now the most exalted of Kalaniopuu's kahunas."

On the beach there at Honaunau, Kamehameha noted that Kalaniopuu was already assuming the mantle of moi of Hawaii, as if the war against Keawe-opala were already won. And yet he was deferential to Kamehameha. After all, Kalaniopuu was his true uncle, his father's brother, and it would seem unlikely that Kamehameha could be forgotten—that is, as long as Kalaniopuu was engaged in a fight to the finish with Keawe-opala for control of the island of Hawaii.

At the Auoro, or thatch-roof headquarters of the military campaign, Kamehameha met the leaders of Kalaniopuu's forces. They were esteemed chiefs from the districts to the south, Ka'u and Puna, and the southern part of Kona. Whether they came from Alikapapa, Honuapo or Keauhou, each had brought his contingent of warriors for the effort against Keawe-opala. In the huge Auoro, a long house with open sides and a roof of thatch, Kalaniopuu was in a hearty mood. He joked with the chief from Pahala on the central coast of the Ka'u district:

"Not too many split ears in your group of warriors, Kimo," he said. He was referring to the usual punishment given to soldiers who tried to evade the "draft" for service in Kalaniopuu's army. Kalaniopuu looked toward the assemblage of Halepai, the small huts put up by the warriors and their families, ranged along the valley slope below.

Kimo was evidently the chief in charge of supply and accounting. "What is the count of our forces as of today?" Kalaniopuu went on. "Was the last count about 4,000?"

"Yes, and it has risen by 200 more today. The group came in with the chief from Kaohe. The chief is not here now. He has gone to secure taro for his warriors and their families."

Kalaniopuu smiled. "Good! If I can bring in the chief of Hookena and another 500 warriors, we should be able to march. I have already promised him one-fifth of the first day's spoils of war, and I believe he will come."

So it was that Kamehameha, a stripling of a boy in age but more a man in appearance, came to his first war.

Many times before, in the war games of the Alii, he had battled with other young nobles, and in these sessions of thrust and parry with pololu, the long spears, he had been nicked by spear points. In the sport of mokomoko, or boxing with no weapons save one's fists, he had several times knocked opponents unconscious. And there were few, among the older warriors or his contemporaries, who chose to oppose him in the mokomoko contests. But now, at last, it seemed he was going to enter his first real contest at arms, and for the first time, to try to kill an enemy, and to avoid that fate himself. He did not know yet that his uncle was going to keep him back from the mortal struggle, and keep him in the rear for this first battle.

And another important development occurred in the life of Kamehameha. Here at Honaunau while waiting for the battle, he met his first love. In the hale of Kalaniopuu, near the military headquarters, life was still to be enjoyed. There were feasts and games. The woman was Kane-kapo-lei, one of the younger wives (then aged about twenty-nine) of his uncle Kalaniopuu.

Kane-kapo-lei was mature and very beautiful, and took a strong fancy to the well-formed nephew of Alapai. She was a favorite partner of his at the Alii's kissing game (kissing, nose-rubbing and other much more athletic endearments were allowed). Soon she was pregnant by the fifteen-year-old Kamehameha.

But of course, the birth came much later, considerably after the battle had been joined by Kalaniopuu, Kamehameha and Ke-e-au-moku with Alapai's appointed heir, Keawe-opala.

The child was a boy, Kamehameha's first, Kao-lei-oku, nicknamed Pauli (pronounced "Pa-oo-lee" or shortened to "Pow-lee"). And both the mother, Kane-kapo-lei, and Kalaniopuu, Kamehameha's uncle, accepted the child as their own. Polynesian society generously accepted all healthy children as good fortune, and disposed of (killed) those handicapped with physical ailments at birth. In the atmosphere of plenty which suffused the vast Polynesian crescent stretching from New Zealand to the Samoas east to Tahiti and the Marquesas, then north to Hawaii, there was always plenty of coconut, banana, taro, breadfruit and fish, for Alii and Kauwa alike, and all their children. When Captain Cook came, on his voyage of discovery, he estimated there were 400,000 native inhabitants in the Hawaiian Islands.

In Polynesia, there were always many people who wanted to take care of healthy children. The boy, although Kamehameha's firstborn, was reared most of the time by Kane-kapo-lei and Kalaniopuu.

The battle to the finish with Keawe was joined a few miles to the north of Honaunau. It was halfway down the west coast of the island of Hawaii, between Honaunau and Keei.

That strip of ground, along the west coast of the "Big Island," is very rough and rugged, with the usual subsoil of multiple lava flows from the slopes of towering Mauna Loa: heavy, jagged-edged tongues of lava congealed into forbidding dikes that rip feet, shoes, gloves or any heavy garment of whoever tries to cross them. Usually, these brownish gray dikes of basalt show a lovely outflowering of small, purple and pink mallow wild flowers which suffuse them with a soft and welcoming look from a distance. But close up, those heavy, rough-edged and intractable dikes are rough as rusty old cutlasses; and they will be for hundreds of years before the weathering processes of wind and rain have softened their contours into more benign hills and dales of older country.

This is an incongruous battlefield, these strips of rough dark rock, for Hawaiian soldiers with greased bodies and usually only a narrow malo or loincloth around their bodies.

It's easy to imagine these virtually unprotected soldiers battling to the death over these rough stone dikes. Or the leaders, the chiefs or Alii, with their lustrous long bird-feather cloaks of red, black and yellow, and their ancient Greek or Spanish conquistador-type of feathered, domed helmet.

This battle, so critically important to Kalaniopuu (and to Kamehameha), was joined in the usual way of forces about to undertake mortal combat. The opposing forces, the armies of Kalaniopuu and Keawe-opala, spread out south of Keei. A day or two was allowed while the kahunas, or holy men, of both sides chanted incantations to the gods, especially to the war god Ku, and made sacrifices of pigs so they could read the entrails and find omens indicating how the battle would be going.

Hundreds of campfires spread over that rough country, and among the hales, the mat-houses of the chiefs, a galaxy of kukui lamps burned like starlight on both sides of the Keei valley.

Everyone knew that the magic of the gods, and the kahunas, would have much to do with the battle.

The spotlight of attention focused upon the two opposing chief priests and their retinue of younger kahunas. These two religious leaders were Holoae, the father of Kekuhaupio, and Kaakau, the priest of Keawe-opala. And Kamehameha was thrilled by the excitement of readying for the mortal fight.

In the daylight hours, the outstanding chiefs and warriors of both sides paraded along the facing slopes of the valley where the battle was to be joined, surveyed the enemy camp, and shouted out insults. They tried to manage as blood-threatening and fright-ening tones as possible and to single out individuals with their taunts when they could. Most of the imprecations reflected upon the alleged fact that the enemy were base-born (even that they were Kauwa lepo, base-born slaves, lepo meaning "mud-sill"). Also, that their much-vaunted chiefs were kulu, meaning womb "drops," of no account; that their mothers were of low birth, even if their fathers were chiefs. Also, that they all lacked courage. "He holo-wale!—The kind who always run away in fright!"

When the battle was joined at last on two successive days, it went very stubbornly. Neither side seemed to have an advantage, and the casualties were fierce on both sides.

Finally, on the third night, Holoae, the kahuna or priest of Kalaniopuu, told his chief that the only way to manage a victory was to lay a trap and kill Kaakau, the priest of Keawe-opala.

Kaakau had been quite reckless about exposing himself at the forefront of the fighting, Holoae said. It was the prayers and other powers of Kaakau which prolonged the contest. But his staying at the crux of the fighting was also important to the enemy's military effort. He had seemed to live a charmed life. Probably he had been lucky, but it was more than that; the soldiers had hesitated to kill a kahuna on either side.

Now they were told to make a deliberate effort to kill Kaakau, and that very morning it was done. He was captured, cruelly killed, then baked—a measure of Holoae's vindictiveness.

Keawe-opala's defenses collapsed; and Keawe-opala was slain. In that one day, Keawe's troops and Alii capitulated and recog-nized Kalaniopuu as their sovereign and the successor to Alapai.

There have been no historical accounts of the details of this, Kamehameha's first exposure to battle. Kamakau and Fornander, who have the fullest stories, say that he was involved, but there is not much further. Nor do we know how Kamehameha's mili-tary tutor, Kekuhaupio, fared in the battle, except that he was not killed or injured in the fighting. It seems likely that Keku stayed close to Kamehameha in this, the prince's first battle.

At any rate, the battle was a resounding victory for Kalaniopuu.

And it seems that Kalaniopuu, a wise commander, kept Kameha from active fighting. Probably the young chief was kept on the sidelines so he could absorb the shock and psychic impact of the fighting. He could see for himself how the first killings of the enemy were dedicated to Ku, and the forelock cut off amidst much running of blood—and how the first victors ground their victims into the earth, and debased them by leaving their bodies for the pigs and dogs. Also, how the first act of degradation of a fallen enemy Alii is to take his god images, and to lift his identifying badge of nobility, his lei niho palaoa, from his neck. It is a polished, carved sperm whale tooth with upcurved fang, supported by two strands of human hair. All this was a practical introduction to the ways of battle for the well-trained novice, and that Kamehameha was.

CHAPTER 4

Trial and Defeat in Maui

IN A SHORT TIME, Kalaniopuu was generally acclaimed as the moi of all Hawaii, and he immediately began building up his fleet of larger war canoes with a view to starting an ambitious military campaign against the island of Maui.

The moi of Maui at this time was the ailing long-term king Kamehameha Nui II.

Kalaniopuu had generally enjoyed good relations with Kamehameha Nui, his uncle. But Kalaniopuu, a great athlete at many sports, was also aggressive and he wanted to conquer at least a part of Maui, where Alapai had failed. Probably in the late 1760s, Kalaniopuu, convinced largely by his warlike kahu Puna, set sail with a wide fleet of double-hulled war canoes for the east side of the island of Maui, near the present town of Hana.

With him went Puna, the developing warrior Kamehameha, Kamehameha's kahu Kekuhaupio, and that other close comrade-in-arms, Ke-e-au-moku.

The target of the invasion fleet was the celebrated fort on Kauwiki hill overlooking Hana Harbor, on the east, or rising sun, coast of Maui.

The fleet of Kalaniopuu effected a tremendous surprise, and somewhat unethically (by the standards of the time), offered no official explanation or declaration of war against Kalaniopuu's cousin Kahekili.

The campaign was a large and stunning success, since Kahekili was unable to mount his defensive forces. The 800 troops of Kalaniopuu moved in and occupied the Kauwiki hill fort at the eastern tip of Maui with a minimum of difficulty.

Kalaniopuu appointed Puna as governor of the conquered districts. Besides Puna, a number of Hawaiian chiefs were left in the Hana district when the Alii leaders, Kalaniopuu, Kamehameha, Ke-e-au-moku and Kekuhaupio returned to the Big Island.

However, there was still a gasp of energy left in Kamehameha Nui II. Caught somewhat off-balance by the initial invasion, he recovered sufficiently to collect forces from various parts of Maui and draw troops from the neighboring islands of Molokai and Lanai. He then set out for Hana and laid siege to the fort at Kauwiki.

Several fierce battles were fought with the army of Hawaii under Puna, and after two large-scale campaigns at Maka-ole-hua and at Aki-ala, the Hawaii forces were defeated. But the fort at Kauwiki resisted all attempts to take it, and after a siege lasting several months, Kamehameha Nui withdrew his forces, leaving Hana and the Kauwiki fort still in possession of Kalaniopuu. The Hawaiians were strongly ensconced now in Hana, and the Hawaiians were not driven out until Kamehameha Nui died. He was succeeded by his fearsome younger brother, Kahekili, as moi.

Kahekili, he of the dreadful tattoos and merciless aggressiveness, began a long and sanguinary campaign against the Hawaiian monarch. And Kalaniopuu responded in kind.

Again, Kamehameha's part in the early campaigns of Kalaniopuu was never told by any of the legend-spinners. But presumably, by the time Kalaniopuu began his second campaign against Maui, probably around 1770, Kamehameha was a full-fledged and fully qualified warrior, and about twenty years old.

Prominent among the chiefs whom Kamehameha Nui raised with their forces were some valiant leaders from Molokai and Lanai, the islands neighboring Maui. Most celebrated in the legend was Kaeo Helelani. There were large battles near the Kauwiki fort north of Hana. The battles were at Maka-ole-hua and at Aki-ala, and in both those places the forces of the new king of Hawaii, Kalaniopuu (and Kamehameha with him), were roundly defeated.

And yet, with the persistence of Job, Kalaniopuu managed to hang onto that fort on Kauwiki, the focal point for the bastion of strength which Kalaniopuu had established on the island of Maui. On this expedition, Kamehameha traveled with Keku. But this time he could also renew contact with his first foster father, Naeole, who came as a senior military adviser to Kalaniopuu. Kalaniopuu had gladly accepted Naeole's assistance when Keawe, Alapai's son, was killed and his forces defeated. One of the chiefs who did not accompany Kalaniopuu on this expedition was the mercurial Ke-e-au-moku. This tall, dynamic, warlike chief who had changed sides, and views, so often before, had made another flip-over. This time he decided, after the first confrontation between Kahekili and Kalaniopuu, to enlist his fortunes with the Maui king.

First, he had rebelled against Kalaniopuu, and there was a short engagement between the forces he had gathered and Kalaniopuu's which culminated in a battle at a fort which Ke-e-au-moku had set up near Pololu, on the island of Hawaii. With him was his mother, Kumaaiku.

Kalaniopuu led his forces up the steep slope to the Pololu fort. But Ke-e-au-moku with his mother, children and wives escaped down the back slopes of the mountain, then out by canoe at cliffside. The battle, or rather the retreat, was called in Hawaiian legend Pohaku-o-mane-o, or "Itching Rock."

Then, Ke-e-au-moku made his way back to the court of Kahekili.

But this time, the rash and fast-moving Ke-e-au-moku made another misjudgment which got him into trouble. He was consumed with passion for Namahana, the kapu wife of the late Kamehameha Nui, Kahekili's elder brother and and predecessor as king of Maui. Namahana was also a half-sister to both Kahekili and his late brother Kamehameha Nui.

This marriage irritated Kahekili considerably because he felt Ke-e-au-moku was beneath the widow's status. In the tempestuous way of Hawaiians moved by passion, Ke-e-au-moku and Namahana fled to a district of Maui called Waihee, and managed to avoid contact with Kahekili, at least for a while.

But eventually, the struggle between Kahekili and Ke-e-au-moku broke into open conflict. Kahekili pursued Ke-e-au-moku to Molokai, and crushed his fleet there. Ke-e-au-moku fled to East Maui.

There, Ke-e-au-moku, his wife Namahana, their mothers and their train of retainers showed up at the Kauwiki fort, which had been a stronghold of the Hawaii forces. The governor of the fort at that time was Mahi-hele-lima, the brother of Kane-kapo-lei, one of the wives of Kalaniopuu.

There, Namahana had another child by Ke-e-au-moku. Following the custom of the Alii of giving birth to their children in some secret place, she chose a cave a short distance north of the Kauwiki fort. The baby was a girl, Kaahumanu. Kalaniopuu came later with a sizable force in 1775 or 1776 to attack Kahekili, and at that time Kamehameha saw Ke-e-au-moku and Namahana, and met the seven-year-old Kaahumanu. Already she was a great beauty. By this time, the changeable and dynamic Ke-e-au-moku, aided by the diplomacy of his highborn wife Namahana, was once again firmly established as a friend and supporter of Kalaniopuu.

Kaahumanu grew to be six feet tall and imperially beautiful. She was also an ardent surfboarder and swimmer, and a lover of battles, intrigue and many men. And apparently, in 1784 when she was sixteen, she was married to Kamehameha. Although he had at least twenty-two wives (and children by other women

who were not his wives, such as Kane-kapo-lei, one of the wives
of Kalaniopuu), Kaahumanu remained his most emotional marital
involvement and the female whom he seemed to love most con-
sistently and for the longest time. However, he never managed to
have any children by Kaahumanu.

The battles between Kahekili and Kalaniopuu raged north
and south of Hana in the early 1770s. This campaign was called
the war of "Beating over the Head with War Clubs" (in
Hawaiian, Kala-eho-haha). Both Kalaniopuu and the Maui defenders seemed to have been guilty of this kind of cruel fortuitous
beating of prisoners in the area around the fort of Kauwiki.

Kamehameha and his military tutor, Kekuhaupio, were involved
in much of this brutal fighting. It was here that Kamehameha
won his first fame in the arts of war. He and Kekuhaupio were
involved in one of the war-canoe sea-land battles common in
Hawaiian history, one of the many Hawaiian precursors of the
amphibious kind of assault which occurred so often during our
World War II history.

The battle began as Kahekili led an amphibious assault upon
the Hawaiian forces commanded by Kekuhaupio. And Keku, the
famous Hawaiian chief and fighter, was accompanied that day by
Kamehameha. Before the day was over, it was a good thing for
Kekuhaupio that his illustrious student of the military arts was
with him.

The attack began as one of Kahekili's reactions to the "Heads
Beaten with Clubs" brutality of the Kaupo campaign.

Kahekili had sent a large canoe-borne effort led by Kane-olae-
lae. Beaten in two engagements, and forced backward toward the
town of Ki'ei, the forces of Keku were withdrawing among the
sandy yam hills, with a cliff on their left wing. There was still an
ascending grade behind them as they were retiring up the long
slope called Kiha Puhala.

But Keku was not the only one of the Hawaiian chiefs in
trouble. On his seaward flank, the main body of Kalaniopuu's
troops were being beset by increasing numbers of Kane-olae-lae's
troops. Kane-olae-lae realized he had his principal enemy on the

run, and closed in for the kill, seeking to drive Kalaniopuu and his ranking leaders over the cliff. It is famed in Hawaiian battle legends that as he came in for the finale, Kane-olae-lae whirled his battle club by its thong over his head and proclaimed that Kalaniopuu was finished.

Kalaniopuu, realizing the desperate circumstances, had dispatched several runners in succession to get word through to his war canoes to come and pick him up at one of several suggested beach points.

The battle for Kamehameha and Keku was of course a withdrawing action. But Kamehameha, now in his mid-twenties, was displaying the prowess which was to win for him the much coveted nickname among honored Hawaiian warriors, Pai'ea, or "hard-shelled crab."

As the retreating horde fell back to the little group of thatch huts called Pa'auhau, they saw scores of Kalaniopuu's war canoes appearing round the "Point of the Dog" (Kalae-o-ka-ilio). Immediately, as hard-pressed soldiery are wont to do, the main body pushed closer to the cliff and the paths leading down to the small beaches of the coast there. The prospect of safety, even if the Kalaniopuu navy should be beset by the opposing fleet of canoes, was too attractive to be resisted. The main body of the retreating Hawaiians began to accelerate their pace so that it became a trot, almost a run.

And the enemy troops, already pushing hard against the forefront of the Hawaiians, saw this and pushed even harder. The frequent hailstorms of stones arched out by the expert sling-men of the Maui troopers grew thicker. The storm of war shouts, the blood-curdling accompaniment of a battle, almost immediately grew louder: It was like the shout of excitement as a quarry is cornered.

Kalaniopuu, moi of Hawaii and famed for his skill at war and the rough sports of mokomoko (boxing) and hakoko (wrestling), was not exactly the aggressive leader at this juncture. In fact, his pace to the rear seemed to be accelerating.

Inland of Kalaniopuu's commanding staff and his sorely pressed forefront troops to the south, the military chief Kamehameha and his kahu Kekuhaupio could see the disturbing shape of the battle.

Standing on the slope with the giant Kamehameha and looking back toward the enemy, Keku smiled, his weathered and leathery visage cracking with dry humor. "Kameha, it seems we will be the rear guard—whether we like it or not."

Kamehameha looked back up the slope. He was a grown man now. Still in his early twenties, he had an awesome warrior's face, battered and scarred from scores of battles—mostly the realistic sham battles of which the Hawaiian fighters were so fond. His left leg and right arm were also marked with long whitening spear and knife scars.

His eyes, seeming even darker brown than ever, nearly black, showed the same remarkable coolness and measured calculation as in the episode with the Naha Stone. Now, concentration and calculation in the ruthless arts of war seemed to have deepened the fierce scowling lines, as in the twisted face of his war god Ku. Yet there remained an air of graveness and thoughtfulness (not quite consideration) which distinguished him from other twenty-year-old braves. He said: "Keku, the potato vines grow thicker as we withdraw up this slope. We must be careful not to become entangled."

He glanced off toward the sea, where four large Hawaiian war canoes were entering a narrow palm-studded cove to the south of the Point of the Dog. "Kalaniopuu will probably be descending the path down the side of the cliff at this moment."

He looked levelly at his kahu, and added: "We should use our last long spears, our pololu, to keep them back so that the king may leave."

Keku smiled again, the crinkles deepening around his mouth. "Yes. There will be plenty of time later for the short weapons and the pahoa, the shark-tooth clubs and the long-bladed daggers."

Keku grew suddenly serious and took Kamehameha by the arm to a craggy outcrop with a better view of the cove of the Point of the Dog.

From this new view, they could see an isolated small lagoon, almost completely landlocked. In it were two small war canoes with sails half-raised, ready to go.

Keku clapped Kamehameha across the shoulders. He pointed down toward the closest canoe, where they could see three tall figures of men, wearing only their narrow war malos, their skins sunburned, beside the mast. Keku smiled again: "When you have been a soldier as long as I, you know that it is wise to have several extra ways out.

"Kings are not always trustworthy. If all goes badly, throw clouds of dust up and let that boatman see where you go down to the water. He will pick you up."

He laughed. "And I hope he picks me up, too."

Kamehameha nodded. "I will remember, kahu." He did not smile, but somehow his face seemed to brighten. "And I will be sure that you are with me."

A new roar of increasing volume rose like a single shout from the battling ranks on the slopes below the two men. And a few seconds later, another storm cloud of sling-tossed rocks smudged the air around the center of the battleline. The crowd of struggling warriors seemed suddenly to have thickened in that area, and Keku interpolated: "I cannot see who is there, but undoubtedly Kane-olae-lae has come to reinforce the center of their battleline."

Kamehameha nodded. "I will go down and hold them together while we fall back through the yam fields."

Kamehameha nodded again. "I will go with you, kahu. With my ihe spear and my shark-tooth club."

Keku smiled his grim, tight smile again. "Yes, Kameha, and we will also have the human ihe and shark-tooth clubs, Keawe Hano, Kane Hailua and Inaina."

A few minutes later, the mighty Kamehameha's figure dominated that same battleline. He was the prominent feature of a mass of his soldiers, somewhat to the rear of that mass, behind the flickering outer edge where it contacted the Maui troops in hand-to-hand action. He was a monument, his six-and-a-half-foot, full-necked, muscular figure, a warlike column swathed in the red and gold feather cape of his ahuula, his battle cloak. His tall helmet, of closely woven yellow feathers on a tight vine and olona fiber, raised his height to more than seven feet. In his hands, now, the short ihe spear on the right, and ready in the left, a long sling or ma'a, made of Hau fiber.

Beside his feet was a pile of smooth sling stones, oval-shaped. And tied to his waist, by a thong, an open-frame shark-tooth club, studded with selected long and reasonably straight shark's teeth. Right now, he was expertly flinging a sling stone, so that it arced high into the cloud of stones soaring overhead.

The noise of the battle shouts engulfed them like a cloud. And around the towering figure of Kamehameha stood the lesser ones of Keku and the same human spears Keku had mentioned: Inaina, Keawe Hano and Kane Hailua.

A kind of shield of men arched in front of the chiefs. They were fighting hand-to-hand against the Maui soldiers, the shouting, panting, screaming of their bodily contact like surf around the chiefs. The warriors of both sides were naked except for narrow strips of malo around their middles, and they had no shield like European or Asian warriors; only the short (about six feet) in-fighting spears of hardwood, highly polished, most with barbed points. Some men had draped improvised turbans of tapa cloth, wetted down for insulating effect, around their heads to afford some extra protection. The spears were used in this close fighting for parrying enemy thrusts by spear and dagger, or for deflecting the blows of war clubs swinging in that melee, the shark-tooth and club-shaped bludgeon weapons. The brown bodies, locked in the clatter of weapons and the blanket of the sounds of effort, pain and ferocity, appeared almost to be wrestling, like one many-legged beast, while their spears waved like scores of wooden arms in and around the tangle. Among that mess of flailing and parrying weapons, there sometimes gleamed the short under-thrusts of the daggers, the pahoa.

Kekuhaupio spoke to Kamehameha as the big man reached

for another sling stone. "Kane-olae-lae, I believe, is to our left. The line seems to have thickened considerably there. And I see many yellow cloaks in that sector, Maui high Alii."

Kamehameha acknowledged with a slight bow. "Yes, kahu. It was he at whom I was throwing my sling stones." Keku was not surprised. Kamehameha had eyes as sharp as many birds of prey, even the black-headed osprey, the sea-eagle. And he had always said, since his first battle at Honaunau, where Keawe's kahuna had been killed and the whole enemy fort had collapsed as a result, that it was always good strategy, if not exactly in accordance with the old rules of warfare, to kill the enemy's leaders whenever possible.

Now a new outcry rose from the immediate forefront of the embattled front line, and the hue and cry indicated some new excitement, he was sure.

Keku said, under his breath, "It's probably the big effort." Kamehameha said, softly:

"Keku, I think the biggest effort will be from the direction of their leader, Kane-olae-lae. Shall I move in that direction, to hold up that line?"

Keku glanced at him admiringly. "Good. I will keep an eye out for you." His face crinkled wryly: "Or perhaps you had better keep an eye out for me."

Kamehameha hesitated, and said with admiration: "Keku, you are never happier than when we are in a fight."

Keku grinned. "Happier, if we are winning."

At that moment, another sharp outcry of excitement and concern seemed to inundate them, coming predominately from the sector Kamehameha had indicated, their left. From that direction, stones and spears were flying, the long pololu spears, and a hailstorm of stones. From that direction, battlecries rose like the frantic gobbling of turkeys at feeding time. "He's coming now!" Kamehameha said. "We can fall back among the potato hills, and kill them in the ravines."

A clatter and clamber of warriors were pushing from their left, with a wide-sounding cry of alarm. The Hawaiians were being compressed backward. Kamehameha saw a chief, identifiable by his long red and yellow cloak and plumed helmet in the middle distance between Kamehameha and the far-off figure of Kane-olae-lae. He didn't recognize the chief, but he knew that he would be the lieutenant of Kane-olae-lae entrusted with this front of the attack. Kamehameha searched for a long pololu spear. He had long since thrown his, but the best source was one thrown by the enemy. He spotted one such lying on the ground and snatched it up. If he could remove this Alii lieutenant with the red and yellow cloak, that would impede the enemy attack considerably.

His years of practice in sham battles and his many recent battle experiences here on Maui and on the Big Island helped him. It would be a long shot to kill the chief or even to wound him, at this distance. The flight of the weapon would have to be long, and if the enemy's eyes were sharp, he would have ample time to dodge the spear or catch it. But it would be worth a try.

For this shot, he would have to make a long run to get the spear up to flying speed. The flight would be at least three times the length of one of the large double-hulled war canoes. He could see the chief a little more clearly as he turned toward Kamehameha. He was tall and dark-skinned and he too carried a long pololu spear. Still, he did not recognize the man.

The spear he had picked up was not heavy enough, and it was cheaply made, with only two barbs carved into its long wooden point. It did not balance right, it was too heavy at the rear. But it would have to do.

Kamehameha hurried backward fourteen or fifteen paces, and crouched over the spear for the beginning of his launching run. He made a quick prayer to his war god, Ku-kaili-moku. "Great God Ku," he breathed, "help my aim and my arm to do justice to you and my family, and to kill."

But at the critical moment of the start, his keyed-up warrior's mentality gave him prescience of a threat coming. In that second, he had glimpsed two long pololu spears flying in his direction, one close behind the other. And in that second, he had dodged the first so that it slid harmlessly over the ground, and caught the second with his upreached right hand. In the quick maneuver, he had dropped his own pololu spear.

But in the next few moments, he gathered that the first of the two spears thrown at him was a better weapon than the one he had dropped. He ran backward to retrieve it and to start again with his throw. At that moment, another surge of enemy activity buckled the lines ahead of him and the Hawaiian line was falling back: the sweating malo-clad warriors were jostling past, and a charging group of Maui troops pounded toward him. In that second, he retrieved the long well-made spear he had sought, and turned to face a Maui trooper, brandishing a short ihe, and doing his best to utter a bloodcurdling war cry.

Kamehameha changed his tactics in a moment. The enemy was no more than twelve paces away and thumping closer. Kamehameha aimed carefully. He had long since learned that in a fight it is best to estimate coolly, rather than be inflamed with emotions which were generated mostly to give one courage.

The spear flew truly, and his warrior's heart leaped despite his resolve to be cool, as the weapon struck the enemy full in the chest and the force of the blow caught him in the middle of a running stride and knocked him over backward.

But other enemies were close, charging like the first. Kamehameha retrieved his short, ihe spear and his shark-tooth club from the ground where he had laid them. Now, he would do best with close-in weapons, where many men were lacking.

In the breathing space of that second, he glanced around to see what friends were with him. Keku had disappeared; so had the other Alii lieutenants, except Kane Hailua. The burly, stalwart chief was at that moment thrusting an ihe spear into the side of a Maui soldier, and turning to ward off a malevolent spear thrust by another Mauian.

The next second, Kamehameha was fending off a spear thrust to the left, with his own ihe, and attempting to dodge a wide swing by another Maui soldier with a huge, smooth-headed war club.

The war club from the right missed; he parried another thrust from the ihe to the left, and with his accustomed fast reactions, managed to jam the smooth point of the ihe into the thigh of the spear carrier on the left.

A group of Hawaiian warriors had appeared around him, and they were locked in close conflict. He suspected Kane Hailua had sent help. Kamehameha took advantage of the relief to find the wielder of the large smooth-headed war club from the right.

He was a sturdy, very dark-skinned, grizzle-haired warrior of the common rank, judging from the fact that he wore the simple malo and nothing else. His body, while large, seemed overfat for a warrior and he was an older man, judging from body fat and grayed hair.

But now, he was aiming a tremendous wide swing with the war club at the towering Kamehameha. And Kamehameha was not about to defer to his superior years and capitulate. In an instinctive reaction, his left hand came up with a short underhand swing which caught the older warrior under the chin and flipped him over, his wide swing of the deadly war club flipping up into the air as he spilled over backward. The excitement and danger of the fight were reaching Kameha like a fever. He liked this excitement almost as much as making love to women.

Now Kamehameha glimpsed an Alii figure next to him, in a ripped and battered feather cloak and helmet of red and gold. It was his treasured battle ally Kane Hailua ("Man-Hailua"), nearly as tall as Kamehameha and, like him, dark-skinned. Kane Hailua was striking out with a wide-swinging shark-tooth dagger like Kamehameha's but in his right hand. The weapon in his other arm was like that of Kamehameha's other hand, a short ihe spear, with a smooth wooden point so that it could be used quickly in mortal wounds and withdrawn without difficulty in disengaging any barbs. Now, the point of Kane Hailua's spear was red with blood.

As Kamehameha noticed him, Kane Hailua's shark-tooth weapon, also running with blood, found a mark. It bashed a Maui soldier on the side of the head and spun him over. Kane Hailua exulted, to Kamehameha: "Pai'ea! We may even be turning them back!" The nickname meant "hard-shelled crab," and it was Kame-hameha's favorite, for it was a battle-earned soubriquet. As Kane Hailua spoke, it seemed that the line of the Maui troopers did seem to be bending backward, did seem to be giving way in this locality at least. The mass of Hawaiian troopers were moving forward, stepping over the dead or dying Mauians they had de-feated. And Kane Hailua shouted in a stentorian voice, for the benefit of all: "Forward, Army of Kalaniopuu. Kill these kau-kau Alii. They have no stomach for battle."

But Kamehameha, his first warmth of battle rage tapering off into the efficacious coolness which was his mark of successful procedure in a fight, was not at all certain that the battle was going as well as Kane Hailua believed.

A quick check showed him that the rest of the line of the Hawaiian army, Kalaniopuu's army, was far behind them on both sides, particularly on their left. There, the Maui forces had been making their great effort under the leadership of Kane-olae-lae. And that, he felt sure, was the direction which Kekuhaupio had followed when the latest attack of the Mauians began. He hur-ried forward to Kane Hailua, who was at that moment preparing to launch a long pololu spear. He waited while Kane Hailua ran forward and bounced the long lance steeply into the air—prob-ably aimed at the same Maui Alii chief whom Kamehameha had eyed as a target earlier. It disappeared into the enemy throng. Then he spoke to Kane Hailua as the chief bent over to retrieve another loose pololu spear:

"Chief, Kekuhaupio has been driven back on our left. Our right flank has also fallen back. If we are not careful, we will soon be surrounded by enemy."

Kane Hailua looked up at him with eyes wide in surprise. He stopped and looked as Kamehameha had, at both flanks. Then he said:

"You are right, Pai'ea. We also must fall back." His white teeth flashed in a quick smile: "But at least, we have held them back a little. And surprised them!"

Kamehameha said: "While you withdraw, Hailua, I will go to

the left and look for Kekuhaupio. I'm afraid he is in deep trouble."

As Kamehameha moved somewhat to the rear, skirting the battleline, he had to work farther and farther to the rear. The front
skirmish line had been beaten far back on this sector, where it ran
out toward the cliff. At the left end of the line, close to the cliff
edge, he made out the most forward elements of the Hawaiian
army, and in this area, a tangle of struggling bodies in hand-to-
hand, close-weapon combat. Near them, among a group of the
yellow robes and helmets of the Alii, he was sure he could recognize the stalwart, lean figure of Kekuhaupio.

Keku really was in bad trouble. Opposite him was the largest
group of the Maui troops, apparently the bulk of the army of Kalaniopuu and Kane-olae-lae's troops. It was clear what they were
about. Here where the access to escape through the canoe fleets
of Kalaniopuu was the most direct, they would concentrate their
forces and try to decimate the remnants of Kalaniopuu's armies.

Kamehameha worked his way closer, satisfied himself that this
was indeed Keku, the great chief and his kahu, and then he knew
what had to be done: to find a vantage point where he could see
the small cove with the canoemen pledged to rescue Keku; to
signal them that they must come to the appointed place to pick
up their chief. Then, to bring the successful and skillful fighters
of Kane Hailua to rescue Kekuhaupio.

There was no time to waste.

He started climbing back up the slight rise toward a point in
line with the vantage spot which Keku had shown him before,
where Keku had pointed out the canoes in the calm little cove,
now well to the south where they could be signalled.

With all the adroitness of a mountain goat from the crags of
Mauna Kea on his home island, he scrambled up the slope toward
a high rise which overlooked the whole battle scene, where he
should be in line with the cove-of-several-pools and its friendly
fleet.

From this high spot, he could look down on what seemed to be
the same precise crag where Keku had taken him before to point
out the canoes. And this time, as before, he found them, although

with some searching. On the high crag, he threw up clouds of dust. As an extra beacon, he removed the narrow red war malo he was wearing and, his long, heavy arms moving like semaphores, he managed to attract the attention of the war canoes of Kekuhaupio. They signalled back, waving their arms. Then the canoes began to move out of the cove, and Kamehameha breathed a prayer to his god Ku that they should make no mistake but find their way to the same cove which Kekuhaupio had earlier designated to the canoemen.

Kamehameha saw the canoes moving in sprightly, precise formation, the paddlers moving in unison with the miraculous precision of the Hawaiian paddle navies—especially with the extra precision insisted upon by Kalaniopuu. Then, Kamehameha began to run down the slope, searching for the forces of Kane Hailua. They would undoubtedly still be closely engaged in mortal combat with the Mauians, if Kane Hailua had his way.

He found Kane Hailua as expected, in the midst of a sweating, bloody entanglement, plying his ihe spear, a now-battered shark-tooth club, and his short hardwood dagger. Kane Hailua had been wounded in the side by now. His yellow cloak was torn where weapons had ripped it and beneath the largest rent, a crude bandage of white tapa showed through. And Kane Hailua's band of warriors were similarly battered, their numbers decimated.

They had fallen back near the thatch-hut village of Pahonu. Here the yam vines were thick and entangling. They had been fighting along the lines of the vines. Good soldiers that they were, they had been using the vines as hazards to the enemy and protection to themselves. Frequently they had managed to trap the Maui soldiers in them so they could be cut down more easily. The bodies of Maui soldiers hung along the lines of the vines like flies in a spider web. And now, the current fighting spread down the lines of several vines and a bulge of Maui soldiers was being driven back down the slope, away from Pahonu.

When Kane Hailua saw that Kamehameha had returned, he disengaged himself and hurried to the chief. Kamehameha told him: "Keku and his men are fighting hard on our left flank. They are heavily outnumbered. I have called for the canoes to pick us up at Kalae-o-ka-ilio, the village on the coast."

"We'll pull back and come with you," Kane Hailua said.

Kamehameha nodded. "Yes. But we will probably have to fight our way out. Helping Keku." Kane Hailua surveyed his battered troops, then driving the remnants of the Maui troops in that sector down the slope, some of the enemy running to escape. "They are ready for that," he said.

By the time Kamehameha and Kane Hailua got back to the left end position of Keku, the forces of that chief were in desperate straits. As he came down the slope above Keku's position, Kamehameha saw the same battle phenomenon he had glimpsed with Kane Hailua's forces but turned the other way around.

Where the bodies strung along the potato vines in Kane Hailua's position were Mauians, here it was Keku's men who were the corpses strewn through the lines of the vines. Even greater numbers of Maui troops were swarming up from the south than before, and there seemed to be only two of the yellow blades of battle cloaks, indicating Alii and commanders, on Keku's side. One of them, he saw rapidly, was Keku, and he was closely entangled with a group of struggling Mauians, his ihe spear moving skillfully in the best master-at-arms fashion. His motions as he parried and struck seemed graceful even in the desperation of a hand-to-hand struggle.

Kamehameha surveyed the scene coolly with his analytical dark-brown gaze. The lights in his eyes seemed to turn almost black as the warrior's rapid concentration held him.

Kane Hailua had halted his men at the top of the rise, well behind the rock which marked its peak. He and Kamehameha surveyed the situation from behind that rock. Kamehameha said: "We can get around to the rear of the Mauians—that way we may catch them by surprise."

Kane Hailua said: "Yes, perhaps we can get through on this side." He grinned. "In fact, it's the only way."

And so it was that the pack of battered fighters under Kamehameha and Kane Hailua came charging into the fight from the enemy's rear. And the most powerful weapon in any military arsenal, surprise, was again a strong influence. Now it wreaked sore confusion and death in the enemy ranks. Kamehameha headed straight for his beleaguered kahu and found him sorely beset from two sides, and wielding his ihe with his right arm and his pahoa, the short wooded dagger, with expert effect in his left.

At the moment Kamehameha came upon Keku, a new opponent was joining the fray. He was a Maui chief, with yellow and red battle cloak and helmet, and Kamehameha surprised *him* completely.

In the few moments available as he pressed his attack, Kamehameha made a quick check to see if it was some Maui chief he would know. It was always possible, in these days of interrelated Hawaiian royalty, that one might kill or cripple one of one's close relatives. But he did not recognize the man. As he cried out, the Alii turned, just in time to receive an ihe thrust to his middle. Kamehameha jerked his spear free and the violence of his assault threw off the two soldiers who were besetting Keku. Keku speared one and the other ran backward. Kamehameha swung at him with his shark-tooth club, but in the close passage, the man ducked away and Kamehameha missed.

Kamehameha called out: "Kahu, I've called for the canoes. We must go to Kalae-o-ka-ilio. Now!"

Kekuhaupio smiled, a brilliant flash of white. "Pai'ea, you won your right to be called Hard Shell Crab today, if never before."

It was only a moment's respite in that engagement, but the effect of surprise had buckled the Maui assault at least for the moment, and the Hawaiian forces, now under three distinguished generals, Kamehameha, Kekuhaupio and Kane Hailua, were in command of a victorious situation. Kane Hailua's indomitables were driving the fleeing Mauians back down the slope, as they had before, and committing mayhem in the lines of yam vines.

Now Kamehameha commanded the dark commander: "Tell them to follow Keku. He will lead us down the cliffside to Kalae-o-ka-ilio."

It was fortunate that they were so close to the extreme left flank of the Hawaiian line, and the cliff which led to sanctuary. Getting down the cliff to the beach at Kalae-o-ka-ilio was surprisingly easy. But the issue was a long way from being solved. As they climbed down the winding trail toward the narrow, rock-trimmed cove, in the bay outside they could see two pitched battles going on between war canoes of the two sides. One of these engagements they could see squarely: Two fleets of canoes, totalling perhaps thirty-five of the double-hulled Polynesian men-of-war, were lambasting each other with showers of sling stones. Several of them were grappled together with the long ropes and hooks. The malo-clad warriors, including the bright pinpoints of yellow cloaks marking the Alii, were locked in hand-to-hand boarding struggles.

The other engagement, at the northern edge of their field of view, disclosed another boarding combat among four canoes. Two of them were already locked together. The torrents of tan-colored bodies, punctuated with the spots of yellow and red, the leaders, were locked in death struggle.

One factor was favorable to the escaping troops: time. The long day's battle had sapped away most of the daylight hours. Now, as Kamehameha's feet touched the cooling sand of the little cove, the light shedding down into it was the luminous, cool, brave light of the before-twilight time, the crepuscular moment always so dramatic in the Hawaiian Islands. In a short time, as the sunset paled into darker colors, and the puffy clouds changed from dark gold to purple, the marauding canoe fleets of King Kahekili and the Mauians would be less able to wreak their havoc on the retreating Hawaiians.

Many deep concerns plagued Kameha and Keku as they reached the beach. The main concern was whether they had come to the correct meeting place to be picked up by the canoes of Kekuhaupio, and whether those canoes would be able to fight their way through the screen of marauding canoes from Kahekili's forces and make the pickup.

Another worry high on Kamehameha's list was the fate of Kalaniopuu. As soon as they had time to spare on the beach while waiting for the canoes to appear, he asked about it. And Kekuhaupio answered with dispatch:

"I saw Kalaniopuu making his way to the canoes," Keku said, smiling. "The fight was so hot I didn't have time to find fresh spears." His grin grew brighter. "I wouldn't have been able to get away at all unless you had come along. I say a heartfelt mahalo."

Kamehameha did not smile, but his face lighted with a kind of enthusiasm, and he said simply: "So far. We probably will not know if he survived until we are back at the fort in Kauwiki. That is, if the Great God Ku favors us."

As if his mentioning Ku were an invocation of the supernatural, four of the smaller-type canoes that moment appeared in a neat echelon formation, the crewmen paddling swiftly and in unison. The four boats entered the narrow entrance to the little lagoon of Kalae-o-ka-ilio. "Glory be to the Great God Ku," said Kamehameha. "Our canoes!"

And behind them, testifying to the real glory of Ku's miraculous power, followed six large canoes of Kalaniopuu's fleet—with enough space for Kane Hailua's valiant band.

Fortunately, the shadows of the night were deep over the purpled ocean by the time the small fleet of canoes picked their way out of the narrow entrance to the lagoon—and found to their joyful surprise that not one of Kahekili's canoes was lying in wait for them.

These favorite canoemen of Kekuhaupio knew well how to navigate by night. Always, there was "hoku-paa," the fixed star which in the European world we call Polaris, or the North Star. The chief boatman, Kanaloa, also could fix his position by the "makali'li," Castor and Pollux, and he could estimate the hour infallibly by the positions of the Twins in the sky, judging by "nana-mua," or the One Going Ahead, and "nana-hope," the

One Following, as the constellation slowly revolved through the watches of the night.

When the night winds blew, the paddlers unshipped their paddles and the canoes sailed nicely with the wind until they were in the vicinity of the fortified hill of Kauwiki. When the tired band came into the moonlit harbor of Kalaniopuu's fleet, there lay the remnant of that fleet. It had been sadly whittled down to about sixty war canoes. Many of them had scars visible even in the faint moonlight, their superstructures broken after the day's desperate encounters.

Kameha found out rapidly before the moon set—it was the time of Holu Palemo, the Sinking Star—that Kalaniopuu had survived that day's ordeal. With him he still had many of his leading generals, including his famous military kahu, Puna. The indefatigible Kalaniopuu was then being paddled among the remnants of his once-proud fleet.

They came upon him as he was boarding one of his largest double canoes, a vessel so badly wrecked by the fighting that the outrigger booms which kept the two hulls apart had been cracked and hastily lashed together. The humpbacked outrigger shape squeaked loudly in the slapping of the small chop in the bay.

In the light of the setting moon, Kalaniopuu climbed atop the deckhouse on this broken canoe, and swore by his war god that he would be revenged. While his head kahuna, Holoae, stood by on one of the hulls with Puna, Kalani summoned the god: "Great God Kaili, I promise to avenge this defeat upon your sacred presence. I will build heiaus for the complete defeat of our enemy, Kahekili. I will raise armies from Kealia to Kapa-ahu. I will raise such an army of chosen alapa [troops] to fight for you, and such a fleet of canoes as Kahekili has never seen, not even in his bad dreams. We will have troops as numerous as the rains of Ikuwa."

There was a pause, and from one of the hulls of the canoe, the tall, stooped, white-haired figure of Holoae, the kahuna, answered him in sonorous tones: "I predict that the waters of the Iao stream will run red with the blood of Kalaniopuu's enemies.

"The god Kaili has heard your promise of heiaus consecrated to the defeat of Kahekili. We will start building them as soon as we are back in Hawaii."

It would be seventeen years before the prophecy of Holoae would come true, literally. During the intervening time, Kamehameha was to suffer the reverse, defeat in the Iao area—and only from the ashes of defeat to build his own dream of aggrandizement and glory in the ranks of Hawaiian royalty.

CHAPTER 5

A New and Formidable Foe

WITHIN THE NEXT YEAR, Kalaniopuu was in mid-flight with his vast project of expanding and glorifying the army of Hawaii to its largest extent.

During two years very important in American history, 1775 and 1776, Kalaniopuu and his chiefs were busy making sure that his promise to the war god Kaili was going to be kept, and the vast amphibious fleet and army prepared for the forthcoming conquest of Maui. He still held the base of operations in east Maui, the Kauwiki fort.

As he had sworn he would do, Kalaniopuu, with the aid of his high priest Holoae, repaired and put into good order his heiaus for Ku-kaili-moku. They were at Kahaluu, and at Kailua in the Kona district. He assembled six army corps or brigades, known by the names of I, Ahu, Mahi, Palena, Luahine and Paia. And the members of the royal family were welded into an elite guard, called Keawe. The other nobles, the Alii-ai-alo, nobles who had the privilege of eating with Kalaniopuu, were composed into two regiments called Alapa and Pi-i-pii.

Also, Kalaniopuu built, over the space of two years, a formidable fleet of dugout canoes, many of them the supersized, sixty-foot-long war canoes with double hulls, usually with a platform between the hulls.

On Maui, the quick-thinking, resourceful and warlike Kahekili kept himself informed of these developments on the Big Island. He instituted a religious program, involving the building of heiaus to rival Kalaniopuu's. In his kingdom he did not have a high priest worthy of comparison in power or mana with the famed Holoae. So he sent to Oahu and prevailed upon Kaleo-puu-puu, the high priest of the recently deceased king of Oahu, to come to him.

Kaleo-puu-puu was one of the most prestigious of the priests of the Hawaiian Islands, and allegedly a descendent of the priests of 700 years before who had been brought back from long voyages to other Pacific islands. The most famous of these far voyagers was Pau Makua.

So Kahekili hung on every instruction of Kaleo-puu-puu, and principally he repaired, expanded and won the priest's approval for a remodelled heiau called Kaluli near Wailuku. Wailuku was the principal royal capital, located at the narrowest neck on the island of Maui, not far from the center of the island. It was fated that the great battle between Kalaniopuu and Kahekili was to be fought not far from this heiau, in the valley of the Iao, to the west of Wailuku. In return for the construction of this handsome heiau, Kaleo-puu-puu prophesized that the Hawaiian forces would be caught and killed like fish in a net: "Ua komo ka ia i ka makaha ua puni i ka nae"; literally "school of fish entering a fish trap."

Kalaniopuu's large navy landed just about midway on Maui, on the southern coast. Wailuku, the objective, is close to the northern coast. In this landing area, near Makena, one of the southernmost points in the island of Maui, the Hawaii warriors ravaged the countryside. The local inhabitants fled to the hills behind the coast.

Kalaniopuu decided he should reembark a large portion of his troops and go closer by sea to Wailuku. To do this, he took most of the fleet and they landed on the southern edge of Maui's narrow isthmus.

The wide span of canoes spread all the way from Kihei, where Maui's narrow neck begins on the east, to Maalaea at the western extremity, a good five miles.

A fleet of more than 300 canoes, perhaps more than half of them the mammoth sixty-footers with a platform between the hulls, had been beached by sunset of that first day of landing. But there were still another hundred to come up from Makena, with troops.

The elite regiment of the Alapa were landed as a unit at Maalaea. With them, Kalaniopuu, Kamehameha and many of the leading chiefs. Kalani set up his headquarters at Maalaea, and conferred immediately with their leaders—Kane Hailua, Keawe Hano, Kuaana and Inaina. He wanted to start immediately with the assault, and these indomitables assured him that the Alapa alone could beat Kahekili.

So Kalaniopuu, his legions, principally the Alapa regiment or detachment of 800 men which was to start the expedition, uttered the war cry "On to Wailuku!" The Alapa started across the narrow isthmus of Maui, and they were a beautiful sight to behold in the sunlight. They were the elite guard of Kalaniopuu's army, with a high percentage of Alii, and chosen to be tall and of equal stature, their spears also of equal height. As they marched, a mass of red and gold feather cloaks and yellow coned feather helmets, it seemed they must be almost all Alii.

The wily Kahekili, consulting moment by moment with his holy man, Kaleo-puu-puu, decided to let the enemy tire themselves somewhat with the crossing north to Wailuku. He had spent two days carefully arranging his forces along the width of the Wailuku perimeter, and was counseled by Kaleo-puu-puu: Wait for the enemy. He too had a picked army, but they were far from being all nobles, although they were all chosen for their expertness in fighting: chiefs, skilled soldiers and lefthanded stone slingers reputed to be the most accurate marksmen in all the islands.

Most important, these troops had the greatest advantage in any war involvement: arithmetic. Kahekili had good intelligence, and his swift runners brought him news that the rash Kalaniopuu was attacking with only the Alapa regiment.

Kalaniopuu dispatched his forces with the ringing exhortation: "Before the day is over, we will drink of the waters of Wailuku."

Kahekili let his enemy penetrate into the sand hill area southwest of Wailuku. This area led into the Iao Valley, and it was here, as they moved into the bottomlands of the Iao River, that Kahekili had planned their total destruction.

Among the forefront of the Alapa were these three young chiefs who had distinguished themselves at the previous battles of Kalaniopuu on the Hana coast of east Maui: Inaina, Keawe Hano and the giant of the dark skin, Kane Hailua.

The Alapa went ahead, full of supreme confidence that they could lay waste the best troops of Kahekili, and that night, indeed drink the waters of Wailuku and the next day rest in the shade of Hekuawa. The other units of Kalaniopuu's army remained in a reserve status. Or to be more exact, most of them were still moving up from the strip of coast near Kihei, or still back at Makena.

Kamehameha and his mentor both cursed their luck, standing on that high hill west of Maalaea, near Kalaniopuu and his other chiefs. They watched the proud spectacle of the Alapa on the march, the waves of golden-uniformed men.

Kalaniopuu was boastful: "How beautiful! They will make ground meat of Kahekili."

Kekuhaupio spoke softly about this to Kameha: "Pai'ea, I know how much you want to go with them."

Kameha in fact was scowling dismally, and this was the cause of his misery.

Keku went on: "But I, for one, am glad we are not going. Kahekili still believes the best prescription for victory is two or three of his for one of his enemy's."

Pai'ea still scowled. Keku said: "I did my best to persuade him of this. But he has blind faith in the Alapa, against any odds."

But the plain fact was that the Alapa, for all their skill with the spear and war club, were no match for the more than 2,500 skilled slingmen of Kahekili's "Smoke Head" and "Red Coconut" divisions. The Kahekili forces outnumbered the Alapa more than three to one.

According to the legends of this Polynesian "Charge of the Light Brigade" assault, the chief holy man of the Maui forces, Kaleo-puu-puu, said to Kahekili: "The fish have entered the sluice; draw in the net."

On the sounding of the hoarse battle cry and the blowing of conch shells, the Smoke Head and Red Coconut hordes rose out of the sand hills to the north of Kahului and came streaming down to the attack. The Alii of the Alapa regiment were overshadowed by a swarming cloud of expertly slung stones, and a fish-school of spears. These marauding divisions, overwhelming in number, came to the attack with their short ihe spears, long daggers, two-bladed, with a handle and thong in the middle so that strikes could be made in two directions. And in the first assault fell the valiant dark warrior who had fought so well beside Kamehameha on the Hana coast before, Kane Hailua, dead with a spear thrust through his chest.

Hemmed in from all sides, the gallant Alapa fell by the score, and Kahekili's warriors carried out their instructions, "No quarter. Kill them all."

The locust swarms of Kahekili's divisions beset them from all sides, and being so vastly outnumbered, the Alapa were eliminated almost to a man. Two survivors managed to extricate themselves and found their way back to the command post at Kihei-Pukoa. According to Kamakau, one of the two survivors stood before Kalaniopuu and said: "O Heavenly One! Our men are lost. We two remain to tell of our escape. The chiefs Inaina, Kane Hailua, Kuaana and Keawe Hano and the whole host of the Alapa are dead."

Then Kalaniopuu leaned his head against his hands, pressing

them against his forehead, grasped his nose with one hand and pulled at it with a mournful wailing for the dead.

That night, in the thatch hut which was his headquarters, Kalaniopuu consulted with his principal chiefs: Keawe-mauhili, his half-brother; Kalani Manouka Poowaha, of Kohala; Keawe Aheulu, descendent of the great family of I; Nuuanu, of Ka'u; Kekuhaupio, the great chief and military kahu of Kamehameha; Kamehameha; and many other relatives of Kalaniopuu.

At that council of war it was decided that the following day the remainder of Kalaniopuu's army would march to attack Kahekili's legions in the outskirts of Wailuku.

The chiefs broke up the meeting that night with the same battle cry on their lips, "We will drink the waters of Wailuku and rest in the shade of the Hekuawa."

During the night before the battle, Kahekili had also been active. He took advantage of the opportunity to push in reinforcements under his ally, the Oahu king Kahahana. He stationed a large reserve force at the turn of the Waikapu stream, and predicated his campaign on the assumption that the Hawaiian forces would again attack from the direction of the Kealia salt ponds. At this juncture, the Waikapu turn, he set up vast forces of arms so that a great barrage of long and short spears and sling stones could break like a thunderstorm upon the attacking forces.

Again, the spectacle of Kalaniopuu's armed force marching to battle over the low sand hills south of Wailuku was awe-inspiring: this time, the full force. His six divisions, each from a district of the island of Hawaii, were there: I, Mahi, Palena, Luahine, Ahu and Paia, more than 2,000 men strong. Today they marched as the Alapa had marched, with their uniforms streaming with red and green, their Alii resplendent like the Alapa in yellow, red and green feather-cloaks, and helmets.

But, once again, Kahekili had somehow managed to raise a force more than twice the size of his enemy. This was principally because of the assistance in men and weapons tendered him that night by the ruling chief of Oahu and Molokai, Kahahana.

When the splendid vanguard of Kalaniopuu's divisions reached the foot of the sand hills where Kahekili's troops were waiting, suddenly the most devastating wall of missiles known in contemporary Hawaiian history soared up and into them from Kahekili's massed legions.

Hundreds of the pick of the Hawaiian troops fell with the weight of that first onslaught. But Kahekili had planned well and had provided several rows of backup ammunition, sling stones and spears of varying lengths. Almost immediately, a similar wall of missiles was airborne, sloping up and arching down into the massed legions of Kalaniopuu. Once again, the best soldiers of Kalaniopuu fell in rows under the onslaught. In the verbiage of the Hawaiian historian Kamakau: "Like grasshoppers on the plain, easily to be caught by women, so they lay in the heat of the sun snuggled close to the blossoms of the grasses."

Within a few seconds, still one more curtain of fire, spears and sling stones rose like a dark gray mass from the northern sand hills overlooking the plain of Kama-o-mao. The missiles reaped their dreadful handiwork in blood and gore. The Hawaiian soldiers, looking around them, saw that the devastation was appalling. Many of the soldiers began to fall back: at first, a relatively sparse number, but soon a tide that grew furiously. Then, whole sheaves of the assaulting army were peeling off and breaking into individual groups bent on retreat.

Some groups charged on. They left their dead and wounded and charged up into the sand hills with a fury to get at and bowl over the enemy, and drive through the enemy defenses to the sea. There, they hoped to find, in Kahului Bay, a part of the Hawaiian fleet. That fleet would be bringing them reinforcements.

One of these aggressive groups was the legion led by Kekuhaupio, with his faithful military student Kamehameha close beside him. They took their share of casualties, but pushed ahead, mainly trying to find the source of the mysterious attack.

Nevertheless, Kekuhaupio's and Kamehameha's legion, led by the two energetic warriors, sprinted up the first of the hills. From the top, they looked down upon a wide valley full of troops.

Beyond the valley, presumably further troops of Kahekili's spread on endlessly toward the sea and Kahului Bay.

Kamehameha looked down at the massed slingsmen and lancers with their long spears, and whole munition piles of spears and sling stones stacked in banks among them. In the multitude of soldiery, Kamehameha noted the predominance of red among the uniforms: All of the Alii wore cloaks that were mostly of red, with red helmets.

"The Niu-ula!" he said. "The Red Coconuts." The fame of the left-handed slingsmen was great. And their ranks stretched on and on.

At that moment, the slingsmen let fly a short-range cloud of missile stones. The troops of Kekuhaupio, and the commanding Alii, were hard put to dodge as the hailstonelike attack came clattering into them. And again, many men fell.

Kamehameha was quick to lead the counterbattery fire. "There they are! Give them damnation with your slings!" He fitted a large oval stone into his sling, took careful aim at a tall Alii in red robe and helmet near the front of the host of the Red Coconut division at the foot of the hill, and sailed the missile on its way with a mighty heave.

Before the stone could find its target, a dozen others had followed from his troop.

But Kamehameha's sharp eyes held on the tall enemy and saw him dodge as he must have spotted the incoming missile. Then he did a comical little dance as four or five of the troop must have followed Kamehameha's point of aim. But evidently, the Alii was not struck, because he still stood.

By that time, it seemed that the whole of Kamehameha's and Keku's legion were firing their sling stones. A famed combat in Hawaiian folklore had begun. A large dark cloud of stones could be seen descending en masse upon the Red Coconuts. And at that moment, Kameha heard a stentorian voice shouting out to them. It was evidently the tall Alii in the red cloak. His remarks were addressed toward Kekuhaupio: "Kekuhaupio! The son of Holoae! I am O-uli. You provoke me with your clumsy sling stones. Don't you know that the stones from my sling have a crack like thunder and strike like lightning? You are mad to provoke me. Because I will strike you dead!"

It seemed that in a moment, a dead silence had fallen over the battlefield. Everyone was listening to the boastful O-uli.

And Kekuhaupio, equal to any challenge in the field of combat, answered him similarly with a taunt: "Kekuhaupio knows you, O-uli. And he knows too that the thunder of your sling stones is more like the pitter-patter of rain at Honaunau, in the dry season. And the long lightning in your strokes will be just enough to warm my soles and make me hot for battle with you, to finish you off as any craven coward deserves to be finished!"

With Keku's last words, O-uli rapidly, in one movement, with a marvelous short, pistonlike movement of his left arm, flung a stone whistling in the direction of Kekuhaupio. It was true that the stone had little of the upward trajectory of most sling stones: It traveled at a low level, like surf sent roaring through a narrow blowhole at seaside.

But Keku had sharp eyes, and he dodged that, and also the second which came with unbelievable rapidity after it.

Then there was a pause, and in the hiatus, Keku called out to him in loud, clear tones: "Is that the best you can do, O-uli? It is a child's performance."

With that, in the same quick convulsion of musculature from the direction of O-uli, another low-zooming, rapid-traveling stone went winging in the direction of Keku, which Keku again dodged, easily.

Without a moment's delay, Kamehameha had picked up a long spear from the ground, and now, with a careful, painstaking aim as he ran to launch, he flung the barbed weapon well up into the air, sailing in the direction of O-uli. So expertly was the spear launched, and with such speed, that as O-uli tried to dodge, the weapon caught him in the thigh and penetrated the flesh, so that he fell. Indignant and mortified with the disgrace of being hit, he fought to his feet and wrenched the spear from his leg. His thigh was covered with an instant sheet of blood. As if that sight were the signal, Kamehameha shouted to the men behind: "Come! Let us shed the blood of all these cowards and braggarts. Let us make them eat the dirt of Iao!" With that, and a knot of ihe spearsmen behind him and Kekuhaupio at his flank, Kamehameha started running down the slope, grasping a short ihe spear himself in his right hand, and his shark-tooth battle club in his left.

"Death now to you! Die!" With that hoarse battle cry roaring in his throat, the giant of a man with his yellow plumed helmet and huge yellow cape around his huge shoulders, ran with incredible speed toward the enemy line. The first enemy immediately in front of him was a red-robed, red-plumed Alii leader, a sturdy, broad-chested man armed with ihe and battle club, with a long pahoa dagger stuck in his cincture of plaited green tapa cloth. He was endeavoring to display a fierce face, twisting his mouth into a grimace like the grotesque features of a war god, and it crossed Kamehameha's mind immediately that the grimace was a measure of uneasiness: The Alii was overawed with Kamehameha's fearsomeness as a warrior.

Kamehameha growled out: "Ho-he wale! Coward!" And with that as impetus he drove his ihe, shafted along by the brute force of his long body, straight into the side of his opponent. He saw the complete look of surprise striking the face of the enemy, and with a precise movement he reversed his direction and extracted the spear as his foe fell spewing blood, and he charged on amidst the foremost of the men behind. In that moment he saw the other of the supporters behind the Alii turning to flee, and in the same glance, saw that his new opponent was deflecting the spear thrust with a parrying stroke. He knew from the expertness of that parry that his opponent was a formidable foe. The parry turned into an expert thrust, with an almost imperceptible change from defensive to offensive motion. And he was hard put to divert the enemy's quick and forceful counterthrust.

He spun backward, turning his body so that it would be a minimal target, and with the vehemence of his movement, he threw himself somewhat off balance to the rear. If the opponent were fast enough to take advantage of his position, he would be in trouble. That is, if the foe could keep on coming. As a measure of desperation, Kameha thrust his ihe spear into the air to block any move in that direction, and luckily he made the move with such force that the enemy's spear went flinging out of his hand.

If Kamehameha had been in better balance, he might have converted his parry stroke into a thrust which would have finished off his enemy. But his body was now too far forward.

Instead, the enemy came charging back with indomitable energy, whirling his war club overhead with his right arm. Now, thought Kamehameha, let him charge, onto my spear. He let his body sink backward and braced his legs for the charge with the spear coming up to chest level, his legs and lower body forming a low tripod to support the weapon.

The foe came crashing ahead, and Kamehameha's spear came up to meet that assault squarely. Unerringly, Kamehameha's quick-set plan worked: The enemy rammed himself onto the ihe, and a wide-eyed look of complete astonishment came over his face. But in that moment, the battle club, on its thong, came crashing into Kamehameha's shoulder. In the last second, Kamehameha was able to dodge a little—his eyes were quick and sharp, but the ball-like missile, with low, bent shark's teeth in it, grazed his shoulder and ripped his skin. He shrugged, stood up and waved to his men behind.

"Come on, loyal followers of Keku! Destroy this unworthy enemy!"

Keku had come up behind him, and had seen the recent wound. "Is it a deep or shallow wound, Pai'ea?" he asked.

"Troublesome, but not deep, Keku," Kamehameha told him. "Let us lead the charge."

From somewhere ahead, a new Alii, a tall, white-skinned young man in a red cloak and helmet which had some spots of yellow on them, had appeared from nowhere to take the place of the Alii whom Kamehameha had killed. Just beyond the expiring body of the first Alii, whose chest was heaving with a final death rattle, stood his new foe: a tall, pale noble with a long pololu spear in his hand. He is poorly armed, Kamehameha thought. But with the long spear, he can be dangerous.

Kamehameha wrenched the spear from the chest of his expiring last opponent, and parried the long, somewhat awkward thrust of his new foe. With another swift, muscular parry, as violent and disturbing as the last, Kamehameha's short ihe spear drove the enemy's long lance abruptly upward and back, and almost as if part of the same movement, the parry became a thrust and the lance point plunged into the upper thigh of the foe. That chief fell back, blood running down his thigh, and Kamehameha wrenched the spear free for the mortal wound.

But before he could make the stroke, Kekuhaupio had come up from behind and now stood next to him, his face drawn with concern. "Kamehameha, the supporting troops are not coming up behind us. We had better retire, while we have a local advantage."

Kamehameha looked back up the slope. Except for the knot of perhaps 100 troopers gathering around him at the foot of the slope, that sand hill was bare. There were no Kalaniopuu troops on either flank. It was clear that back there on the other side of the hill, the bulk of the army was probably retreating.

On the top of the sand hill, he spotted a small group of his own troops. "Keku, we had better send back our rear guard, and find out what is happening—whether the army is retreating back there. I'll finish off this Alii and take his forelock and his lei niho."

The force of Kamehameha's and Keku's assault had driven the enemy back. There seemed to be a strange hiatus as the Red Coconut troopers held back. For the moment, they were not even slinging stones. They had been according him the highest compliment of a fighting man: the admiration of the enemy.

Then, Kialoa, one of the rear guard, reported to Kamehameha and Kekuhaupio. "Great Chiefs! The main body of the army is retreating. All along the line, the field is strewn with our dead! They must number more than 1,200."

Kekuhaupio said: "In that case, Kamehameha, we must withdraw. If we go ahead with our small number, the only final result will be our annihilation, like the Alapa. Let us withdraw, now! And forget finishing off that chief." The white, tight smile creased his face. "He didn't give you much of a fight, anyhow."

Kamehameha was still grim from the fight. "All the more reason to finish him off," he said. "I recognize him now, Keku. He is Pua, the Two-Handed, supposed to be able to fight equally well with both hands. But you are right, we must go quickly."

He sprang a few steps up the slope, and called out: "Follow me, soldiers! Now!" And he and Keku led the way swiftly back up the bank. They kept a wary eye in the direction of the Red Coconut division, for the shower of spears or sling stones which was certain to come at some point in their retreat. They had climbed halfway up the slope when the first shower of long pololu spears sailed into the sky in their direction from the ranks of the Red Coconuts. Kamehameha set the example, turning to face the incoming squall, dodging some of the missiles and seizing some directly from the air. He was the first to heave the spears back at the enemy, and then he quickly led in resuming the withdrawal.

Before the second spear attack could be launched, the first of the Kekuhaupio legion were over the ridge of that sand hill, and on their way to the valley.

They hurried through the desolation of bloody bodies strewn in that valley floor, both Hawaiian and Kahekili troops, the pitiful remnants of those forces strewn as human wreckage on the sandy floor.

There was a cry and loud roaring behind them, suddenly. Kameha glanced back to see, but he knew what it was. The temporary lull during his combat with O-uli, Pua the Two-Handed, and his most intense battle with the nameless Alii had gone, and the Red Coconuts were at last closing in for the kill.

The Red Coconuts were slashing at his rearmost troopers. The enemy were pouring over the sand hill behind them in droves. He stopped and looked back. Keku was with him.

It was the first time defeat and annihilation had ever been so close to him. For the first time, he could feel the icy fingers of fear on his warlike confidence.

"Keku," he said. "Shall we stop and fight? And go down that way?"

Keku looked up. A gray rain squall was moving toward them from leaden clouds in the northeast. They could see the wide sheet of rain marching. "That may save us," Keku said. "Ku is with us."

In a few moments the squall struck and inundated the fighting. At the outer extremity of the fighting it persisted. But the other enemy fell back, separated. And the bulk of Keku's surviving troops were free to retreat.

By the time the teeming rain squall had passed, Keku and Kameha had led their survivors quickly over the next sand hill to the east, toward Keopala.

Then when the sun peeped through the silver clouds, Kameha steered them south toward Maalaea and Kalaniopuu's rear headquarters.

At the head of the column with Kameha, Keku could joke again. "The great god Ku was with us." The wry smile: "But Kalani certainly was not."

Kameha almost smiled. "Keku, now I believe what you almost taught me in the Kauwiki campaign—that one must protect himself from the mistakes of his king."

And yet, when this disastrous battle was resolved with the withdrawal of Kalaniopuu and his surviving forces to Hawaii, and a vengeful Kalaniopuu came back again with raiding forces to attack the wily Kahekili, Kameha and Keku were both with him.

In the meanwhile, there was the exceedingly difficult diplomatic maneuver of arranging the peace.

They were not the only bearers of ill tidings that the battle had gone badly. In his headquarters, Kalaniopuu was even then consulting with the council of his chiefs, and he had summoned his wife, Kalola. She of course was the sister of Kahekili, and evidently at that moment Kalaniopuu had been importuning her to go as an ambassadress to ask for peace from her brother.

She was a tall, dark-skinned chiefess who was long-legged and beautiful. Once Kameha's stepmother before she married Kalaniopuu, she was a true love of Kameha. Now she was saying: "But my husband, remember this has been a raider's war of devastation and ruthless conquest, a Kaua hulia mahi, and it would not be safe. They would kill me, though I am the king's sister. I would suggest that you send our son Kiwalao. He is my brother's nephew, and my brother knows that he has one of the holiest kapus, the Niau-pio, and is your heir apparent. Send him with the twins, Kameeiamoku and Kamanawa. After all, they are half-brothers to Kahekili."

Kalaniopuu laughed, even in this desperate moment. "You are right, Kalola. Kiwalao has the Niau-pio even if I did declare this kapu myself, and he did not inherit it by birth. A higher kapu than Kahekili. He is a sacred personage, and will be accorded the proper reverence for a peace emissary. And because of his kapu, Kahekili will have to speak to him through a lower caste."

Kalola said, "Husband, who will go with him?"

Kalaniopuu said: "Kameeiamoku and Kamanawa, the half-brothers of your brother. Kameeiamoku will carry the awa spittoon for him. It should be a prestigious negotiating body."

And that it was. According to the famous legend of this encounter, Kiwalao was carefully dressed in the most splendid garments of a chief, so that he glittered like a rainbow. The twin half-brothers of Kahekili also wore regal vestments. Kameeiamoku carried the ipu-kuha, or royal spittoon, of the Niau-pio. Kamanawa carried the towering kahili, or symbol of authority. The kahili was always carried ahead of a royal personage, like the Roman lictors of the centurion, but it was much more benign as might befit the Hawaiian Islands; it was made of flowers.

By a leisurely route, according to legend, the three high Alii made their way toward Wailuku where the aging, but still formidable Kahekili awaited them. He waited with his womenfolk and the old men and women, the center of a multitude. As the high Alii approached, the soldiers and the multitude around Kahekili prostrated themselves around their path. They knew that not to fall down prostrate before the advancing kahili of a divine-rank Niau-pio was a death offense, a death offense prescribing burning as the means—the burning kapu.

Kahekili heard of course that they were coming, and he draped himself over a lauhala mat with his face turning upward, to indicate a friendly reception according to tradition. However, it would have been difficult for Kahekili to look amiable. With his black tattooed eyelids and half of his body, down to his toes, tattooed in black, he was a fearsome spectacle.

Kamanawa was the first into the room with the kahili, followed immediately by Kiwalao. Kahekili of course recognized his half-brother with the kahili, but he knew that his function in this context was to announce the arrival of Kiwalao. So he did not acknowledge Kamanawa immediately.

Kiwalao walked to the reclining form of Kahekili and, according to the form, sat briefly on his half-black tattooed chest. They rubbed noses. Then, also following the tradition, they began to wail in grief over the dead in the battle.

Meanwhile, the twins, Kameeiamoku and Kamanawa, crept forward and kissed Kahekili's hands. Kahekili observed the fact that Kiwalao was of the high Niau-pio caste and could not be addressed directly by a lower caste (like Kahekili), so he addressed his questions to the twins. Kahekili was of the third-ranking caste, the Naha.

Kahekili asked the twins: "Why did you bring Kiwalao here? He might have been killed, by accident. You could have come by yourselves if you are in trouble."

Kamanawa answered: "The chief has been sent by Kalaniopuu, the moi of Hawaii, to ask for all our lives. We ask our lives. Kalaniopuu has commanded that if Chief Kiwalao dies, we shall die with him."

Kiwalao had sat up by now, and Kahekili joined him. There was something regal as well as fierce in the lean, erect, if grizzled, bearing as he sat, his body and face half-blue with ornate tattoo. He replied: "Let live! Let us make an end of the battle, and the dying!"

He asked Kamanawa: "Where is your sister Kalola?" Kalola, of course, was one of the wives of Kalaniopuu, and besides being the sister of the twins, she was also the half-sister of Kahekili.

Kamanawa said: "She is with Kalaniopuu at Kihei-pukoa. She might have come to you, but she decided that we should come with the Chief to visit with Great Chief Kahekili."

Kahekili answered benignly: "Take fish and vegetables down to Kihei-pukoa." And with that gesture of generosity, the hostility between the two armies officially ended.

After these negotiations, Kahekili met with Kalaniopuu to discuss peace terms in general, and one of the terms was that Kalaniopuu would withdraw his army from Maui. Actually, after the severe losses of this campaign, it was only the wreckage of an army, and the rambunctious Kalaniopuu was eager for vengeance.

When Kalaniopuu's fleet carried the remnants of his fighting force back to the island of Hawaii, he made secret plans for yet another conquest of Maui. Again, he levied an army from all of the districts of the Big Island, and one year later, he had launched yet another expedition to Kahekili's terrain. This time his forces were smaller and he made small expeditions to find a soft spot and loot provisions and other booty. He came back to one of his initial old targets, the Kaupo district on the south coast of Maui, where he renewed his cruel raids upon the Maui people around Mokolau.

But the quick-reacting Kahekili marshaled troops in large quantity again, and sent them to Kaupo. The Hawaiians were driven off, and limped back to the Kauwiki base.

Then Kalaniopuu led a larger force to Lahaina, on the west side of Maui.

Once again, the tactics of the brilliant Kahekili overcame the invading force. As before, Kahekili made sure that arithmetic was on his side: With his own armies reinforced by his allies from the island of Oahu, Kahekili's army outnumbered Kalaniopuu's forces by at least two to one.

Here again, in the annals of Kahekili forces, it is recorded that Kamehameha and Kekuhaupio were involved in some of the most bitter fighting. And the ruling chief of the Oahu forces aiding Kahekili's army in the engagement later related that at Hale-ili near Lahaina, Kamehameha had distinguished himself.

Soldiers of this high chief, Kahahana, according to Kamakau, paid an ironic compliment to Kamehameha's size and military prowess. He quotes them as if it were one man. "There was one bit of a soldier of Hawaii named Kamehameha, whom they call an Aikane [friend] of Kalaniopuu. He was a brave little fellow."

The stories of Kamehameha's military valor filled many of the Kahekili soldiers with respect, and a soothsayer with Kahahana's army, Keaulu-moku, eventually made the famous prophecy that Kamehameha would be the great king of Hawaii.

This seer, over a circle of burning kukui flames, chanted his magic mele for Kahahana. His eyes misted over, he told of the greatest king who would bring fire and war into Maui, Oahu, Lanai and Molokai; who would eventually bring the islands together for a golden age of peace.

Kahahana smiled. "And, wise Kahuna, who is that great king. Is it I?"

The old one hesitated. "His name is—is Pai'ea!"

"Pai'ea!" said Kahahana. "This man is pupule, crazy. King Hard Shell Crab!"

Later, some of Kahahana's soldier chiefs gathered courage and told him that Pai'ea was Kamehameha. But by that time, Keaulu-moku had defected to Hawaii.

Once again, Kahekili dispatched forces to the defense of the beleaguered Mauians.

But for once, the forces which Kahekili was able to muster were not overwhelming in number. So the war, in the Lahaina vicinity, surged back and forth, and as previously in his attempts at conquest in Maui, Kalaniopuu's tactics with the inhabitants were generally cruel and repressive.

After some time, Kalaniopuu led his forces to the smaller off-shore island of Lanai. Here on Lanai, as in Maui, Kalaniopuu made ruthless raids on the inhabitants, and drove the chiefs and soldiers up to a hill stronghold called Ho-okio. It was up in the hills above the beaches where Kalaniopuu had landed, near Mauna-lei.

Here at Ho-okio, the Lanai chiefs held a practically invulnerable fortress, but it had one weak spot. That weak spot was that there was no water supply there on the hill of Ho-okio. And in itself, it had no vegetable gardens for growing food. Kalaniopuu stubbornly beseiged the Lanai defenders, and eventually closed in and took the fort, and killed all of the chiefs.

This kind of ruthless, bloody guerrilla war, coupled with long and bloody memories of fighting in Maui, was the school of combat which hardened the young Chief Kamehameha and made him even more formidable an opponent in battle. But undoubtedly, they led him to further questioning of Kalaniopuu's wisdom and planning as a military commander.

It was during the campaign on Lanai that Kamehameha, like the other soldiers of Kalaniopuu, endured some severe hardships. Not only did they cut off the supplies and water of the chiefs, in the final stand of the Lanaians at Ho-okio, but they themselves were reduced to eating the root of a wild plant called Kupala. This diet had a loosening effect upon the bowels when eaten, and that bloody war is therefore called Ka-moku-hi, "the War of the Land of Loose Bowels."

On the west coast of Lanai, about eight miles from the fort of Ho-okio, is the spot famed as Kahekili's Jump. Kahekili, fond of cliff-jumping, had himself made this leap, for sport.

It was here that one of the captives taken by Kalaniopuu, a man famed for jumping from cliffs into the sea on Lanai, was being led along as a captive with his hands tied, near a very steep cliff. This famed cliff-jumper, whose name was Kini, pretended pain from the fact that his wrists were too tightly lashed, and asked that they be loosened a little.

When that was done, he ran to the edge of the cliff, and sailed through some sixty feet of air to land in fifteen feet of water. Kalaniopuu was impressed and permitted the man to escape.

After the Lanai campaign, Kalaniopuu decided to go back to the section of Maui where he knew food was generally abundant: It was Kaanapali, and there he fed his soldiers well, for a change, upon the taro of Hono-kahua.

This time, Kahekili, blessed as usual with good advance intelligence, had prepared a more than ample welcome, to meet the army of Kalaniopuu.

Defeated in a number of decisive battles by the masterful tactician and strategist Kahekili, Kalaniopuu had developed a new technique for making guerrilla-type raids with smaller forces and withdrawing before he could be brought to major battle. At one point in the long series of harassing engagements that went on in 1778, the raiding bands of Kalaniopuu committed indignities upon the inhabitants of many of the communities around Kaanapali and Lahaina.

The degree of barbarity increased as the campaign went on. At Hama-kua-loa, Kalaniopuu made a raid, but here Kahekili had a large force in readiness, and he summoned his reserve to drive Kalaniopuu back to his canoes with heavy casualties.

In the next raid made by Kalaniopuu, the soldiers under his command seemed especially vindictive and vengeful after their defeat at Hama-kua-loa. The killing of the locals, even those who were not soldiers, was especially ruthless and bloody, and the Hawaiian soldiers won extra notoriety by urinating into the eyes of their captives.

It was in this stage of this long and brutal guerrilla conflict that the first of the "floating heiaus," the two ships of the British explorer Captain James Cook, arrived in this part of the Hawaiian Islands. The two Cook ships, *HMS Resolution* and *Discovery*, had discovered the Hawaiian Islands in 1778. However, they had stayed only on Kauai, for fourteen days. Then they went north to search for the fabled "Northwest Passage" across North America. They were unsuccessful, of course, and were battered and chilled from cruising the icy wastes off northern Alaska. Now they appeared off the very coast where Kalaniopuu and Kahekili were engaged in their long, exhaustive war struggles.

In the sixteenth century, Spanish explorers had touched upon or been shipwrecked in the Hawaiian Islands, and it is probably from these early visitors that the Hawaiians learned to fashion their tall, plumed helmets, that warlike headgear the Spaniards and Portuguese had adapted into iron from early Greek and Roman models. Of course, the Hawaiian variety of helmet, in the absence of iron, was fashioned from plaited wicker work, with a tightly woven cover of feathers, usually from birds with red or yellow plumage.

Fornander, in a fairly detailed investigation of various evidences, concludes that the Hawaiian group was discovered in 1555 by Juan Gaetano. Those islands, called *Los Majos*, are placed on some Spanish charts at the correct latitude but erroneous longitude. Yet besides the more than coincidental shape of their war helmets, the Hawaiians in Kauai, where Cook's ships first touched, were able to produce iron parts of ships, and knew of the material iron from these early explorers. And yet it is more than passing strange, as Captain Cook points out in his *Voyages*, that the Spanish galleons did not stop subsequently in the Hawaiian Islands during the seventeenth and early eighteenth centuries while they were sailing the long route between California and the Philippines.

At any rate, Cook was the first European explorer to make sightings, bring back drawings, and record in log books and accounts of voyages a visit to these islands of blissful climate and beautiful scenery, just inside the northern limits of the tropics.

So it was that on January 18, 1778, coming northeast from Christmas Island in the Pacific, Cook's two ships of exploration sighted the island of Oahu, and soon after, the island of Kauai, due north of it. They did not then see the islands of Maui or Hawaii.

The first landing of the Cook ships was at Waimea Bay, on the south coast of the island of Kauai.

Cook and his exploratory party stayed in the vicinity of Kauai and the neighboring small island of Niihau not quite half a month, until February 2, 1778. Then they headed north toward the strait in search of the mythical Northwest Passage.

Coming back ten months later, on November 26, for the first time they sighted the island of Maui. This time they were approaching the islands from the northeast.

Cook wrote in his journal: "We were now satisfied that the group of the Sandwich Islands [he had named the Hawaiian Islands after his patron, and the First Lord of the Admiralty, the Earl of Sandwich] had been only imperfectly discovered, as those which we visited in our progress northward all lie to the leeward of our present station."

On the 26, at noon, Cook hove to and received a few curious natives who ventured close in their canoes. He traded nails and other bits of iron for cuttlefish.

The next day, Cook brought his two tall ships closer to this, the north coast of Maui. He hove to and waited for more visitors.

They came in more canoes, with breadfruit, taro, sweet potatoes, quite brave about facing the "floating heiaus" and the strange men in them with white faces. These first Hawaiians from Maui hadn't yet decided that the strangers in the tall ships might be the god Lono and his followers. Later, on the Big Island of Hawaii, Kalaniopuu's men were to make that decision —and fall down in homage before Cook.

But first he made a peaceful, leisurely progress along the Maui north coast. Cook noted that some of these "Indians" had skin sores characteristic of venereal disease. Some of his infected sailors had introduced this virtually incurable "Pox" to the islands on their visit to Kauai.

On November 27, as the two ships stood in close to shore,

canoes came to trade. And in a large canoe came King Kahekili, bringing a red feather warrior's cloak to Charles Clerke, Cook's second in command and the skipper of the *Discovery*.

On the afternoon of November 30, off the northeast coast of Maui, another group of canoes approached. These were mostly the canoes of Kalaniopuu (or "Terreeoboo," in Cook's attempt at phoneticizing the Polynesian name). The Cook party had gained some familiarity with Polynesian people, customs and language in many Pacific islands, notably Otaheite (Tahiti), Bola Bola (Bora Bora), and Atooi or Kowi (Kauai) and Oneeheow (Niihau) in the Sandwich (Hawaiian) Islands.

The first canoes to reach the ship were those bent on trading, the favorite commodity sought by the Hawaiians being bits of iron such as nails, which they had already learned were extremely useful.

But after the trading canoes came the impressive larger canoes of the commander, Kalaniopuu. They were paddled by expert canoemen and drove their double-hulled craft with uniform strokes as well drilled and precise as a choral ballet.

The fleet of three royal barges, with Kalaniopuu and his top-flight party in the lead, circled the Cook ships carefully while one of the royal party (perhaps Kamehameha himself) sternly ordered the trading canoes away from the side of the *Resolution*, and the lead canoe of the royal formation hove alongside.

First, the kahili bearers of Kalaniopuu, with their ornate flower-structured lictors or symbols of authority, scrambled up the Jacob's Ladder that was let down from the quarterdeck. Then, Kalaniopuu, followed by Kiwalao, Kamehameha, the aged chief kahuna of Kalaniopuu, Holoae, and others of the high command in Kalaniopuu's court nimbly followed their chief up the rope ladder. In the royal train followed bearers with suckling pigs for the outlanders with the "skin with loose pockets," or clothing. They also had remarkable pale faces of fish-belly-white, and many of them had outlandish blue eyes, a most shocking color to the Hawaiians.

And the British in their turn were impressed with the size and fierce, warlike appearance of the Hawaiians. They were particularly struck with the appearance of Kamehameha, evidently at this time a close favorite of Kalaniopuu. In their rather strained attempts to render the Hawaiian sounds into English, they called him Maihamaiha, and Lieutenant King, the third in command to Cook, later observed in his diary that Kamehameha had "as savage a looking face as I ever saw, it however by no means seemed an emblem of his disposition, which was good natur'd & humourous, although his manner shew'd somewhat of an overbearing spirit."

After the visit, six or eight of Kalaniopuu's party requested permission from Cook to remain on board a short while, and a sailing canoe was attached to the stern of the *Resolution* to care for their needs when they should want to leave.

Kamehameha was one of them. He was filled to overbrimming with curiosity about the wonders of this floating heiau and these strange white-faced men, and he wondered, as many of the Hawaiians did, whether Cook, the tall, straight, conciliatory leader of the expedition, with his bright blue eyes and frame of more than six feet, might be the good-natured god Lono on a visit to Earth. Some of the others in the regal party of Kalaniopuu had mentioned this possibility already to Kamehameha. But the main item of curiosity on Kamehameha's mind was the wonder of the material objects which the outlanders had with them.

They were in fact visitors from some other strange land, and they had secrets of power which fascinated Kamehameha. The main item was this huge sailing canoe of wood fastened with pegs of a strange hard substance, which the Hawaiians already had learned about. It was called, in their language, hao, something forceful or hard.

And then he had learned about the wondrous weapons which they had, the great heavy tubes of hao which spoke with red mouths when some magic made them belch fire and thunder, and send balls of hao flying to kill at a great distance. And then there were the smaller weapons which the men carried, which also spoke with the same magic, and launched with the same red mouths a cloud of thunder and smoke that projected a small, hard ball of hao with the capability of killing men several canoelengths away from the weapon.

Kameha didn't know whether to believe the outlander who told him about this or not. That man was a burly, smiling fellow who called himself "Bo-sun." He had eyes the color of the water at the first break of the surf off Kawaihae. It was shocking and startling to see eyes in this very unnatural color. And he had hair also a shocking and unreal color, pale reddish brown like the Uki-Uki flower.

This man had one of those small weapons with a long tube of hao embedded in wood, shaped so it could be gripped. He showed Kameha the ball of hao which this weapon "fired," the word which the man used for the way the magic worked.

He also took Kameha to show him a "cano"—that was something like his word, and the big balls it "fired." "Boom-boom— house fall down!" the man said. It seemed most unlikely, like ko-hu-ole, a child's wild story, but Kameha wondered. Later, on his home island, he was to have proof of this "fired" magic, and the blood it could shed. And he was to harness this power himself, to conquer the island of Oahu.

Kamehameha was carried away with curiosity, and insisted on staying on board as the evening fell, and his sailboat was towed astern into the night. This was the dawn of Kamehameha's Age of Discovery of the skills and techniques of the white man, which he embraced so wholeheartedly and with such intelligence, and which he used as one of the principal sources of the strength he needed to conquer and enrich the islands. Through his liberal attitude toward Europeans with miraculous knowledge of ships, weapons and many other techniques and advances of the Western world, he was to seek out and make friends with many Europeans and Americans who could show him the way.

CHAPTER 6
The Fate of Lono

CAPTAIN COOK's two converted Whitby coal ships, the *Resolution* and the *Discovery*, left Maui and ranged along the eastern shores of the Big Island, Hawaii, looking for a fit anchorage.

In a storm, and at nightfall, on Christmas Eve, December 24, 1778, the two tall ships lost contact. They didn't see each other for twelve days. On the twelfth day, January 6, 1779, they met again. That afternoon, they began to cruise together up the west coast of Hawaii.

Periodically, they stood in close to shore and received Hawaiians in their canoes. By now, the word had spread by the rapid magic of Hawaiian hearsay that the white-faced men in their floating heiaus were interested in peaceful trading—specifically that they offered scraps of that precious hard stuff, hao, which they called "ai-lon," for yams, breadfruit and especially for puaa, pigs. So as they moved up the west of the Kona coast of the Big Island, Cook gradually reprovisioned.

The explorers were struck with the fact that the two mountains on this island of Owhyhee were very high, and the peaks covered with snow. They were also seen to be igneous in origin, with parts of it "having been laid waste by a volcano."

At daybreak on January 16, "seeing the appearance of a bay, I sent Mr. Bligh [William Bligh, the *Resolution*'s master] with a boat from each ship to examine it, being at this time three leagues [approximately nine miles] off."

This was Kealakekua (Kay-ala-kay-ku-a) Bay, where Cook was to meet his end, not quite a month later, stabbed and speared to death by Kalaniopuu's men. Rendering the name in his best phonetic English, Cook heard it as Karakaooa, with the same peculiar Tahitian intonation as his rendition of Kalaniopuu as Terreeoboo and Kamehameha as Maiha-maiha.

On the evening of the 16, Bligh (the same officer who, as a captain, later became the villain of the true-life South Pacific epic, *Mutiny on the Bounty*) returned from his harbor-scouting expedition and reported that the bay was all right, with "good anchorage and fresh water."

The two ships had been lying to, not anchored yet, about three miles from the shore of the bay, all during that day.

The ships were beleaguered by many hundreds of handsome, sturdy, laughing people who descended upon them in canoes. "Canoes now began to arrive from all parts, so that before 10 o'clock, there were not fewer than a thousand people about the two ships, most of them [the canoes] crowded with people, and well laden with hogs and other productions of the island."

The visitors swarmed over the ships. There was a goodly proportion of women, dressed in the same abbreviated malos around their middles as the males, and nothing else. The surviving journals of the officers and crewmen comment on the handsome bodies, the intriguing smiles, the beautiful teeth, and the females' propensity for and uninhibited interest in sex.

Cook wrote: "No women I ever met were more ready to bestow

their favors, indeed it appeared to me that they came with no other view."

This time, the conscionable but humanistic Cook did not try to prevent his crewmen from slipping below decks to take advantage of these favors. At the time of the Kauai landing a year before, he had attempted to hold back the sex-starved crew from dallying with the Polynesian beauties because he was afraid that the European sexual curse of gonorrhea and syphilis might infect the untouched "Indians."

But now, since the first contact with the Indians at Maui on this visit, he had known that the dread venereal pox of Europe had slipped through his attempts at restraining the men at Kauai. Now, he knew, the damage had been done, for he had seen the telltale lesions in the skins of the Hawaiians both on "Mowee" and "Owhyhee." So he looked the other way if the sex-starved crewmen took one or more Polynesian belles to the below-decks privacy.

Cook was more disturbed by the thievery of the Hawaiians— or should it be called a penchant for souvenir-hunting?—which became evident on this, the first day at Kealakekua, when hundreds of laughing Hawaiians clambered over the ships.

One large episode of thievery occurred on this first day: Some of the Indians made off with the rudder of one of the ship's longboats. Cook saw the canoe paddling madly away with the loot. He was angry, but really quite temperate in reacting to his distress.

Cook's journal reports (as of course rewritten by one of the three ghost writers who were successively employed to give the logbook a measure of conventional eighteenth-century "elegance"):

"I thought this a good opportunity to show these people the use of firearms, and two or three muskets, and as many fourpounders were fired over the canoe which carried off the rudder. As it was not intended that any of the shot should take effect, the surrounding multitude of natives seemed rather more surprised than frightened."

The last entry made in the logbook of the *Resolution* by Cook was the next day, January 17, 1779. Cook was not killed, however, until twenty-eight days later. Now, at 11 A.M. on January 17, the ships anchored in the northern portion of the bay and were immediately surrounded by a vast swarm of brown-skinned, shapely Hawaiians. Most were in canoes, but many swam naked in the clear water around the ships.

Cook's *Voyages* recorded (in the last translation of the logbooks, as done by John Barrow, FRS, FSA, in 1860): "I had nowhere, in the course of my voyages, seen so numerous a body of people assembled at one place. For besides those in canoes, all the shore was covered with spectators, and many hundreds were swimming round the ships like schools of fish."

Lieutenant King estimated the crowd here at more than 10,000. That was a fitting turnout for the island of Hawaii, the largest in area of the Hawaiian Islands, and then the largest in population. King's estimate at that time was that this Big Island (incidentally, equal in area to the sum of all the others in area) had about 150,000 inhabitants. Second in his estimate was Maui, with 65,400. The total population of the islands in King's estimate was about 400,000, a sad contrast with the situation 100 years later, when there were only 81,000 Hawaiians left after the White Man had brought his particular variety of viruses, physical and psychic.

King, by the way, took over the job of keeping the journal of the expedition after Cook's demise on February 14. He had been nominally third-in-command. But Captain Clerke, the second-in-command, was invalided with a bad heart, to die shortly after. So King became captain and the leader of the expedition.

There at anchor in Kealakekua Bay, the far-voyaging Englishmen were moved by the spectacle of this rich green and mountainous land with such beautiful children of nature in it.

Ashore, they saw groves of nodding coconut palms like tall flowers, villages of grass and thatch, a few tawny strips of sand edged by lucent water the color of emerald and aquamarine, and, rising above the hardened lava flows around it, the snow-covered peak of Mauna Loa, sloping up to a summit more than 13,000 feet high.

Cook wrote, as rewritten by Barrow: "Few now lamented our having failed in our endeavors to find a northern passage homeward [the Northwest Passage] last summer. To this disappointment we owed our having it in our power to revisit the Sandwich Islands, and to enrich our voyage with a discovery which, though the last, seemed in many respects to be the most important that had hitherto been made by Europeans throughout the extent of the Pacific Ocean."

Cook describes the bay as about a mile long from north to south, bounded by the village of Kaawaloa (Ka-a-wa-lo-a) on a bare point of land on the north and Kekua (now called Napo-opo-o) on a sandy beach at the southern extremity. Cook's rendering of Kekua and Kaawaloa as Kakooa and Kowrowa seems closer to the modern Hawaiian spelling than most of his phonetic attempts.

Anchored as the ships were less than a quarter-mile from the shore, the Anglo-Saxons were inundated with endless waves of eager, naked Polynesian females and hundreds of sturdy Hawaiian braves who had an insatiable appetite for whatever bits and pieces of "ai-lon" they could manage to take by hook or crook.

Among the visiting throngs of those first days at Kealakekua came two handsome young chiefs called Kanaina and Palea—whose spelling Cook and King rendered as Kaneena and Pareea. Kanaina, King reported, "was one of the finest men I ever saw. He was about six feet high, had regular and expressive features, with lively dark eyes: his carriage was easy, firm, and graceful."

Kanaina and Palea helped the outnumbered Englishmen with the handling of the Hawaiian multitudes who swarmed over the decks. Their absolute command over the crowds and their imperious airs impressed Cook and King. Once, as the crowds made the ship list alarmingly, Kanaina shooed them off the ship like chickens.

Kanaina explained that the moi or king was not here, that he was on a war campaign on Maui. But this chief, Kalaniopuu, would be back soon and would give a proper welcome to the British commander. Cook didn't realize that he had already met Kalaniopuu, off the Maui coast.

The two young men brought aboard an exalted kahuna named Koa. "He was a little old man, of an emaciated figure; his eyes exceedingly sore and red, and his body covered with a white leprous scurf, the effects of an immoderate use of the ava [awa]."

Koa was led into the Captain's cabin and went ahead with a small ceremony he had planned. With great deference, he reached up to drape a wide red strip of tapa cloth—red being the usual color of the clothing on the Hawaiian god images—around Cook's shoulders.

Then he took a dead suckling pig from the hands of an attendant and began a long, sonorous chanting and invocation as he approached Cook with the pig.

After that, Cook invited the kahuna to dinner, and the old man ate noisily and spiritedly everything that was set in front of him. However, one quick taste of the White Man's drink was enough for Koa. He had to fight to avoid making a face at his first sampling of the visitor's wine, and had an even more violent reaction to the after-dinner brandy. "Like the rest of the inhabitants in these seas, (he) could scarcely be prevailed on to taste a second time our wine or spirits." Oh, what a change time was to work in that attitude with the Pacific islanders as they grew more used to our addictions.

As twilight came, the old kahuna, Koa, invited Captain Cook to come ashore with him. Cook went willingly, because he was anxious to locate a spot where he could set up an observatory for a forthcoming astronomical phenomenon, the Transit of Venus. He had been ordered to make observations of this passing of the planet across the sun's face, viewed from a new perspective, the wide spaces of the world's largest ocean. This transit was imminent, and Cook had decided that almost any spot near any of the villages on the level ground along Kealakekua Bay would do.

Going ashore in a long boat from the *Discovery*, Cook took Lieutenant King and William Bayley, the naturalist and astronomer. They landed at the small Kealakekua beach near the village of Kekua.

There the party—the three Britishers and Koa and his two young chief friends—were met by four kahunas carrying wands tipped with plumes of dog hair. The visitors were astonished to see that the crowd of people in the village had almost disappeared. Those who were caught in the open promptly prostrated themselves and stayed on the ground as if in awestruck reverence.

This was mystifying and somewhat disturbing to Cook, though something like it had happened on Kauai. Another mystifying occurrence was that the four subkahunas marched before the visitors chanting at length and sonorously. But the only word the Englishmen could make out sounded like "Orono, Orono." The word was actually "Lono" with the affirmative particle "O" indicating "It is." The kahunas believed that Cook was the god Lono returning to Hawaii. According to legend, this good-natured god had promised the Hawaiians that he would come back. Now the kahunas marching with their dog-hair wands before the returning god and his two followers were ordering utmost obeisance.

Koa led the visitors toward a large, evenly arranged pile of stones, with a flat top surmounted by a forest of wooden god images, most of them clothed in capes of red tapa. The Englishmen noted that the god images were grotesque, with hideously twisted mouths evidently supposed to indicate fierceness and severity.

Another spectacular feature of this temple, the Hiki-au Heiau, was a wooden rail which surrounded the structure's flat upper deck. On the rail were fixed rows of skulls. King, who had learned enough of the Polynesian argot to serve as interpreter, understood that these deceased were captives taken in battle and sacrificed to commemorate the deaths of their chiefs.

Hiki-au is a generic place name, literally meaning "comes the current"—signifying that the current, and the surf, are good for riding here. Heiau means "worship" or "place of worship."

On the mauka, or inland, side of the heiau platform, stood a semicircle of twelve god images, with a kind of altar platform of rickety wood behind it, supported on poles more than twenty feet high. The centermost of the god images was evidently, King decided, the most honored because it was the only one with red drapes around it. Evidently it was the image of Lono, and the heiau was for the moment at least consecrated to this good-tempered god in his appointed season.

A young kahuna with a rather long beard—long for a Polynesian—had joined Koa in his chanting, and the party moved to the altar platform. There they halted in front of a six-foot-high table where a decaying and smelly hog carcass was the centerpiece. Under it were ranged liberal offerings of sugar cane, plantains, sweet potatoes, coconuts and breadfruit. King decided that these offerings were intended for the centermost of the god images, evidently Lono.

Now that the man believed to be the returning Lono was here, he was led before the offering table, and the bearded young priest, Keli-ikea, stood by while Koa began another lengthy chant. This time his tone became more vehement, probably because the group was reaching the climax of the ceremony which the old priest had planned.

Then Koa took the odoriferous hog carcass from the sacrificial table and extended it to Lono's reincarnation. Cook was embarrassed and didn't move to accept the gift, if gift it was. Eventually, Koa let the foul-smelling animal fall to the ground.

But the ceremony had only started. Next, the old kahuna insisted that the English captain should join him in a climb to the top of the shaky altar structure. While his officers worried, Cook valiantly climbed the rotting ladder and old Koa assisted by holding his arm.

At the top, Koa draped yet another piece of red tapa cloth around the shoulders of Cook. Keli-ikea had scaled the scaffolding with the cloth, and carrying a large live hog—quite a feat but not so much for a muscular Hawaiian. Up there, Koa now chanted at greater length, and tried again to give Cook this second hog—this time a live and squealing animal, not so putrescent. But again

Cook was embarrassed and Koa lost his grip on the beast and it fell squealing the twenty-five or so feet to the ground.

Next, Koa led the way to the ground. The ceremony continued at the semicircle of god images, where the old kahuna said something evidently contemptuous about and snapped his fingers toward each of the images, except the center one, that of Lono. Ten subpriests had appeared by this time, and they watched while Koa prostrated himself before the god image and kissed it. He indicated that Cook should do the same and Cook obligingly did so.

Then they broke for one of the Hawaiians' favorite pursuits, eating. Cook had already eaten dinner once before, this evening, and he was disconcerted when another procession appeared bearing baked pig, breadfruit, coconuts, sweet potatoes, plaintains, the same variety as before, in the offerings.

After his experience with the putrid hog, Cook's appetite had scarcely renewed itself. Old Koa, who must indeed have been a considerate soul in his own insular way, tried hard to help by chewing the barbequed pork in advance for the Captain and passing the masticated mouthfuls on to the English Lono. Cook had to decline with apologies.

Poor Cook also had to endure an especially noxious treatment in the awa ceremony. In the course of other stops in Polynesia, in Tahiti, the Friendly Islands, and on Kauai, he had often been accorded the dubious honor of sitting down with the highest chiefs to take his turn at chewing the awa root and sipping the resulting awa juice. It was foul-tasting, but he would have to give it at least the virtue of being somewhat intoxicating.

Now, since he was being honored as the returning god presence, the young, bearded kahuna Keli-ikea prepared a special anointment for Cook. He chewed part of the kernel of a coconut, and then took the kernel, wrapped it in a cloth, and used this moist sop to rub the Captain's face, head and shoulders. Cook patiently endured this, but he hardly enjoyed it, and he was concerned about potential stains on his dress uniform and gilded epaulets.

As soon as the ceremony and the eating festivity could be gracefully ended, Cook distributed some beads and other bangles from the trinket chest he had found useful on every stop in the Pacific trip. The Hawaiian chiefs accepted with a show of thanks, but they were most truly grateful for a few nails and other scraps of iron from the carpentry shop. These, Cook was discovering, were very highly (and later embarrassingly) in demand, a kind of foreshadowing of the great cupidity and appetite for iron and other fabrications of the Western world which Kamehameha was to display.

Kamehameha, by the way, was still over on Maui, engaged in Kalaniopuu's long and racking war against Kahekili. The senior kahuna here at Kealakekua, Koa, and the two young chiefs, Kanaina and Palea, repeated several times that the moi or king was Kalaniopuu, and that his leading chiefs were on Maui with him. However, they said that the king and the leaders of his forces would be coming back soon, perhaps before muku, the end of the moon month. This, by the lunar charts, would be inside two weeks.

The kahuna subpriests who had welcomed them at landing again led the way with their dog-hair wands and their annunciatory chant about Lono. Again, as before, the Hawaiians who were caught in the open by the passage of the English officers prostrated themselves in his path and remained face down until he had passed. And in the longboat en route back to the ships, the Englishmen remembered that they had done nothing, in the hurly-burly of this evening, about finding a site for the astronomical observatory for the upcoming Transit of Venus.

The next day, January 19, Lieutenant King and William Bayley, the astronomer-naturalist, with a guard of eight marines, went ashore and found a fit place for the observatory in a yam field near the Hiki-au Heiau, or temple. Cook called it a morai, the South Pacific word he'd picked up south of the equator.

Lieutenant King and Bayley observed that the kahunas immediately marked the area as off limits, or kapu, by putting up their dog-hair wands on top of a wall nearby. In honor of Captain Cook's godhead, no ordinary Hawaiian would cross the wall unless specifically invited by one of the white-faced followers of Lono.

The fact which most upset the English workers in the observatory was that no amount of cajolery or even bribery could induce any passing woman to violate the kapu and come into the enclosure. This was the source of much amusement among the other crewmen on the ships, where "the crowds of people, and particularly the women that continued to flock thither, obliged them almost every hour to clear the vessel, in order to have room to do the necessary duties of the ship."

During the next five days, Bayley and his assistants made their observations, Cook was greeted like a god each time he went ashore, and without any prompting, canoes laden with hogs and vegetables went to the ships every day to discharge their cargos. They never stopped for any payment. It developed that this was being done under the direction of the old kahuna, Koa.

On the 24, five days after the first move to set up the observatory, Palea and Koa, the young chief and the old kahuna, left for another part of the island. They told the Englishmen that they were going to meet the moi, Kalaniopuu, and royal party returning from Maui. That same day, the natives stayed close to their houses, no canoes plied Kealakekua Bay, and Captain Cook's crew learned that the bay had been kapued in expectation of Kalaniopuu's imminent return.

On the afternoon of the 25, without fanfare, a single canoe came to the *Resolution*. The kapu was still on, and the crewmen and officers had expected Kalaniopuu would appear with all the magnificence he could muster. But the single canoe carried the king "in a private manner." He came aboard with a wife and several children. Cook and Lieutenant King did not bother to note which wife or which children these were. Despite some exposure to Polynesian customs, they hadn't yet gathered that a king would have many of both varieties of human beings.

Kalaniopuu and this unnamed wife and these unidentified children stayed on the ship long after sundown, and didn't go ashore until nearly ten o'clock.

But the next day, a formation of three large and sumptuous war canoes appeared about noon. In the first was Kalaniopuu, in a sleek, golden war cloak of the yellow feathers of the O'o bird, and a crested helmet to match. He carried a long pololu spear.

Around the moi clustered his leading chiefs, a dazzling splash of red, yellow and black, a colorful pincushion of uplifted spears.

In the second canoe came the kahunas, led by an old man who was the foremost of the priests. King soon remembered that he had seen this old priest previously. It was Holoae, who had come aboard the *Resolution* before with Kalaniopuu, off the northeast coast of Maui. For some reason, Cook and King referred to him as Kaoo.

In the canoe with the kahunas, a red tapa cloth had been spread and four god statues set upon it. Like the other god images the Englishmen had seen, these were made of wicker work, but covered over with black, red, white and yellow feathers. And as usual, they had twisted, grimacing mouths full of shark or dog teeth, and glittering, mother-of-pearl eyes.

The third canoe was loaded to the gunwales with hogs and vegetables, "four very large hogs, with sugarcanes, coconuts and breadfruit," besides sweet potatoes and bananas.

But the three canoes didn't come close to the *Resolution*. Instead, they circled the ship while the kahunas chanted their deep basso paean of dedication to Lono. Then they turned to head back for the shore. They landed near the small beach and the observatory, where Lieutenant King had set up tents for the scientific activities within the kapu area.

Seeing them approach, King mustered his small marine guard and sent them to the beach to welcome the royal retinue. At the same time, Cook ordered the *Resolution*'s pinnace, the largest of the expedition's longboats, to stand by to take him and his officers ashore. They followed close behind the royal fleet.

On the beach, the marine guard smartly escorted Kalaniopuu

to the tent. His chiefs, his kahunas, and many Hawaiians bearing a long train of gifts, followed.

It was then that the Englishmen saw Kamehameha again. Lieutenant King remembered having seen him off the coast of Maui when the royal party had come aboard—and Kamehameha had been so curious that he had stayed on the ship overnight with a few other chiefs. Now, King recorded that the formidable Hawaiian warrior had "the most savage face I ever beheld."

He also specified that the English "at first had some difficulty recollecting Kamehameha," because his hair was "plastered over with a dirty brown paste and powder"—which was, in fact, only a style intended to render the hair lighter in color. During the playing out of the Cook drama, Kamehameha was close to Kalaniopuu. He was also one of the small group of Hawaiians whose blood was shed as the story evolved.

Lieutenant King also reported that in close attendance on the wizened old king were his two younger sons, both called Keoua, but with two other names to differentiate them, Keoua Ku-ahu-ula and Keoua Pe-eale. The older of these two, whose name means approximately "inheritor of the Red-or-sacred-Cloak," was to be Kamehameha's principal foe in a later fight for the kingship of the island of Hawaii.

The presentation ceremonies at the Cook scientific camp were of the usual kind, but of a much more splendid order. This time there were more feather war cloaks, and Kalaniopuu draped his own yellow cloak around Cook's shoulders and put his tall feather helmet on the English captain's head.

This time the train of food—pigs, breadfruit, yams, bananas, sugar cane, coconuts, etc.—was nearly endless. And this time the Hawaiian king had evidently thought out the most lavish ceremonies he could call forth. For the first time in Hawaii he invoked also the friendliest gesture a Polynesian might offer a white stranger, the exchange of names.

This meant that Kalaniopuu told Cook his most intimate personal names and nicknames. And he invented new familiar (but respectful) soubriquets for the English leader. Some verged on humor and on disrespect, like *iwi loa*, meaning literally "tall bone" or less exactly, "tall person." Since Kalaniopuu and his kahunas had ordained that Cook was indeed the god Lono returning here to Hawaii, the Center of the World, the King had to be gentle in his humor. But the fact that Cook was among the tallest of the Englishmen (about six feet two inches), it was a safe, complimentary and obvious jest.

After the ceremonies in the British camp ashore, Cook took Kalaniopuu and many of his leading chiefs to the *Resolution* in the pinnace. It is a safe assumption that Kamehameha was one of them. On board Cook did his best to repay some of the magnificent hospitality that had been lavished on his expedition. He managed to find a fine linen shirt which he draped around the shoulders of Kalaniopuu. He also presented one of his dress swords, a flashy nickle-plated parade item with unsharpened edges.

It was a poor show compared to the long parade of adulation and lavish gifts which had been showered upon Cook. Each of the six feather cloaks which the Hawaiian king had bestowed upon Cook this day represented years of skilled work and would equate to at least a thousand times the dollar value of the parade sword and the linen shirt.

But on the other hand, the value of such items of clothing to the Englishmen was very high. In fact, they were irreplaceable. The expedition had been away from England nearly three years, and neither the shirt nor the sword could be replaced without a hazardous year-long sail back to civilization. And Kalaniopuu could command new feather cloaks at any time from his wardrobe stocks. The same was true of the food. So Cook's gifts, though modest, did represent much greater sacrifices.

Cook made a blunder in diplomacy when he took Kalaniopuu and his leading chiefs out to the *Resolution* and left all of the kahunas on the shore. Of course, Cook was unfamiliar with the importance of the kahunas in the planning of all state affairs, including the most important and costliest of all state affairs, war.

It was a glaring oversight, especially since the English captain did not take along the chief kahuna, Holoae, who had been with Kalaniopuu on the Maui campaign. However, that was probably one of the diplomatic mistakes which contributed to Cook's death twenty days later.

During the festivities on shore and on the ship the whole of the bay remained under priestly kapu. King's chronicle reported: "Not a canoe was seen in the bay, and the natives either kept within their huts, or lay prostrate on the ground."

For the next few days, relations between the English and the Hawaiians continued in flawless peace, but there were several episodes which boded ill for the Cook expedition. One was the public burial of Captain Cook's old batman, or orderly, William Watman, who died on January 29 aboard the *Resolution*.

This was the first death among the crew since the ships had come to Kealakekua Bay. Cook mentioned to Kalaniopuu that he wanted to bury Watman's body on the beach, and Kalaniopuu suggested the ceremonies be conducted and the body buried in the heiau grounds where Lono, the visitor, had been welcomed so enthusiastically.

Lieutenant King reported in the journal that the kahunas stood in respectful silence while Captain Cook read the burial ceremony. Then, when the English had placed Watman's body in the grave and were filling it up, they approached it with reverence and dropped a dead pig, and some coconuts and bananas, into the grave. Then, that night and for two successive nights, they sang prayers and Hawaiian hymns and sacrificed pigs in ceremonies that lasted until daybreak.

Lieutenant King, who was the most popular of the younger officers with the Hawaiians, was better educated in Polynesian customs, and had his misgivings about this notice afforded to the death of the seaman. "May not this public display of their visitors have tended to lessen the exalted ideas which the natives at first seemed to entertain?" he mused in a footnote to that page in the *Journal*. Gods, after all, did not die.

If he had grasped the effect this kind of doubt could work on the Hawaiians, and how it might even lead to lessened respect and even trouble for the English, it seems certain that Cook would have buried Watman at sea and in an inconspicuous ceremony. But Cook, compared to King, had only the most primitive understanding of Hawaiian customs and beliefs.

Then came another blunder which added to the uneasiness of the Hawaiians about the presence of their visitors. It was an indiscretion of Captain Cook which certainly exacerbated any growing frictions between Cook's people and Kalaniopuu's.

Cook was short of firewood for both ships, so he sent Lieutenant King to ask Holoae, the chief kahuna, for one obvious source of wood which Cook had noted. It was the railing which he had seen around the top deck of the heiau, the Lono temple.

It would seem from this distance in history that he might almost as easily have made use of any other timber, almost any of the trees in the vicinity. But he was finishing his work of spot repairs to the ship, the astronomical observations were almost over, and the ships had been well stocked with provisions. He wanted to leave, and least thoughtful and most sacrilegious of all points, he was willing to *pay* for the wood.

Lieutenant King went to his mission with considerable misgivings. "I must confess I had at first some doubt about the decency of this proposal, and was apprehensive that even the bare mention of it might be considered by them as a piece of shocking impiety."

But Holoae surprised King by agreeing without any dispute and he did not even want anything in return. And the crewmen sent to take the wooden railing added another provocation on their own; they demonstrated initiative which was even more of an ignorant and undiplomatic blunder. They took all of the god images which were made of wood.

The priests acquiesced in all this, except the loss of the image of Lono, the largest of the god statues in the temple. It was odd that they should give up the railings and the smaller statues to the reincarnated Lono—but not their image of the god.

Perhaps, with the death of Watman and Cook's blunders in the heiau, they *were* beginning to doubt the divinity of their visitor.

Lieutenant King, who knew enough of the Polynesian language to talk to some of the Hawaiians, said all that he could discover about the Hawaiians' opinion of the English was that "they imagined we came from some country where provisions had failed, and that our visit to them was merely for the purpose of filling our bellies. It was ridiculous enough to see them stroking the sides and patting the bellies of the sailors (who were certainly much improved in the sleekness of their looks during our short stay in the island), and telling them, partly by signs and partly by words, that it was time for them to go, but if they would come again the next breadfruit season, they should be better able to supply their wants."

At this time not only Kalaniopuu but others of his chiefs asked repeatedly when the English were going to leave. And the hospitality of the Hawaiians persisted even to the end of this, the Englishmen's first attempt to leave Hawaii. When Lieutenant King told Kalaniopuu that they were going to sail away in two days on February 4, King noticed that a royal announcement was immediately proclaimed through the villages of that area, "to require the people to bring in their hogs and vegetables for the King to present to the Orono on his departure."

On February 3, Kalaniopuu himself asked Captain Cook and Lieutenant King to visit him at the house of Holoae, the chief of the kahunas. The English officers found the ground around Holoae's grass dwelling crowded with parcels of cloth and a pile of hatchets and other bits of iron which obviously had come from the English in barter.

Nearby lay a mountain of vegetables and fruits, and near that, a large herd of hogs nuzzled the grass. At first Cook and King assumed that all of this loot was to be a gift to the expedition, but they were mystified at the return of the iron objects. Soon King was told that all of the treasure was a present from the people of the district to Kalaniopuu.

In short order, the visitors were surprised when two-thirds of the cloth, and all of the hogs, vegetables and fruit, were bestowed upon them by Kalaniopuu. It was a fitting finale to the stay of the Cook expedition at Kealakekua Bay. It was the largest example of generosity toward the explorers in all of their voyages through the Polynesian islands.

So far, despite a few blunders, the relations of the vastly different ethnic groups had been generally harmonious. The Cook expedition, with its total of about 180 men, had imposed a severe drain upon Kalaniopuu's supply system. But on the other hand the visit had also consumed much of the sparse supply of manufactured goods, and principally, the iron and steel objects left in the ships. These had proved to be the best bartering objects to be offered in return for the good-natured present of the women's café-au-lait charms to the crewmen.

Now, as the ships prepared to sail, Cook's plan was not to leave the Hawaiian Islands forever, but to find a more sheltered harbor than Kealakekua Bay. The inveterate and indefatigable explorer still had the plan of surveying the rest of the island of Hawaii before he finished his observations and notes on the other islands of the group.

Before the ships left, Lieutenant King had seen a chance to stay behind. He had won many friends among the Hawaiian chiefs, and several of them offered him land and Alii privileges if he would remain at the court of Kalaniopuu.

It was a heartfelt compliment and tribute to King, and it was amplified greatly when Kalaniopuu appealed to Cook directly to leave the lieutenant behind. The Hawaiian moi told Cook that he believed Lieutenant King was the Captain's son, but that he was formally requesting that King stay on the island.

Cook did not want to refuse this hospitable offer flatly. He said instead that he would be returning with King to Hawaii the next year, and at that time perhaps he could settle the matter amicably.

And so, on February 4, 1779, the ships weighed anchor and sailed northward, looking for a better harbor, which also would supply drinking water. On the 7, a fairly heavy storm hit the west coast of the island, and on the 8, as the storm subsided, they found that part of the foremast had cracked. This left Captain Cook with no real alternative except to return to Kealakekua

Bay and undertake a major repair job on the mast, and also repair the sails which had been ripped in the storm.

When the ships found anchor in Kealakekua Bay again on February 11, the crew noted with dismay that no canoes and no boisterous swimmers, male or female, came clamoring to meet them this time.

A boat sent ashore brought comforting word that the bay had been put under a kapu because Kalaniopuu was absent. The officers and crew conjectured that perhaps this time Kalaniopuu had chosen to be absent while he debated with his chiefs what should be done with the English visitors who had so unaccountably returned.

At any rate, the foremast was unshipped, and Lieutenant King took it and the ripped sails to the beach. The same day, February 12, the astronomer-naturalist, William Bayley, and Lieutenant King again took the scientific instruments and tents ashore and set it all up with a marine guard at the Hiki-au Heiau.

This time they saw the kahunas again, and these priests seemed cooperative. They set up kapu wands around the mast to protect the crewmen working on it from the curiosity and possible thievery of the kanakas, the Hawaiian natives. They had done the same before to protect the scientific camp set up to study the Transit of Venus.

On the morning of the 13, Kalaniopuu came to the *Resolution* with some of his courtiers, undoubtedly including Kamehameha. This somewhat allayed the suspicions of the English.

But later that day, the young officer who led the watering party came back to the ship to give Lieutenant King a disturbed, and disturbing, report. The Hawaiian kanakas who had been rolling the barrels of water from the spring down to the beach for the English had been driven away from this job by a group of Alii. It developed that these chiefs seemed to be leading some sort of revolt against the visitors.

King gave the young officer a single marine to go back with him. And at King's order, the marine took along only his pistols, not his musket.

But the watering officer came back soon and said that the natives (the "Indians") had armed themselves with stones and were growing very restive and rambunctious. King and Captain Cook went back with the officer to the beach and took along another marine, this time armed with a musket.

They went right to the point of trouble and noted that when the mob saw him coming, they threw away their stones. King's popularity and his friendliness, and especially his ability to communicate in Hawaiian, were well known among the kanakas. And the mob also knew that Cook was the leader of the visitors even if there might be some doubt that he really was the god Lono returning to Hawaii. They also by this time had heard that Kalaniopuu himself had asked Captain Cook to leave his son, Lieutenant King, on the island.

King then spoke with amiable face to the chiefs and they obligingly drove away the mob who had been threatening with their stones. They also permitted those who wanted to work for hire to assist the English crewmen in filling the casks and rolling them down to the ships' boats at the beach.

But soon after that, when King had gone to the scientific tents, he and Cook were alarmed to hear a fusillade of musket fire coming from the direction of the ships. Cook and King saw a native canoe paddling frantically away, pursued by a ship's longboat.

The shore party concluded that the firing from the *Resolution* was directed against some visiting natives who had stolen something. Judging from the volume and prolongation of the firing, they concluded that something had been an item or items of considerable value. Cook had been suffering from the depredations of the "Indians" since the beginning, and of late they had developed a talent for swimming under the ships and extracting the nails with improvised tools. Cook had ordered the crew to fire over the heads of such raiders, preferably using bird shot so they would not be stung nor seriously injured. Once, Cook had ordered such a raider caught and flogged.

Of course, it was dreadful that Englishmen were so ignorant and careless and clumsy about Hawaiian customs and the generally easy-going attitudes about private property, except if it belonged to the Alii.

On the other hand, if we blame the English for being ignorant, clumsy and thoughtless, by the same standard we should find fault with the Hawaiians for not knowing and reflecting that the English were unable to find any replacement in the wide Pacific wastes for the stolen bits of iron which held their ships together, and tools which made repairs possible.

Now, Cook, followed by King, ran toward the spot where they guessed the raiding canoe would be landing. But they arrived too late. The officer, Thomas Edgar, had found the stolen goods hidden in a canoe. They were a pair of armorer's tools and a chisel.

Edgar was returning to the ship with the recovered loot when he saw Cook and King hurrying around the beach, looking for the thieves.

Then followed one of those comedies of errors which frequently lead almost innocently to tragedy. Edgar decided that he should seize the canoe on the shore, believing it was the same one he had chased before.

So he came storming up to the canoe, which belonged to the young chief Palea. Of course, Edgar didn't know this. He decided he must seize the canoe, because Cook was evidently quite concerned about the theft.

Meanwhile, Cook and King and their two supporting marines, not knowing that the missing tools had been discovered, began to look around for the stolen goods. They had seen Edgar's boat trying hard to catch the canoe with the thieves in it, and they had seen some natives scrambling up the slope above the beach.

This time, Cook had no kahuna escort to wave wands and proclaim Cook's divinity. The mob which accumulated around the English captain was surly and some of them had begun to mutter threats and curses. Cook was jumpy and had King tell the throng that he would have the marines fire at them if they didn't produce the thief. One of the marines raised his musket and the crowd retreated. But Cook didn't give the order to fire and the crowd laughed and jeered.

Night was coming and Cook and King gave up and went down to the beach. There they found a packet of grief. Edgar had been opposed by Palea in seizing the canoe and they had been immediately surrounded by a mob. Palea protested his innocence of the theft, and his and Edgar's tempers were straining.

Palea and Edgar suddenly were locked in a struggle, and one of the sailors hit Palea with an oar and knocked him down. The mob closed in and began to beat up Edgar and a young midshipman named George Vancouver. The crowd began to throw stones at the English and at their boats drawn up on the shore. They overran the boats and broke some of the oars and copper fittings —no doubt trying to detach some of that magical hard substance called "ai-lon."

The sailors of the shore party scrambled for safety and took refuge on some rocks along the shore. Palea got himself together and despite his aching head seemed to have forgotten his grievances immediately and helped the battered Edgar and Vancouver. He told the sailors in their rock refuge to come back to the sand and take over the pinnace and ship's boat. And he seemed genuinely concerned that he might have offended Captain Cook and asked if "Lono" would kill him. He was worried about whether he would be able to go on board Cook's flagship the next day. He also returned a midshipman's cap (probably Vancouver's) and promised he would get back the tools, which had been stolen again by the mob.

When the disordered shore party got back to the *Resolution*, King and Edgar reported to Cook and he was disturbed. He ordered all Hawaiians from the ships. According to the last and final version of King's journals, he said: "I am afraid that these people will oblige me to use some violent measures. They must not be left to imagine that they have gained an advantage over us."

The next day, February 14, Valentine's Day, was a fateful and tragic one for the Cook expedition. Early in the morning, Captain Clerke of the *Discovery* noted that their cutter, attached to a buoy near his ship, had been stolen. This was a serious loss. The cutter was a big ship's boat, designed to carry a large load and an able sailing craft. Each of the ships had only one cutter.

Almost immediately, Cook determined to go ashore, taking nine marines with him, and Lieutenant Molesworth Phillips, the marine commander. Lieutenant King had spent the night at the scientific tents ashore, and mounted a double-strength guard there. During the night, a prowler bothered a sentry and the sentry drove him away by firing over his head.

Coming aboard the *Resolution* shortly after daybreak, King found Captain Cook loading his double-barrelled musket and the marine detachment arming for the excursion ashore. Cook's strategy for the day was a technique he had used successfully elsewhere in the Pacific. When something particularly valuable was stolen, he habitually seized the principal chiefs and held them as hostages until the item was returned.

Today he planned another step. To prevent the cutter's sailing out of the bay to some new hiding place, he sent out heavily armed boats to form a blockade. And the gunnery officers of the two ships were instructed to fire their batteries as needed to reinforce the blockade.

As a group of canoes went out, the gunners of the *Discovery* fired in their direction and the thunder of the guns and their cannon splashes ahead of the canoes turned them back toward shore.

Ashore, Cook conjectured, the kahunas at the Lono heiau would probably be alarmed by the warlike sounds from the ships, the cannonading, the drum rolls as the marines mustered, and the maneuvers of the blockading ships' boats. He would go to Kaawalao, at the northern edge of Kealakekua Bay, visit old Kalaniopuu, and bring him along as a hostage. He told Lieutenant King that he must reassure Holoae and the other kahunas that no harm would come to them, that he simply wanted to get his cutter back.

Cook shoved off in three boats, moving this time in considerable strength. This did not include the boat that went to the heiau area with Lieutenant King.

The three boats with Cook were larger than the regular longboats. There were a pinnace, the cutter from the *Resolution*, and a launch under the command of Lieutenant Williamson. Leaving the ship, Cook said the seizure of Kalaniopuu might provoke the "Indians" somewhat, but that he was sure they would not stand up to the fire of a single musket.

Lieutenant King went directly to the heiau and ordered his marines to load their muskets with solid ball ammunition rather than bird- or buckshot. In other words, they were to be prepared to kill if necessary.

Lieutenant King immediately began to reassure Holoae and other kahunas that no evil was intended for them, since they had been friendly with the English ever since they first came to Kealakekua. The kahunas were still greatly concerned, and anxious that Kalaniopuu might not be harmed.

Meanwhile, Captain Cook's three boats reached the point of land at Kaawaloa and took the marine commander, Lieutenant Phillips, and his nine marines with him. Two of the boats stood by in the shallows. The third hovered off the point as a kind of final security.

At Kalaniopuu's hale, Cook and his ten marines found that the great chief had just roused himself from sleep. It was not 9 A.M. yet.

When Cook's party reached the village of Kaawaloa, the people prostrated themselves before him, as before. And in the house of Kalaniopuu, the courtiers received him with utmost deference and the customary offerings of small hogs. Cook's mind was somewhat eased, and his approach to Kalaniopuu was gentle.

He told the old monarch about the theft of the cutter. Kalaniopuu denied any responsibility for it, and Cook invited him and his twin sons, both Keouas, to come aboard the *Resolution* and spend the day with him.

Kalaniopuu and Cook and the marines started for the pinnace, but didn't quite reach it. The two boys, both Keouas, had run ahead to get to the pinnace. Now, one of Kalaniopuu's favorite wives, Kane-kapo-lei, came running after him and halted the procession. Kane-kapo-lei had been Kamehameha's first love, and the mother of his first child, Kao-lei-oku, or Pauli.

A runner had probably come over from the heiau and told some of the courtiers about their concern for Kalaniopuu's safety, and she had heard about it. Also, all of the chiefs, undoubtedly including Kamehameha, had seen and heard some of the military preparations on the ships and the blockading boats. And all had heard the cannonading of the ships' batteries.

Now Kane-kapo-lei attached herself to him in tears and begged him not to go to the ships. Two of the chiefs—apparently Kamehameha was not one of them—laid hold of him and tried to dissuade him from going. Lieutenant King recorded that Kalaniopuu was forced to sit down. By this time a vast mob had gathered around the king. According to Lieutenant Phillips, the marine commander, the crowd had rapidly grown to between 2,000 and 3,000. Phillips reported in his diary that the crowd was pressing so close that the marines didn't have room to unlimber their muskets in case they should be ordered to do so.

The mood of the mob was not friendly, and more of the chiefs began to urge the old king to stay on shore. Cook saw the need for intercession and began to urge Kalaniopuu to come along without delay.

Kalaniopuu grew alarmed at all the tensions "with the strongest marks of terror and dejection in his countenance," according to Lieutenant King. Cook was urging him to stand up and come along, and the mood of the crowd was turning ugly.

All of the chiefs were insistent now that Kalaniopuu should stay on shore. Lieutenant Phillips was growing concerned and urged Cook to give up the project of bringing Kalaniopuu on board. According to his diary, he said: "We can never think of compelling him to go on board without killing a number of these people."

Cook determined that Phillips was right. He and Phillips decided the marines should line up at the water's edge, facing the crowd. Cook started to walk across the thirty or so yards to the water's edge when a canoe landed and a chief hurried up from it. He was Kekuhaupio, Kamehameha's military kahu and a very famous warrior through some of the most desperate of Kalaniopuu's battles. Also, as noted in the account of Kalaniopuu's war against Keawe, he was the son of old Holoae, chief of the kahunas.

Now the redoubtable old fighter reported to Kalaniopuu, with Kamehameha and the other chiefs gathered around him, that one of the English boats had fired at him and another chief named Kalimu. He and Kalimu had been trying to cross from a northern village on the bay, an English boat had opened fire on them, and Kalimu had been killed. Kekuhaupio had not been overawed by this bit of foreigners' magic—only angered.

He managed to communicate some of this to the leading Alii, clustered around Kalaniopuu, probably including Kamehameha. At this moment, another Alii with a spear in his hand appeared. He was overbrimming with anger and had worked himself into a warlike rage.

He was Palia, the brother of Kalimu. He was threatening loudly that he would kill Captain Cook because Cook had been responsible for the death of his brother.

It was not difficult to locate Cook. The Captain was tall and physically distinguished; he had a commanding mien, and he wore his sword. Now he had turned to face the multitude near the water's edge. By now, the crowd was thoroughly enraged.

Cook saw that Palia's face was twisted with fury, and that he wore a crude body armor of pandanus mat. Cook saw that many of the warriors in the crowd had taken this precaution to-day. This kind of armor had been adopted by the Hawaiians since the English had been peppering them with birdshot in an attempt to drive them away as they tried to dive under the ships to extract iron nails and other metal fastenings.

In the heat of the moment, Cook still waited before killing anyone. He was concerned about Palia's vengeful appearance, but still didn't want to kill him, only to drive him back and discourage him. In that split second, he could scarcely reflect whether or not the birdshot and the blast of the musket would really deter the attack. He could only hope.

He fired. In the confusion of the onrush of the mob, Palia disappeared. Others pressed toward Cook and his detachment. The English began to fall back toward the water.

Cook had expended one of the two barrels of his musket, the one loaded with birdshot. He had the important one left, the barrel charged with solid iron ball, and he could kill one man with that when necessary. But to reload was a detailed, three-minute job and in that time the onrushing mob could finish him.

Things were getting out of hand. Suddenly, many men in the crowd were throwing stones at the marines in their line along the edge of the water.

The crowd pressed closer to the marines. More stones were hitting among them and still they did not yet fire because Captain Cook had not ordered it, and neither of course had Lieutenant Phillips, without an order from the commander.

Lieutenant Williamson was hovering off the rocks in the launch, with his crew of sailors. The marine commander, Lieutenant Phillips, ahead of the line of marines at the water's edge, was holding his musket at the ready trying to face down the mob. He was jumped by a large and fierce Hawaiian who tried to stab him with a dagger. Phillips dodged and parried by swinging the butt of the weapon.

Cook too was being overwhelmed by the press of the mob and he fired his lethal musket barrel carefully and killed one of the assailants. But the Hawaiians did not fall back. They kept pushing forward and threw more stones and Cook ordered the marines to fire. Several of the Hawaiians fell and the mob at last began to fall back.

If the marines had been able to fire again immediately and kill and wound more of the Hawaiians, they might have withdrawn completely, at least long enough to allow the shore party to leave. This was the first time the Hawaiians had seen many muskets fired to kill.

But the marines were busy reloading their single-barrelled muskets, and strangely enough Lieutenant Williamson, in the launch offshore, had not yet given the order to his men to fire.

While the marines scrambled to reload, and fell back into the water, the mob came surging back with vengeance in their hearts. Cook tried to draw his sword. A large, well-meaning Alii, Kanaina, who had been friendly with Cook and his officers, struggled with Cook, possibly to prevent him from inflicting more carnage.

The mob read this as a mortal struggle, and threw more stones while they pushed toward the Englishmen. And at that moment, the sailors in the boats at last began to fire their muskets, in a ragged way. Lieutenant Williamson hadn't yet given the order to open fire.

Then the catastrophe happened. Cook turned toward the boats. The legend has been that he was asking the sailors with muskets to hold their fire, and this is perpetuated in the etching by the expedition's artist, James Webber.

It seems more likely that far from asking the sailors and marines to stop firing, he was in effect trying to say to them: "In the name of the Deity, will you give me some supporting fire? And quickly!"

Cook was an experienced field commander and he had lived through considerable experience as boss of a fighting ship in His Majesty's Navy. He could see now that his whole position was about to go under if the mob overran him.

But now they did. In the hurly-burly, the shouting and struggling crowd, Cook was struck from behind with a stick and he fell. Four of the marines were inundated by the flood of the mob's violence, and soon they were stomped, beaten and stabbed to death. The others fell back into the water.

Now the marines were firing another volley into the crowd of the Hawaiians and many had fallen. Cook was trying to get back to his feet, but before he could, he was stabbed in the back with a dagger. He fell back into the water.

The mob was crushing toward the remaining marines. These

brave men had no time to reload. They scrambled on through waist-deep water toward the pinnace, which was lying a few feet offshore.

The marine commander, Lieutenant Phillips, was mobbed by the throng, knocked down and stabbed in the shallows. But his stab wound wasn't as bad as Cook's. From the water, he managed to shoot his opponent dead and haul himself aboard the pinnace. The pinnace was getting under way, but they stopped long enough in the confusion to pick up the marines scrambling in the water. Phillips, battered as he was, jumped in to save one marine who appeared to be drowning, and pull him aboard.

The mob was charging into the water and getting closer to the pinnace. The pinnace began to make speed to get away. The cutter was also close to the shore, the sailors in it standing to fire their muskets into the rampaging crowd. The third boat, the launch commanded by Lieutenant Williamson, was still too far off and the men in it were firing in the most desultory and disorganized fashion.

It was too late to pick up the remains of Captain Cook. He was being trampled, stabbed and beaten to death by the mob, and his shirt had already been taken by the man who had first stabbed him.

We can only conjecture what Kamehameha was doing at this time. It would seem likely that his quick and amenable intelligence would have found him trying to hold back the forces of destruction in the mob which were leading to such a tragic outcome. He had already shown immense curiosity about the technical inventions and scientific superiorities of the White Man, and probably did not want to lose the English as friends.

At the heiau observatory for Lono near the small sandy beach to the south, Lieutenant King had seen much of the fighting and heard the firing there at the rocky point at Kaawaloa.

King believed he had been successful with his reassurances to the kahunas that Cook's intentions were benign—until the outbreak of violence at Kaawaloa. Then, the ship *Discovery* suddenly began to fire with two of her main battery of four-inch guns in the general direction of the beach near the heiau and the scientific observatory of the Cook expedition there. Later King learned that Captain Clerke, who had been left in command of the ships during Cook's absence ashore, had heard reports of the massing of hundreds of Hawaiian natives around the heiau. Clerke had wanted to deter the aggressive ambitions of *that* mob, but the firing of those few cannonballs probably exacerbated the situation rather than helped it.

Lieutenant King hurriedly sent a boat back to the ships. He had witnessed and heard some of the fighting at Kaawaloa, and had seen the boats shuttling back and forth between the ships.

The next half-hour, while the boat was on its way, was nerve-racking. "Our situation was at this time extremely critical and important. Not only our own lives, but the event of the expedition, and the return of at least one of the ships, being involved in the same common danger. We had the mast of the *Resolution* and the greatest part of our sails on shore, under the protection of only six marines—their loss would have been irreparable."

Then Mr. Bligh, the sailing master of the *Resolution*, came in a boat from the ship. He confirmed that Cook was dead, and had orders from Clerke to strike the tents and move the sails to the ship.

At that moment, the bearded kahuna of the Lono temple, Keli-ikea, came up in a dreadful state of "great sorrow and dejection" to ask if it was true that Cook had been killed. He said he'd heard this from Kaawaloa and wanted to know from "Tinny" whether it was true.

King thought it best to deny the story, and to convey this answer to everyone. He wanted as much time as possible to get the *Resolution*'s mast and sails to the ship. He instructed Bligh to take command of the post while he, King, made a quick trip to the ship to get some marine reinforcements so that he could move the mast, sails, tents and instruments out to the *Resolution* with a little more security.

King had scarcely reached the *Resolution* when they heard firing from the direction of the observatory. King hurried back and en route saw a mob of Hawaiians moving across the top of the cliff from Kaawaloa in the direction of the observatory camp.

When he reached the camp, King saw large numbers of Hawaiians with spears and their antigunfire-type body armor of mats wet down with seawater for extra resistance to birdshot. Stones began to fall upon the garrison at the post. Some of the Hawaiians crept up to the camp by using a line of rocks for cover, and tried an assault. The marines fired from the top of the temple and killed one of the attackers. Then they fell back.

Fortunately for King and the men of the post, the durable marine commander, Lieutenant Phillips, arrived at this time with well-armed reinforcements. The Hawaiian warriors retreated at the sight and King was able to contact the kahunas.

Aided by the strong psychological ploy of the reinforcements and extra arms, Lieutenant King arranged a kind of truce to get the repaired mast and sails and the instruments to the ship and by noon all the people at the station were out.

Back on the ships, the officers took sorrowful toll of the day's tragic losses. Captain Clerke, although he had been chronically sick with what was apparently a heart ailment, took over on the spot as the new commander of the expedition.

First priority, Clerke said, was to get back the body of Captain Cook. Lieutenant King, in a strange reaction for an officer who had been the friendliest of all toward the Hawaiians, suggested some punishment be inflicted upon them. Clearly, he felt the English had been deeply wronged.

After considerable discussion among the officers, it was decided that conciliation should be tried before force, and King was to be sent as the envoy. At four in the afternoon, a fleet of boats from both ships left for shore. The men in the boats were conspicuously armed and the Hawaiians reacted in kind. Mobs of men were massing along the beach, protected by their home-made antigunfire body armor of wet matting and carrying long spears, and the womenfolk were taking the children from the scene, an ominous foreshadowing of expected war action.

King didn't like the look of this at all, and as commander of the expedition, he ordered the armed boats to fall back, and went ahead in a single boat "with a white flag in my hand, which by a general cry of joy from the natives, I had the satisfaction to find was instantly understood."

Shortly, the old kahuna named Koa, whom King anyhow believed to be a two-faced backbiter, came swimming out to the boat. He too carried a white flag in his hand as he swam.

King noted that the kahuna was armed (he didn't say how), but he believed the prudent and fair course was to receive him into the boat. On the spot, King said he demanded that Cook's body be restored to the Englishmen immediately, and that if this were not done, the English would make war on the Hawaiians. Koa said he would take care of that chore, begged (and got) a piece of iron, and shouted to the people ashore that everything was all right and that they were all friends again. Then he jumped back into the water and swam ashore; quite an athletic feat for an old man.

But the Hawaiians continued to be anything but friendly. King waited for Koa's return for an hour, then reluctantly started back for the ships. As he was leaving, a Hawaiian male climbed up on a rock, exhibited his backside to the English and made numerous gestures indicating sexual disrespect.

The other boats returning to the ship reported that they had been told that Cook's body had been dissected and the parts carried into the hills. That night there were large and ominous fires along the beach and in the moonless darkness two Hawaiians approached the *Resolution* in a canoe and were fired upon by the sentries.

One was a minor kahuna (unnamed in King's chronicle) who had been an outspoken admirer of Captain Cook and he tearfully presented a bundle wrapped in tapa cloth. It turned out to be the "nether parts" of the captain, that part of the body assigned to the head kahuna, Holoae. Holoae was frail and peaceful but occasionally very bloodthirsty, as we have seen earlier in his life during Kalaniopuu's war against Keawe. But Holoae had been disturbed by the imminence of all-out warfare with the formidable English. So he had dispatched the two Hawaiians with this bit of flesh, all that he could lay a hand upon at that moment.

When they killed such a formidable opponent as Cook in what was loosely called "battle," Pacific Island warriors generally kept the bones, and sometimes ate the flesh, pervasive with the mana (Hawaiian word for "power") of the dead man. This belief is curiously prophetic of the findings of modern geneticists that animal life can acquire certain kinds of intelligence through diet. Thus B. F. Skinner and others have postulated the theory that perhaps humans might similarly benefit from cannibalism. If this should prove to be the case, it would be far from the first case in which the ancient Hawaiians were the voice of our future, with their views on sex and many other social problems.

So head kahuna Holoae had sacrificed some very powerful mana when he gave up his share of the Cook body. Yet the emotional climate ashore was stretched well beyond a breaking point. The two messengers from Holoae had come by night because, they said, anyone dealing with the Englishmen on a friendly basis might be killed.

Tempers ashore had been inflamed by the casualties in the day's battles with the English. At Kaawaloa, seventeen Hawaiians had been killed; five of these were chiefs, including Keli-ikea, the long-bearded kahuna who had been so friendly with the English from the very beginning, and his brother, another good friend. That at least was the wawa rumor.

And at the observatory where Lieutenant King had held forth, eight Hawaiians had been killed, including three first-rank chiefs.

Because of this apparent disastrous defeat for his power, old King Kalaniopuu, fearing a coup and a violent overturn by the more aggressive chiefs, had retired to a secret cave in a cliff and was being kept alive by food baskets lowered by rope.

There is no indication in any of the known sources how Kamehameha fitted into this situation. It is known that he had been given Cook's scalp, an honorable part of the anatomy for a warrior to have. The opponent's scalp and forelock, as we have already indicated in previous accounts of Hawaiian battles, were among the first trophies garnered by a victorious Hawaiian gladiator, right after a fight to the death. That is, at just about the same time as the victor removed the niho palaoa, or tooth of a whale (or walrus), the mark of a high chief, usually worn on a necklace of human hair.

It seems unlikely that Kamehameha would side with the dissident revolutionaries who wanted old Kalaniopuu to take a more vigorous course of action against the English. From the first contact with Cook and his men, Kamehameha had been friendly. And from the beginning, he had been fascinated by the magic weapons and sizable ships they commanded. The very next day those weapons and ships were to impress him in a way he would never forget as long as he lived.

During that night, from the distance of the ships' anchorage, perhaps three-quarters of a mile from shore, the English could hear loud wailing, and there were many bonfires. Evidently, the chiefs and some of the kahunas were drumming up public grief over the losses of the engagement at Kaawaloa and the scientific camp.

By the next morning, the English resentment over their unsuccessful efforts to get back Cook's body (except for the ghastly piece of hip) or the stolen and invaluable cutter, was mounting. "Indeed," King wrote, "our situation was become extremely awkward and uncompromising: none of the purposes for which this Pacific course of proceeding had been adopted having hitherto been in the least forwarded by it."

Captain Clerke certainly showed no visible evidence of doubt in the ability of the English to force their will on the Hawaiians by whatever degree of power should be required. Of course, they were perhaps overconfident of the superiority which their weapons seemed to give them.

That day the matter of the failure seemed to come to a head, with a show of braggadocio, insolence and insult in full view of a crowd of admirers on the shore. A young brave came out in a canoe and pulled up ahead of the *Resolution*, close enough so that he could have been easily knocked down with a musket shot. Then he stood up, started throwing stones, shouting insults and waving Captain Cook's hat.

Nothing could have been better calculated at that moment to drive the English sailors into a towering rage. This warrior's provocation was well done in the tradition of prebattle insults, where the soldiers and Alii try to distinguish themselves by being insulting to a prominent member of the enemy camp. It had been offensive enough to be presented with the captain's dismembered hip the night before, however unselfish old Holoae might have been in giving up this priceless bit of mana.

"Our people were all in a flame at this insult, and coming in a body on the quarter deck, begged they might no longer be obliged to put up with these repeated provocations, and requested me to obtain permission for them from Captain Clerke to avail themselves of the first fair occasion of revenging the death of their commander."

That was the account of Lieutenant King, and he did as the men requested. He went straight to Captain Clerke and the captain came through with a quick decision: He ordered the ship's great guns to give the natives ashore a good dose of whatfor. He also told the crew something they had been dying to hear. Clerke was planning to send a party ashore to replenish the water casks as if nothing untoward were happening. Now he said that if that shore party were harassed, they should take whatever punitive measures they chose.

In a short time the big guns were loaded, but the hustle and bustle of the preparations to fire, the scurrying around, the trundling of the bags of gunpowder and the cannonballs and the commands were sufficient to alert the villagers near the coast. They accordingly took shelter behind walls and rock features. But even so, the gunners did well enough with their targets of opportunity—which were any large groups of people.

The guns thundered. The gunners saw the cannonballs smashing into the soft houses and sending them down in showers

of thatch and splintered bamboo. In that quick, ricocheting bed-
lam Kamehameha was caught, knocked down and cut up. And
three or four other Hawaiians were killed.

The facile and inventive kahuna Koa came paddling out posthaste, still flying a homemade white flag, and carrying a peace
offering of more pigs. He was getting to be as quick to react to
a bombardment or threat as a weather prophet, and as unreliable.
By now the crew, even in the midst of all this grievous travail,
had begun to joke about this two-faced and inventive diplomat.

Now he was ushered to Captain Clerke with many a grim
jest. This time he seemed genuinely agitated, and he said that
many Alii had been killed by the guns, including Kamehameha,
Kalaniopuu's nephew. He begged Clerke to stop firing and promised that the chiefs were friendly. However, the English had
heard that song before.

That night, the two subkahunas came back aboard again from
Holoae under cover of the darkness. They said that the afternoon's bombardment had wreaked considerable havoc and killed
some of the Alii, and that it had frightened the chiefs. But even
though the chiefs were frightened, these two friendly kahunas
warned that the chiefs were not through fighting. In fact, the
English should be on their guard against trickery.

The next morning, the watering party went ashore with empty
casks. They were bristling with arms and spoiling for vengeance.
Ashore, the Hawaiians were "resolved to take every opportunity
of annoying us, when it could be done without much risk."

The Englishmen never knew it, but as they went ashore, the
warrior who was to become the first king of all the Hawaiian
Islands, Kamehameha the Great, lay seriously injured, under the
care of a kahuna. He had been washed down with sea water
and a new hut of ironwood, or hale hau, had been put up for him.
Certain kinds of squid, sea urchin and sea cucumber were dropped
from his diet, the ina, wana and haueke.

The usual chant of the kahuna for a sick Alii was frequently
recited, a calling for supernatural help against the magical spell
which some enemy might have worked against the ailing Alii.

Some ana-ana.
"What if the wandering ghosts strike evilly?
I am safe against the ana-ana,
By the day which the god has made clear,
Like the water of life."

This was a customary chant of kahunas, and it was sung each time medicine was given. But it was especially pertinent in this case, because it was the White Man's special magic with the miraculous tubes of hao, that hard stuff with supernatural strength that barked out fire and death.

And in this case the injuries must have had special interior magic in them because the wounds on Kamehameha's face and torso did not seem serious. But the beating about the head which had been inflicted by stones sent flying by the cannonballs had stunned the huge, muscular and redoubtable warrior. That beating had left him dizzy, niniu, with blurred vision, headache and fever.

The kahunas did their best. Even the chief kahuna, old Holoae, came in to help. But the kahunas could do little more than sing their chants fervently and administer the standard remedy for fever, raw taro juice or yam juice.

The fact that Kamehameha was the king's nephew and one of the most famous warriors in Kalaniopuu's commanding echelon made his being healed a top-priority project.

To be as sure as they could be that the preparations for healing were as propitious as possible, kahunas repeated their initial steps. Last night had been stormy and rainy, a bad omen, after the initial washing down with sea water and the sacrifice of a pig to Ku-kaili-moku, the war god who was also the aukamahua, or family god. So they made another sacrifice of a pig and a baked dog, and built another ironwood house, where the patient might rest while renewed chants were recited.

That same morning, the watering party from the *Resolution* came ashore with murder and mayhem in their eyes. And the Hawaiians had prepared a series of general offensive tactics in the high ground above the Hiki-au Heiau, the former site of the scientific camp.

In the caves in the cliff above the former camp area, they had prepared piles of stones to be thrown, and boulders to be dropped so that they could harass anyone visiting the spring below.

The watering party went energetically about their business of filling their casks, but they were met with such a constant barrage of stones and occasional loosened boulders that they had to stop behind one of the stone walls on the flat, unlimber their muskets, and pop away at the scurrying pelters above.

However, their best efforts at marksmanship yielded no results. The assailants above simply ducked back into the caves, or took shelter behind natural stone walls up there and lobbed stones down at the English.

The result of this activity was that by 11:30 they had managed to get only one cask of water out to their boats. Captain Clerke was informed of the situation and he decided to invoke the final solution again. He ordered another barrage of the great guns to be levelled at the cave area. Quickly the cannonballs created a successful hell of flying rock and debris up there.

This barrage had the immediate result of keeping the Hawaiians under cover. For a while, the watering party was able to go about its business unmolested. Then it started again: stones and boulders falling on them.

Now the long-taut nerves of the English snapped. The shore party was now beginning to be pelted with stones from the grass huts of the nearby village. The officers in charge decided to burn down the huts nearest the spring area and the beach. But once the sailors had torches in their hands, they could not be held back. They not only burned down the whole village, but they also destroyed the huts of the kahunas near the heiau. And the kahunas had generally been the best friends of the English.

But that wasn't enough. The rampaging sailors shot some of the Hawaiians as they ran from the burning houses. They caught some of the villagers and cut their heads off, to take back to the ship with them.

It was sad that Lieutenant King, who had long been a friend of the Hawaiians, had not come to the beach with the watering party. This day he had been ill and confined to his bunk. But he wrote about the day's proceedings when he heard about them:

"I cannot enough lament the illness that confined me on board this day. The priests had always been under my protection."

At any rate, the mayhem carried out by the watering party, barbaric as it was, produced a much desired effect for the English. As the shore party was leaving the beach in their boats, a procession of a score of boys carrying pieces of white tapa and green boughs in their hands appeared. They were led by a man who also carried a white cloth and branches of green. He was Keli-ikea, the amiable and honest kahuna who had befriended the English from the beginning, the bearded young priest whom the crew jestingly called "the Rector."

Keli-ikea was very grave and asked to be taken to the *Resolution*. When he came on board the flagship, he grew still more grave as he saw two decapitated Hawaiian heads on the deck. He asked Captain Clerke very agitatedly that they be thrown overboard. Captain Clerke complied with the request, and Keli-ikea, after some remonstrances about the unfair treatment of the kahunas, left with promises to try for peace and the return of Captain Cook's body. Later in the day, the two-faced kahuna, Koa, came back in a canoe with his usual offerings of hogs and bananas. This time Lieutenant King had suffered enough indignities at Koa's hands and he told him abruptly to shove off, and that if he came back without Cook's body one more time, he would be shot.

After that, Koa's performance was down to his usual level of duplicity. He went back and joined the Hawaiians who were still flinging stones at the English who hadn't yet left the beach. King was dismayed later when he heard from a crewman returning aboard from the shore party that the midshipman in charge (perhaps Vancouver) had been aiming a cocked and loaded musket at Koa as he was throwing stones. But unfortunately, King reported in his journal, the "midshipman's piece missed fire."

The remainder of the watering party finished its chores unharassed after the last bit of shooting to discourage stone-throwers. No doubt the Hawaiians had learned—and they seemed to be very quick at learning and adapting to the tactics of the English—that if a few musket shots didn't work, the English would invoke their big guns and their torches.

Nevertheless, that night was a dismal one aboard the ships. There were more bonfires ashore and a louder wailing and lamenting than even the night before. The English didn't know it, but Kalaniopuu had come back from his hideaway and was urgently conferring with his chiefs about restoring some of the pieces of Cook's body and some of his personal property to the English. It was too late to do anything about the stolen cutter. It had been burned so that the bits of connecting metal-like nails, and the iron and brass fixtures, could be detached. Kalaniopuu decided to send a high chief named Eapo (meaning approximately "King of the Night") to make arrangements to restore some of Cook's flesh and bones to Captain Clerke.

Most of the bones had been shredded of their flesh after cooking. Probably some of that flesh had been eaten for the rare and superpotent mana. Kalaniopuu had the legs, thighs and arms, the valuable long bones. Kamehameha, vaguely conscious in his house of ironwood (hale hau), in the interests of peace had given up his treasured forelock and scalp of the great voyager from far-off Beretani (Hawaiian version of Britain). However, he apparently had kept some of the hair as a last-ditch source of mana. The English noted that Cook's hair had been chopped very short.

The next morning, a column of men was seen moving slowly down the slope to the beach. They carried sugar cane, bread-fruit and bananas. They were led by two drummers with a large temple pahu.

The procession came to the water's edge and stopped there, and the drummers sat down and began to sound a low-toned call. Someone put up a white flag next to them. The marchers put their presents of food on the rocks.

They kept playing while the figure of a large, solidly built chief, in a long cloak of yellow and black feathers, came slowly down the slope. It was Eapo.

He was reverently carrying a package wrapped in white tapa. The officers and crewmen surmised correctly that the package contained some of the remains of Captain Cook. At the water's edge, Eapo signalled to the *Resolution* that he would like a boat to be sent to him.

Clerke, King and the others had seen Eapo occasionally and knew him to be a very high-ranking chief. So Clerke set out immediately in the pinnace, telling King to attend him in the remaining cutter.

Aboard the pinnace, Eapo very reverently gave his bundle to Clerke. Now it was additionally wrapped in a splendid feather cloak of black and white.

Eapo went along with Clerke to the *Resolution*, but wouldn't go aboard, King thought because he did not want to embarrass the English officers by being there while they unwrapped the bones and other remains of Cook. It was a sad sight: the bones of both arms and legs, somewhat scarred with deep heat but with flesh and ligaments still attached; the skull with the face bones missing, the scalp with ears still attached, and the hands almost intact, identified by a distinctive long scar Cook had between thumb and forefinger. The whole sad mess had been heavily salted down, to somewhat preserve the cooked flesh.

Eapo waited in the pinnace while the officers unwrapped the remains of Cook. When they came back to the boat he apologized that the lower section and jaw and feet were missing, and explained that Kalaniopuu had been unable to convince the two chiefs who had these parts to give them up, and that he was still trying. He also explained what had happened to the cutter, how it had been burned for the metal by Palea's men before Kalaniopuu could intercede.

Captain Clerke and the officers, though horrified by the relics of Cook, were satisfied with the good intentions of Kalaniopuu. They were relieved, and worked energetically to complete the work on the foremast and sails so that they could leave in a day or two. Eapo said he would return the next day and he hoped he would have more of Captain Cook's remains and possessions.

He appeared the next morning at the ship with Kalaniopuu's favorite and highest-caste son, Kiwalao. On the evening before, he had visited with Kamehameha in his hale hau. Kamehameha, strong as a shark, was recovering from his concussion and was strong enough to urge Eapo to get together and return more of Cook's body and possessions. Eapo had gathered more bones and Cook's shoes, and went early to deliver them.

Eapo also returned to Clerke the pieces of Cook's musket. The barrels had been beaten flat as the first step in an attempt to convert it into some tools or weapons more understandable to the Hawaiians.

Eapo assured Captain Clerke that Kalaniopuu, Kamehameha and he had been opposed by some other chiefs when they wanted to remain friendly with Captain Cook.

Clerke told Eapo he wanted the whole of Kealakekua Bay declared kapu that afternoon. He was planning funeral ceremonies for his late and much lamented commander.

Very rapidly, the bay was cleared and the ship's carpenter finished a coffin for Cook's remains. Clerke read the military honors, the coffin was weighted and dropped into the deep water.

The ship's company was deeply moved, and the usually articulate Lieutenant King found himself at a loss for words. "Those who were present know that it is not in my power to express them [the feelings of officers and men]."

Cook had spent long, hard and dangerous years exploring this widest and one of the most remote and inaccessible areas of the world. This Yorkshire coastal sailor, a self-taught farmer's son, had been an unselfish, decisive, very wise and ingenious leader. And above all he had always been brave. World history had found few men to equal Captain Cook, and it would find only a few afterwards.

Clerke now prepared to leave the unhappy reaches of Kealake-

kua Bay. The ships were ready to sail except that last-minute provisions had to be brought aboard. It was too late to do that this
evening.

However, the next morning Eapo came to the ship early and
Clerke asked him to remove the kapu so that the Hawaiians
could come to carry on their trading as before. Clerke and King
told the chief that the English were now satisfied, and that now
that Cook was buried, the strife with the Hawaiians was buried
with him.

And so on February 22, 1779, a horde of trading canoes gathered around the ships. Many chiefs came to extend their friendship, and to express their sorrow at the commander's death. In
some ways, it was like the first boisterous days of good fellowship
when the ships arrived at Kealakekua Bay. In many other ways
things had changed so radically that the relationships between
Hawaiians and British would never be the same. Yet the quality
and quantity which most interested the sailors, the willingness of
the women, was still there.

Ashore, Kamehameha, still striving to recuperate from the concussion that struck with the British cannonballs, had learned more
respect than ever for the English scientific skill and technical
inventiveness. His hard experience at the wrong end of a cannon
had greatly encouraged his hunger for the magic war techniques
of the Europeans. Undoubtedly he already had the vision that
the ships and guns of the foreigners would give him the power
to gain control of all the islands and become their first king. He
had long since learned the simple lesson which Kalaniopuu had
stubbornly resisted: that ten men can always beat one, with equal
weapons.

That evening, in the purple shades of the Hawaiian twilight,
Clerke gave the order to hoist anchor and get under way. The
ships moved along the coast of the bay. "The natives were collected on the shore in great numbers; and as we passed along,
received our last farewells with every mark of affection and good
will" (Lieutenant King's journal).

King also, in another version of his journal, wrote in a graceful epitaph: "Thus we left Kealakekua Bay, a place become too remarkably famous for the very unfortunate and tragical death of one of the greatest Navigators our nation or any nation ever had."

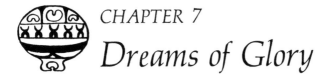

CHAPTER 7
Dreams of Glory

Two years after the Cook expedition left Kealakekua Bay, in 1781, old Kalaniopuu's infirmity had grown acute. His shakiness, and unsteadiness, which the kahunas said came from long-time awa drinking, had developed into a genuine palsy and he was continually sick at his stomach.

The old king had a presentiment of the imminence of death and called together his high chiefs, his sons and his formidable warrior nephew, Kamehameha.

Kamehameha had recovered rapidly from his severe beating by the British bombardment. He was endlessly strong and his will seemed equally indomitable. He had been a dutiful supporter of the old king. He had not involved himself in the endless intrigues and power struggles always happening among the Alii.

But he had learned a new ambition: to assimilate the powerful weapons of the white foreigners when they should come back again to Hawaii. He was not sure yet how he was going to use this knowledge and skill.

At this top echelon council which Kalaniopuu called in 1781, in the Waipio Valley of the Kohala district, the seeds of Kamehameha's climb to power were sown. The chiefs of course were vitally concerned with the division of the lands which Kalaniopuu controlled. The old king had brought most of the Big Island under his sovereignty. His control varied in degree of strength from one section to another, and he had to keep the local lords generally friendly by whatever means were necessary: gifts, privileges, force and threats of force. He had been through the mill of intrigue, murder and war which preceded any of the usual mortal struggles with one's relatives for suzerainty in the Hawaiian Islands.

The central fact remained that no moi or king in the islands had been strong enough to control more than one island and, at the most, small bits of other islands.

It was in this latter tradition that Kalaniopuu had managed to gain control of the easternmost part of the Hana and Kaupo sections of Maui. He had tried at great expense in blood and taxes over those many years of campaigning to expand his holdings on Maui.

Despite the valiant and persistent efforts of his military stalwarts like Kamehameha and Kekuhaupio, he was unable to seize control of the other Maui districts such as Lahaina, Kaanapali and Wailuku. After the all-but-decisive defeats by his cousin Kahekili at Wailuku and Kaanapali, all he had left of his holdings on Maui was the far-eastern tip, Hana. There he still managed control of the nearly impregnable Kauwiki fort. Now it looked as if he were going to lose control even of Kauwiki.

At this high-level conclave of the leading chiefs, Kalaniopuu had reached some central decisions about the future of his realm. The main question in the minds of all the chiefs was: "Who will succeed Kalaniopuu?"

The aged king's answer was definite, but it had a face-saving facet for Kamehameha. The heir would be his most kapu son Kiwalao, the child of his favorite wife Kalola.

But Kalaniopuu, though aged and infirm, had not lost his mental acuity. He knew that Kiwalao was essentially a weak young man, and that there was one young military leader in his court who towered literally and figuratively above all the others: Kamehameha.

The old king also knew that if he did not give Kamehameha a good reason for supporting Kiwalao, the fierce, supersize warrior would be involved in the inevitable intrigues against Kiwalao and that any intrigue vehemently supported by Kamehameha would probably succeed.

So practically in the same breath in which he had declared that Kiwalao would succeed him as moi, Kalaniopuu said that he was entrusting his and the family's war god, Ku-kaili-moku, to the redoubtable and battle-scarred warrior Kamehameha. This was like making him "Minister of Defense" in a modern state, meaning of course in the less taxonomic and hypocritical language of World War II times, Minister of War.

But the idea didn't work. Kamehameha didn't relish the idea of playing second fiddle, even if his appointment did give him in effect the most important job under Kiwalao's authority. It was still under Kiwalao's authority.

Like Kalaniopuu, Kamehameha had little respect for Kiwalao as a man. With his long and successful career in violence, Kamehameha had little respect for a man who was indecisive or unwilling to act or use force. After the Waipio conference, he began to scheme with Ke-e-au-moku, whom he was seeing frequently these days anyhow because he was romantically interested in Ke-e-au-moku's daughter, Kaahumanu.

Ke-e-au-moku had long since returned to Kalaniopuu's fold, as we have seen earlier. He was a fast and convincing talker, a man of tempestuous passions, and a notable turncoat. He had flipped allegiance again after having first deserted from Kalaniopuu and gone to Kahekili. Then, he had quarrelled with Kahekili because he had the audacity to marry Namahana, the widow of the king who had preceded Kahekili as moi of Maui.

He had come back to the Kalaniopuu fold at Kauwiki fort, in the Hana district of Maui, and there Namahana had given birth to Kaahumanu. Kamehameha had seen that child in Kauwiki and observed that she was beautiful. But when he saw her at age fourteen at Kalaniopuu's court at Kawaihae in early 1782, he was surprised to see just how beautiful she had become.

Ke-e-au-moku had been a friend of Kamehameha for many years, since before the outbreak of Kalaniopuu's war against Alapai's son and heir, Keawe-opala.

In Kauwiki on Maui, Ke-e-au-moku had spoken, somewhat in jest, about Kamehameha's marrying Kaahumanu when she grew a little older. It was a joke because she was then about three years old. However, in 1882, she had grown into a straight, tall, beautiful girl, already nearly six feet tall. She was a marvelous surfer and swimmer and in the usual costume for those sports—nothing—her athletic beauty was overwhelming. Kamehameha could not have failed to reflect that in looks and bearing, and in her quick intelligence, she was as close to being a natural-born queen as any woman he had ever seen.

The Hawaiian Alii, both chiefs and chiefesses, had a free-wheeling attitude about the pleasures (even sports, to use the Hawaiian word Hono-ipo) of sex and love. Both sexes had many mates, officially married or not. And the Alii were encouraged to have children by relatives, in wedlock or out. In fact, the closest incest, the wedding of brother and sister, yielded the highest-caste children, the Pio.

Kamehameha, as a very young man, had probably made love to his stepmother, Kalola. Kamakau and Fornander, the old historians who were Victorian in their morality, generally refused to admit this—trying to imply that Kamehameha's early mate was another lady of the same name.

The old chroniclers also fudged on his affair with his aunt, Kane-kapo-lei, another of the wives of King Kalaniopuu. This union, never recognized by marriage rites, yielded his first son,

Kao-lei-oku, or Pauli. Kamehameha, up to the death of Cook, had been joined in ritual marriage to one other Alii chiefess, Peli-uli.

Peli-uli had met Kamehameha while he was recovering from the wounds of the English bombardment, and had gone to see him when he was living in his convalescent house, the hale hau. Like many other nurses who won the hearts of famous men while they were recovering from an illness, Peli-uli was moved not only by motherly feelings of compassion and unselfishness, but also by the rank of his solicitous visitors, like the moi himself, Kalaniopuu.

In the three years she had lived with Kamehameha as his wife, first in fact and later in official marriage, Peli-uli had given birth to three children by Kamehameha: Maheha, a daughter; Kinau, a son; and a third son, Kai-ko-o-kalani.

But the blaze of hua'i (passion) never had moved Kamehameha before at the aspect of a female as much as when he now saw Kaahumanu flowered into full-blown femininity. And this time Ke-e-au-moku did not have to bring up the subject of marriage; Kamehameha did that, and this time with enthusiasm.

This marriage development gave a special urgency to the plans which Kamehameha and Ke-e-au-moku were then hatching. Ke-e-au-moku had been a long-time friend of Kamehameha and was only about seven years older. Kamehameha never completely trusted this emotional and glib third cousin, but both were ambitious and nearly fearless.

Kamehameha's first son, Kao-lei-oku, or Pauli, was already three years older than Kaahumanu. So Kao-lei-oku (the name literally means "Erect Spear with a Wreath of Flowers") was seventeen when this beautiful girl was fourteen, in 1882. But Ke-e-au-moku had already sired six other children by various other wives and lovers.

Pauli had been reared by Kalaniopuu, and Kamehameha had been fond of him as a first-born child, but the Hawaiian traditions of chiefhood and caste militated against his being recognized as a favored heir to whatever laurels Kamehameha thus far had accrued.

Probably the somewhat anomalous social position of Kao-lei-oku—even in the liberal-minded Polynesian society the bastard, especially a chief's bastard, was not given the father's rights and privileges as the offspring of official wedlock—strengthened Kamehameha's wish to officialize the relationship. So, when he began to live as man and wife with Kaahumanu, he wanted to make it formal. Himself the offspring victim of considerable public doubt about his antecedents, he later had official marriage ties with at least twenty-one women.

And in any case, when Kamehameha became the first king of all the Hawaiian Islands, it must be pointed out that he always looked out for the rights and privileges of Kao-lei-oku: that is, his privileges as a member of the Naha caste and a genuine offspring of King Kamehameha.

Now, with the connivance of his friend and sometime father-in-law Ke-e-au-moku, Kamehameha moved to the first step of revolt against the expected sovereignty of Kalaniopuu's designated successor, Kiwalao.

As the wise Kalaniopuu had anticipated, a number of chiefs were scheming while Kalaniopuu was still alive and still the king, against the weak Kiwalao. One of those ambitious chiefs was the youngest son of Kalaniopuu, Keoua of the Red (or Royal) Cloak.

Another highly placed chief now scheming against Kiwalao was Kamehameha's military kahu and friend, Kekuhaupio. Naturally, Keku took Kamehameha into his confidence.

Many of the chiefs who had met with Kalaniopuu about his plans at the Waipio Valley for this summit conference of 1781 were dissatisfied with the distribution of the lands of Kalaniopuu. This had been indicated when he assigned his throne on his demise to Kiwaloa, and made Kamehameha the custodian of the war god Ku.

Younger brother Keoua had also been disappointed with the assignment of real estate. His portion was to be principally the southern region of Ka'u, a rather barren area bordering on several of the active volcanoes of the great mountain, Mauna Loa.

Kamehameha made his first overt move against Kiwalao in Ka'u, when a local chief who had been rebelling against him for several years was caught and turned over at last to the infirm old king, Kalaniopuu. When the rebellious Ka'u chief was about to be sacrificed at the heiau of Pakini, Kiwalao came to officiate in his father's place. The form of the sacrifice was that Kiwalao would offer first a pig and then some bananas on the altar, and then carry the dead body of the chief for the climax.

Kamehameha chose that moment to step forward and pick up the body himself and place it on the altar. Then he barked curtly that the ceremony was over and that the assembled group of spectators should leave.

This was apparently a calculated insult to Kiwalao, designed to humiliate him publicly. But Kiwalao—the name, incidentally, means "untidy"—chose not to react decisively. Kiwalao might not have lived up to that name literally, but he certainly was untidy in his decisions.

Kiwalao was in fact so given to procrastinating and hedging that he had done nothing to still the rebellious voices he heard rumbling. And when his father, the old king Kalaniopuu, died in 1882, the surges of rebellion broke out against him in full force.

The immediate issue was the final division of Kalaniopuu's lands and fiefs. Again, Kiwalao was slow to act, and his uncle, Keawe-mauhili, moved to take over control of the division. He assigned himself the best of the lands, including territories which Kalaniopuu had assigned to Kamehameha and Ke-e-au-moku.

At this point, the impulsive Ke-e-au-moku felt the need for an immediate move. Kamehameha was more cautious, but he consulted the omens, as read by the kahunas, and let it be known to Ke-e-au-moku that he generally supported Ke-e-au-moku's position.

The leading chiefs had gathered in the Honaunau vicinity, a few miles south of Kealakekua Bay midway on the west or Kona coast of the island of Hawaii. There, in the wake of Kalaniopuu's death, civil war broke out.

The impulsive and fiery-tempered Ke-e-au-moku had marshaled

all the troops he could mobilize and managed as well to include some who owed allegiance to Kamehameha. In this time of crisis, all of the major chiefs were gathering all the fighting men they could muster. Even the smaller of the chiefs had scented a major struggle in the air and they knew that the way to curry favor with the top leaders was to have many troops available to throw onto the scales on the side of the prospective moi of their choice. The picture wasn't too different from the usual turbulent history of medieval Europe.

The flamboyant and ambitious Keoua of the Red Cloak, a younger brother of Kiwalao, struck the first blow at Ke-e-au-moku. He sent a sizable force of fighting men to attack Kamehameha's troops. There followed a quick choosing of sides. Some of the chiefs supporting Kamehameha shifted to the agglomerating opposite faction, that of Kiwalao, Keoua and Keawe-mauhili.

The two opposing armies skirmished. Then, at Moku-a-hai (Dividing Place of the Waters), two of the commanders collided with vehemence.

Then the flamboyant Keoua of the Red Cloak struck the first blows. He mustered his chiefs and a fighting force and went to the vicinity of Keei. There he started a series of provocative actions intended to insult Kamehameha.

First, he and his followers started cutting down coconut trees belonging to his cousin Kamehameha. That, in a Polynesian society, was a slap in the face, almost equal to a declaration of war. Then he and some of his followers picked a fight with some of his cousin's men, and took the bodies to Honaunau and prevailed upon the weak-willed Kiwalao to sacrifice these men as offerings.

Kamehameha responded vehemently. He gathered three of his official brothers, Ke-e-au-moku, Kamanawa and an assortment of other Kona chiefs with their troops. Followers of Kamehameha and Keoua of the Red Cloak began skirmishing in the vicinity of Moku-a-hai. Kiwalao began to commit troops to the fight. The troops began to gather and a conventional battle was beginning. Soon a body of troops led by Kiwalao and one under Ke-e-au-moku were locked in close combat. The great warrior Kamehameha had stopped to consult the auguries with Holoae, the chief kahuna and father of Kekuhaupio, at Kealakekua.

At first, the tides of the battle seemed to be leaning strongly in favor of the Kiwalao-Keoua forces. Soon, the rebel armies were driven back, and Ke-e-au-moku was caught in the forefront of the attack.

Kiwalao, pushing forward with his troops, saw Ke-e-au-moku closely engaged and moved closer, hoping to be in at the kill. Without the massive warlike presence and commanding leadership of Kamehameha, he had begun to despair of the day's outcome. He didn't know it, but Kamehameha was bending every nerve to get to the battle scene as fast as he could. Old Holoae was insistent on following the full routine of reading the omens, both those in the sky and in the quivering entrails of animals sacrificed to Ku. His voluptuous daughter Pi-ne had appeared at the critical moment in the reading and had given the libidinous Kamehameha a secular reason for staying longer. He had no way of knowing yet that the battle was actually joined or that it was going badly for Ke-e-au-moku.

But Kamehameha knew instinctively that he must leave and his compulsions toward war were even stronger than those toward women.

Meanwhile, back at Moku-a-hai, Ke-e-au-moku was mortally beset. In the close fight, he was tripped or fell and three warriors jumped him as he got to his feet again. Two dealt strokes with their daggers and a high chief named Kini charged up with his short spear and stuck him from the back. According to Hawaiian legends, as he drove home the blow, he shouted: "The spear has pierced the yellow-backed crab." This was supposed to be a play on words based on the meaning of the other name of Ke-e-au-moku, which is Papai-ahi-ahi. This means approximately "night-walking crab."

However, this does seem an unlikely mouthful for such a desperate moment of combat. The feeble play of words seems more like the invention of a later and aged (and tired) savant reconstructing history in one of Hawaii's many oral legends.

Probably he'd be more apt to say "I got you, you bastard." And if Kini were such a spontaneous wit, given to bright flashes in the midst of a life-and-death struggle, "bastard" would be a clever and pointed sort of triple pun because Ke-e-au-moku was such a close friend of Kamehameha, and one of the words for "bastard" is Kameha-i. As mentioned during the account of Kamehameha's childhood, this pun had been invoked to Kamehameha's face by people who wanted to provoke him; not, however, without disastrous consequences for the perpetrator of the jibe.

Kiwalao was close enough by this time to the scene of action to see Ke-e-au-moku being stabbed and falling and the three soldiers bending over him. Kiwalao ran and he made a slight mistake which was to cost him his life.

Kiwalao was not experienced in battle and he was anxious to recover the whale's tooth, or niho palaoa, which the exalted and eminent Ke-e-au-moku would be wearing around his neck as the badge of his high chiefhood. So he called out to the three warriors who had knocked Ke-e-au-moku down with dagger and spear thrusts. "Wait!" he shouted. The soldiers hesitated; Kiwalao hurried to be close by and to recover Ke-e-au-moku's niho.

In that hiatus and moment of indecision—it was Kiwalao's last such moment—he called to the soldiers not to break or get blood on Ke-e-au-moku's whale's tooth.

On the ground, Ke-e-au-moku was badly wounded and bleeding, but through the haze of shock he heard Kiwalao's voice and the bit of conversation about his niho palaoa. This had a galvanic effect on him. It gave him a burst of strength. And in that split second he realized that the final blow of death was not being struck and that he had a quick chance to live.

Then fortune—Kamehameha would have said that it was the intercession of the war god Ku—intervened to help the fallen Ke-e-au-moku.

Ke-e-au-moku's half-brother Kamanawa was also in the vicinity of this engagement, and he had seen that Ke-e-au-moku was in trouble. Now he sent a small group of slingsmen and spearsmen to raid the crux of that struggle and if not to save his brother, at least to recover his body.

One of Kamanawa's slingsmen saw Ke-e-au-moku fall, and the peculiar hiatus as Kiwalao hurried to the spot. That slingsman, Keakua-wahine, aimed carefully, and his stone hit Kiwalao hard on the temple. Kiwalao fell stunned, and the raiding group shouted as they charged the soldiers fighting around the two felled chiefs, both Ke-e-au-moku and Kiwalao on the ground.

A melee followed, with spears, war clubs and knives flashing, and in the melee, Ke-e-au-moku saw Kiwalao down among the struggling legs of the warriors. He crawled to Kiwalao and cut his throat with one of the smaller weapons of close combat, a knife made of a large, single shark's tooth.

At that moment so fortunate for the future of Kamehameha, Ke-e-au-moku and the Kingdom of Hawaii, Kamehameha arrived on the field of battle with fresh reinforcements. A heaving, hoarse cry of jubilation and dismay swept across the battlefield as the news of Kiwalao's death spread with almost the speed of electricity.

Like a virus, the news turned the hosts of Kiwalao, Keoua of the Red Cloak and Keawe-mauhili into reverse, from advance to retreat—much abetted, of course, by the arrival of the celebrated warrior Kamehameha upon the scene with fresh troops. Keoua managed to escape from the field with a handful of his high chiefs and they were picked up by a fleet of his canoes.

Some of the other chiefs, and several hundred of the troops, managed to find their way to the mountains. But Keawe-mauhili was trapped in a cul-de-sac and captured. He was kept a few days in a canoe shed on Kealakekua Bay. One of his jailers was impressed with the fact that he was of a burning caste, the Niau-pio. The jailer permitted him to escape during the night. Keawe-mauhili climbed over the rugged volcanic saddle of towering Mauna Loa in the night and came to Hilo. There he announced his independence of both Kamehameha and Keoua of the Red Cloak.

Meanwhile, Keoua had landed in the southern district of Ka'u.

He gathered forces again and was acclaimed as moi of the entire island and successor to Kalaniopuu. But in fact the island remained divided into three nearly equal sections, under Kamehameha, Keoua and Keawe-mauhili.

Kamehameha had the northwest and west coast area, which is Kona, Kohala and the northern part of Hamakua. Keoua had the southeastern area, Ka'u and part of the province to the north of it, Puna. Keawe-mauhili had the rest of the island, the east coast and northeast section, which was Hilo and the parts of Hamakua and Puna that bordered on Kamehameha to the north and Keoua to the south.

In general, the kingdom which Kalaniopuu had built up fell into partition and decline in the years between his death in 1782 and 1790. The dominant force in the Hawaiian Islands during these years was not Kamehameha but Kahekili, the sinister old moi of Maui.

Kahekili, the hideously tattooed, crafty and bloodthirsty scion of the Maui ruling family, had recovered the east Maui section of Hana and surrounding territories which Kalaniopuu had taken from his predecessor. And in 1782, the same year Kalaniopuu died, he had mounted an amphibious expedition against the nearby and populous island of Oahu. The expedition had been very successful. Kahekili had conquered the island and the armies of the king, Kahahana. He killed his former ally Kahahana, and established a capital at Waikiki. The Oahu Alii planned to over-throw Kahekili, but one of Kahekili's sons got wind of the conspiracy and the violent Maui king killed not only the leaders but also their women and children near Moanalua in south-central Oahu.

It was said in the legends of the time that the streams of Makaho and Ho-ai-ai in the Moanalua vicinity were filled to overflowing with the bodies of the victims, and that one of Kahekili's chiefs built for Kahekili a house of the baked bones of the rebelling chiefs. It was called Kauwa-lua, or literally "Baked Bones or Oven of Kauwa (Slaves)." The skulls of the highest of the rebel chiefs received special treatment. They were worked into the top of the doorway.

At any rate, fierce old Kahekili prepared to leave Oahu. While he was still in Waikiki, he received his half-brother Kaeo, who had mastered the power politics of the northern island of Kauai and had become its moi or king. Now Kahekili worked to cement his grip on the title of king of all of the islands. He had first driven the Hawaiians out of their toehold of Hana, that eastern tip of Maui, and all of that island was firm under his control.

Next, he had conquered Oahu and he was grooming his popular son Kalanikupule (literally "Kalani of the Prayer-Time"—perhaps born in a Prayer-Time) to be the monarch here. Through his half-brother Kaeo he would probably be able to hold on to control of the island of Kauai. He had regained control of the smaller islands of Molokai and Lanai, immediately off the shores of Maui, largely by diplomatic maneuvering and threats.

The only major piece of terrain that remained for him to seize was the Big Island of Hawaii, the island now split into three nearly equal parts under Kamehameha, Keawe-mauhili and Keoua of the Red Cloak.

Of the three men, Kamehameha was the man Kahekili respected and feared by far the most. Keoua was a firebrand given to emotional tantrums. Keawe-mauhili was an impossible social snob who believed that with his ultra-ultra high caste he was the only person who could rightfully rule the island of Hawaii. And both Keoua and Keawe-mauhili had been soundly trounced by Kamehameha at the Battle of Moku-a-hai.

By the way, Kahekili had not yet told Kamehameha that he was probably his father. Nor had he sent word to Kamehameha through any emissary. And besides, the half-black-tattooed Kahekili still had the vaulting ambitions of a young warrior and the craftiness of an old, unscrupulous and experienced politician. He was not about to help Kamehameha against his two weak Hawaiian rivals.

Besides, Keoua and Keawe-mauhili had made a military bond

against Kamehameha. Back in his capital at Wailuku, Maui, Kahe-kili saw another fortunate break developing on the Big Island. Kamehameha, still hungry for conquest, had launched a two-pronged military assault upon Keoua and Keawe-mauhili. Kahekili decided to throw his lot with Keawe-mauhili.

Kamehameha's plan was an ambitious one. One prong was a thrust by a fleet of canoes, carrying warriors, into the Hilo vicinity, headquarters of Keawe-mauhili. The other prong was an overland assault on Keoua's headquarters in Ka'u. Kamehameha led this attack from the west over the saddle of the towering Mauna Loa, through the area of the steaming and frequently erupting fire pit at Kilauea.

When word of Kamehameha's expedition leaked, Keawe-mauhili and Keoua had a council of war and sent emissaries to Kahekili to ask for his military assistance.

Kahekili was pleased. He was ready to send the aid. He obliged with considerable force: a fleet of canoes loaded with warriors and weapons.

Kamehameha, with all the forces he could muster, was descending from the Saddle between the two high peaks, Mauna Kea and Mauna Loa, toward the Pele Fire Pit. There, amid fumes and sulfur scent, he was jumped by Kahekili's commander with a host of battle-tested fighters. That commander was a valorous veteran named Ka-haha-wai (probably "Proud Water").

The Maui warriors, especially well trained spearsmen this time, wreaked heavy slaughter upon the Kamehameha soldiers with their long pololu spears delivered from long range. A contemporary bard sang romantically and graphically of this defeat for Kamehameha. The bard was called Moa (chicken) and his supposedly eyewitness account compared the close-in struggle of the spearsmen to the ruffled tail feathers of the boatswain bird, or koa-e, flowing in a strong wind. Blood flowed into dry earth like rain, and it was absorbed hungrily.

The Kamehameha forces were quite soundly thrashed, and probably would have been annihilated, there on the east slopes of Mauna Loa. But Kamehameha had prepared for a last-ditch escape if things turned into catastrophe. No doubt he had in mind his bitter experience on the Maui east coast with Kekuhaupio and King Kalaniopuu during the war with Kahekili, nine years earlier.

The plan this time was that Ke-e-au-moku should stand by, close to the coastal area called Puu Kapu-kapu (Sacred Hill) with his fleet of war canoes. And Ke-e-au-moku was very reliably on the scene.

Kamehameha fortunately knew the trails that covered the nine-mile distance to the sea. This section south of Kilauea Fire Pit is between Ka'u and Puna, lightly settled, nearly desert and not much traveled. Lying off the nob that was the 1,000-foot top high point of a long escarpment, Ke-e-au-moku saw a scattering of figures of the bedraggled armies hurrying down the slope. He put in with most of his fleet at Keauhou Landing and the battered Kamehameha forces scrambled aboard. The canoe fleet was well offshore by the time the Maui force of pursuers had found their way to the sea. Fortunately for Kamehameha, they were largely unfamiliar with the geography of the Big Island.

Ke-e-au-moku's canoes took the beaten warriors to the north-eastern section of the Big Island, the part of Hamakua bordering on Keawe-mauhili's territory to the north. It was Laupa-hoe-hoe. There, Kamehameha tried to mend the wounds of his beaten army and get his revenge on his archenemy Kahekili.

But the exhausted army was very short of the basic necessities of life, like food. In fact, the main effort was to forage for taro, breadfruit, cane, coconuts, fish, pigs and bananas.

And thus, on a hungry foraging expedition Kamehameha came to the first of his humanistic and peaceable legislative acts, the famed Law of the Splintered Paddle.

It happened just south of Hilo on the very northernmost coast of Puna. Kamehameha was traveling with only one canoe that day, and only the canoe's crew to reinforce his foraging demands.

Traveling with such a light complement of warrior support, especially in a hostile terrain and bent on pillage, seems a severe lapse from his usual good, hardheaded military sense. But then the Battle of the Kilauea Fire Pit had also shown him to bad advantage. Undoubtedly he was somewhat bemused these days by his great passion for the young Kaahumanu, his tall, athletic and fascinatingly feminine young sweetheart, the daughter of Ke-e-au-moku, now seventeen. Perhaps also his defeat at Kilauea had undermined his usual explosive will to triumph over whatever enemies he found at hand.

At any rate, he saw three fishermen with a large and appetizing catch of fresh fish. His will to act was powerfully stimulated by hunger. The fishermen were accompanied by some women and playful children, and the fishermen were shooing these impedimenta away from their work while they pulled in their nets.

The women and children had been driven away, but not quite all; one small child clung to the back of a fisherman. Kamehameha's short, hunger-keyed patience wore out. He decided to attack and seize the catch.

But the fishermen resisted fiercely, motivated mainly by anxiety to hang onto the fruit of their labor, but also by an altruistic urge to help the man with the child.

In the struggle, Kamehameha's foot slipped into a crevice in the underlying waterside rock and he couldn't wrench it loose. The two unencumbered fishermen started beating him about the head with their canoe paddles, so vehemently that the paddle blades were splintered and the tough-headed warrior was stunned. He was saved by the intercession of canoe crewmen from being beaten to death, but he long remembered that day.

It always stuck in his mind, first because he was well reminded to be prepared with ample force when launching an expedition, and secondly, because that particular sore head taught him more respect for the rights of noncombatants. Years later the lesson was perpetuated in the Mama-la-hoe (chewed-up paddle) rule generally known as the Law of the Splintered Paddle. That law, one of the flowerings of the golden age of peace which followed Kamehameha's conquests, protected innocent citizens from the depredations of rampaging men-at-arms and government officials bent on looting and pillaging.

After rebuilding his strength at Laupa-hoe-hoe, Kamehameha

tried a few inconclusive skirmishes along the northern periphery of the south Hamakua territory of Keawe-mauhili. At last, chewing the bitter cud of defeat, he withdrew with Ke-e-au-moku and the remnant of their forces to his home territory of Kohala, the northwest corner of the island.

There, he plotted ways of subverting his enemies: Keawe-mauhili, Keoua of the Red Cloak and the menacing and sinister figure of the half-black-tattooed Kahekili. One thing Kamehameha was certain of was that he would have his revenge upon Kahekili, and then the other enemies would be relatively easy.

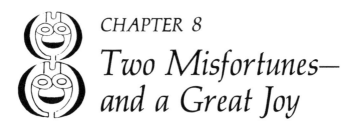

CHAPTER 8

Two Misfortunes— and a Great Joy

K AMEHAMEHA did not have long to wait before he could try for vengeance with another attack on Maui in 1786.

But before he found Kahekili in an inviting position of weakness, Kamehameha had two important personal involvements, sad and happy. The sad occasion was the loss of a close friend and counselor; the joyful event was his marriage to Kaahumanu, the daughter of Ke-e-au-moku, and always his favorite wife, in 1785.

The grievous loss of the close friend came first, in 1784, during a mock battle at Napo-o-po-o. It was his military kahu and comrade-in-arms, Kekuhaupio.

The aging warrior, veteran of so many battle wounds, was as valiant as ever in the mock battle. But his footwork was not up to its proper mortal pitch when it came to dodging spears. He evaded a number of spears, but did not see the next one soon enough. It caught him squarely in the ribs, and he was mortally wounded. The next day, despite the best efforts of the kahunas, he died. Kamehameha was by his side. But the old warrior was delirious when he expired.

The marriage to Kaahumanu came in 1785, at Kawaihae. The six-foot bride was seventeen years old. Ke-e-au-moku, the explosive old friend and companion-at-arms, was present at Kawaihae. There were the sports the imperious Kaahumanu loved and demanded: surfing, swimming, the ti-leaf slide, and the kissing game of the Alii, Kilu. There was feasting, there was the chanting of the kahunas to seek the blessing of the marriage god, Laka, there were the inevitable sacrifices of the porkers. And of course, there was dancing, the abandoned Scheherazade of half-naked hula girls and men.

The crux of the ceremony was oddly simple compared to our more intricate and conscience-ridden ways of the so-called Western world (Eastern, to Hawaii).

The kahunas, and Kamehameha's highest-caste followers like Ke-e-au-moku and Kamehameha's brother, called Kelii-maikai, placed the couple in a fragrant bed of sandalwood leaves, they jested heartily about Kamehameha's warlike might and his prowess —and they covered the couple with a spotless, fresh blanket of white and red tapa.

The love-making and the appetites of the moment were not shameful or necessarily private, they were mainly joyful. But the courtiers and kahunas left the couple alone and went back to their feasting. The women of course did not eat with the men: As always, that was strictly kapu. Nor could the women eat pork, coconuts or bananas, the masculine delights, even on this or any other occasion.

They all swam again, both in a freshwater pool with a waterfall in the foothills to the north and in the lucid aquamarine ocean surge of Hapuna. Then Kamehameha came to join his warriors in the chewing of the awa—and to laugh again at their hearty jokes about his love-making.

And that night around the bonfires, the games, the feasting, the dancing continued—and the Alii couples slipped off into the dark to make love. And Kamehameha, abandoning the awa and the feasting, followed the beautiful Kaahumanu to their bed of sandalwood again. And afterward, they slept the deep and blissful sleep that comes after the three great Hawaiian delights: swimming, feasting and love-making. All of these pleasures, naturally, the later missionaries viewed with alarm as the work of the devil.

Kamehameha went with his new, stormy-tempered bride to his farm in the northern part of Kohala. But there, besides growing taro and sweet potatoes and learning to know the magnificent beauty of Kaahumanu better, he began to make plans for another attack on his archenemy Kahekili.

He was plotting with his younger brother, Kelii-maikai, to invade and retake the former Maui territory around Hana on the eastern tip. That area, held since it was conquered by Alapai, had been regained by the rapacious Kahekili five years earlier.

Now, Kahekili was plagued with troubles in his newly conquered island of Oahu. The old Maui king had gone to Oahu to quell yet another revolt against his distant and tyrannical authority. Kahekili was assisting his favored son, Kalanikupule, the generally popular ruler of the island, with the handling of the revolt.

Kelii-maikai, who was young and very ambitious, had suggested to his famous warrior brother that with Kahekili and his best troops and generals gone to Oahu, an expedition to Hana should have easy pickings. It would be hiki-wale, literally "as slick as spit."

Kelii-maikai also had the aristocratic name Kalani ("From Heaven") with a long appendage afterward, apparently intended to convey some esoteric happening of his birthday. It was Kalani-malo-kuloku-i-kapookalani. It can be translated "malo, or loincloth, against the rain." It was quite common to compound a long name like that with a mysterious significance known only to closest and most intimate friends. To share the esoteric meaning of one's name (always long and complicated, in Hawaiian) with a friend thus became the greatest gesture toward close friendship with a stranger.

This attractive young brother was known by a kind of nickname. That was Kelii-maikai—meaning probably "handsome small person." Fornander calls it "good chief."

At any rate, Kelii-maikai and Kamehameha made a plan to send all available troops in a war canoe fleet to Kipahulu, just to the west of Hana. Kelii-maikai would lead the expedition, leaving Kamehameha to watch over the dangers of his Hawaiian kingdom.

The Good Chief, or "handsome small person," had already endeared himself to the people of Kipahulu when Kalanikupule's army arrived. Kelii-maikai scrupulously avoided the rapine and looting carried on by King Kalaniopuu's troops during his earlier campaigning on the island of Maui.

But Younger Brother's good conduct of the campaign went for naught at first. Kamohomoho, the leader of Kalanikupule's force, led his troops in a head-on attack on the west bank of Lele-kea Gulch.

It was a fierce battle and the Hawaiian army was driven back as far as Maulili, in Kipahulu. Kamehameha had sent large reinforcements to his brother under Kahanau-maikai. But the reinforcements were disordered and the Kamoho forces were pressing them hard. Another head-on battle ensued and the Kelii-maikai army was utterly beaten.

They fell apart and fled to the hills to the west. Kelii-maikai narrowly escaped with his life, and was saved by his kahu, Mulikele, and some Mauians of Kipahulu who remembered his kindness to their people. They hid him away from the Kamoho troops and sent him away that night in a canoe to Hawaii. Kamehameha was overjoyed to have him back and said he was happier to have his favorite brother returned from the defeat than he was sad at the defeat itself.

But the debacle was a grave blow to Kamehameha's military position as one of the rival chiefs seeking to dominate the Big Island. There were still the two other kings on the island, Keoua

of the Red Cloak and the aristocratic Keawe-mauhili, who together claimed about two-thirds of the island.

And Kamehameha's archrival (and probably his father too),
Kahekili, was much stronger than ever because of the overwhelming defeat he had inflicted on Kamehameha's brother.

Kamehameha, had he been a less resourceful man, might have
settled for his status as one of the three kings of the island of
Hawaii. But in 1786, a series of events began which gave him a
bright new idea—an idea which was to contribute a great deal
toward his eventual conquering of all his rivals in all the islands.

CHAPTER 9

Motive Power
for Kamehameha

THESE EVENTS were signaled by the arrival of more tall-masted, square-rigged, white-sailed "floating heiaus" on the Big Island. Now they were trading ships from Europe and America, carrying the treasures of the far-off world of the Haoles, the Foreigners. It had been seven years since the departure of the ships of the great explorer, Captain Cook, who met his end on the shore of Kealakekua Bay. Now, Kamehameha was deeply covetous of the goods the traders carried—especially their magic weapons.

Now, in 1786, two more tall ships sailed into the bay and anchored. They brought another name famous in Hawaiian history, Captain Nathaniel Portlock, skipper of the trading bark *King George*. The other ship was the *Queen Charlotte*, under Captain George Dixon, and they arrived at the same time—which was probably fortunate for them, because it impressed the generally surly natives of Kealakekua Bay with the potential com-

bined might of the visitors. Both, of course, were fully armed
with cannon and carried ample stores of flintlock rifles and ammunition.

One earlier visiting trading ship had stopped at Kauai a year
before, captained by James Hanna. His stay had been short, only
to reprovision and gain rest and repairs. But this time, even on
Kauai, the natives had been generally reserved.

Following Cook's lead, other ships had been visiting the west
coast of what is now Canada to trade for furs. Some of them
had courageously sailed on across the Pacific to the rich markets
of China. But the news of Cook's disaster reported in his and
King's journals at Kealakekua Bay had kept them away from the
Hawaiian Islands.

Now, Portlock and Dixon were opening up a whole new trade
frontier. And yet they, like Hanna, were jumpy about the natives.
Portlock and Dixon were nervy enough to anchor where Cook
had met disaster—but they stayed only two days and the peculiar,
cold reactions of the Hawaiians upset them. Then they shoved off,
nervously still, for another island then called Wahoo, or Oahoo.

At Kealakekua Bay the natives had harried them with studied
inattention and distant demonstrations. At first, as the British anchored and waited for traders, no canoes came. Then a few came
out bearing a small number of hogs, which they traded for
pieces of iron. The crewmen of the British ships were also much
interested in some stout, Hawaiian-made fishing line which they
finally traded for more bits of "ai-lon."

Portlock and Dixon had both been crewmen with the Cook expedition. They grew extremely uneasy when neither Kamehameha
nor any other chief appeared to welcome them. Portlock wrote
that Kamehameha did not come because he feared vengeance of
the English.

When the daylight faded, the natives started huge bonfires on
the shore. As soon as they could get underway, Portlock and
Dixon shoved off to the northwest, and found anchorage at
Waialae Bay, Oahu. Here they found the natives very friendly
and eager to trade. But it was clear now that the natives saw the

visitors no longer as gods, but only as Haoles, white mortals. And the natives were also quite matter-of-fact about prices: The regular price for a two-gallon calabash of drinking water was a six-penny nail.

Another disconcerting fact was that a number of the natives carried iron daggers, the kind which Portlock remembered had come with Captain Cook. The British captains shoved off for the Canadian West Coast, and came back six months later. At that time, Portlock reported that they had stopped at Kauai, and there met not only Kaeo, Kahekili's half-brother, but on Oahu, Kahekili himself.

Portlock's report on Kahekili is disconcerting because he said that Kahekili was only in his fifties—not an old man as others said—and that he was "very stout," sturdy, and that he seemed to be very popular with his people. Not at all the usual picture of the lean, choleric and cruel schemer we have seen elsewhere.

Furthermore, Portlock made no mention of the rather spectacular black tattooing that disfigured half of Kahekili's face and body. It is possible that he met another chief (possibly Kahekili's son Kalanikupule, who was stout, and popular with his people).

Portlock also met on his December, 1786, visit to Kauai a tall, handsome, very intelligent and charming chief named Kaiana. Kaiana was first cousin of Kaeo and of Kahekili. Kaiana later became very important to Kamehameha, and especially to his favorite wife, the stately Kaahumanu. For Kaiana, who learned to speak good English and traveled to Canton, China, with a British trading ship, became one of the favorite lovers in Kaahumanu's multifarious amatory life. Portlock's visit came a year before Kaiana's Canton trip—and before the cultivation of his distinguished black moustache and Van Dyke beard which Kaahumanu found so dashing.

But the really important fact of Portlock's visit to Hawaii was that after it, Kamehameha built up his resolution to move closer to the visiting white traders, and cultivate their friendship to gain the weapons and ships which he now sensed would be pivotally important in his conquests.

Two years later, in December of 1788, Kamehameha saw, and took, his first chance to cultivate a visiting Haole sea captain. It was significant that he told this captain, William Douglas, that King Kalaniopuu had been poisoned by a rebellious group of Alii because he had opposed a plan to kill Captain Cook. The inference which Captain Douglas drew from this was that Kamehameha wanted to establish that he, a staunch supporter of Kalaniopuu, was also blameless in the killing of Cook. Kamehameha knew that some of the Cook crewmen, like Portlock, believed he had been involved.

Kamehameha went into the full theatrical presentation to impress Douglas—and he later reaped full benefit from his efforts.

Douglas then was coming back from a long trading trip to Canton, the great South China port. And besides gaining knowhow about the white man's magical weapons from Douglas, Kamehameha also picked up an ally from him who was a thoroughly mixed blessing for Kamehameha. That was the suave, handsome and personable Kaiana, who also became Kaahumanu's most famous lover.

Kaiana had sailed with one of the same ships, the *Iphigenia*, from Kauai. The overall British leader was Captain John Meares, a fur trader, who had arrived in Kauai in August, 1781, with the 200-ton scow *Nootka*, and the *Iphigenia*. Meares' attention was won by the tall and charming Kaiana, cousin to the king of Kauai, Kaeo, and thus cousin as well to Kamehameha's archenemy Kahekili.

When Meares asked Kaiana to come along on the voyage to China, Kaiana had courage enough to go. He thus became the first Hawaiian chief to visit a foreign land.

Meares sailed to Canton, stayed three months, and there he was busy trading and equipping two of his ships for the fur trade, the *Felice* and the *Iphigenia*.

Kaiana was popular also with the Chinese. When one of Meares' officers, Captain Russell, sailed from Canton for Alaska and North America, Kaiana was with him. And his many Cantonese friends showered him with presents: cattle, turkeys, goats, lime and orange trees.

Russell sailed in the *Iphigenia* to Alaska, and down the North American west coast to Vancouver, accumulating furs. At Nootka Sound (Vancouver), Russell had a small sloop, the *Northwest America*, built. Then the two ships sailed to Hawaii to trade, rest and recondition. The livestock had died in the course of the trip. Kaiana remained a good friend of Russell and even then he saw that this Haole's weapons were his most important asset. He learned all he could about these magical killing tools. And later, he was instrumental in persuading Russell to trade some of these vital weapons to Kamehameha.

When the ship reached the Hawaiian (the so-called Sandwich) Islands, Kaiana was quick to learn that Kaeo, the Kauai king, had turned against him. At Kaiana's request, Captain Russell headed his ship for the Big Island of Hawaii and anchorage of Kawaihae.

Kamehameha, then at Kawaihae, made a maximum effort to impress Captain Douglas and the crews of the *Iphigenia* and *Northwest America*.

This time, Kamehameha managed the same splendid and precise water parade of war canoes decked in red and yellow feathers, loaded with spear-carrying Alii and kahunas carrying god images, as old King Kalaniopuu had mounted for Captain Cook. Accordingly, Captain Russell responded with a seven-cannon salute.

Soon after Kamehameha was aboard the *Iphigenia* he did his best to make friends. In his proud Alii way, he nevertheless was most anxious to assure Russell that he was blameless in the killing of Captain Cook. Apparently, he felt that this issue was the most important in building the confidence of the British.

Another gesture of great friendship toward Russell was Kamehameha's proffering of cordial welcome to the nobly born Kaiana. Kaiana of course was ready by now to throw in his lot with Kamehameha. And the astute Kamehameha was already well acquainted with this bit of military and political intelligence.

Kamehameha also seized the moment to ask the British captain for some of the white man's weapons. Kaiana added his persuasive influence, and Russell promised a weapon which made Kamehameha as eager as any dream ever offered to him; Russell said he would give the Hawaiian king his first cannon: a field-piece mounted on a swivel, which he promised to set up on two canoes. And some of those marvelous muskets too, the British "Brown Betties," the standard military weapon.

Kamehameha could see the great advantage these weapons would give him. But Captain Russell said that the mounting of the cannon would take some preparation and that he would be making those preparations as his ships moved around the islands—that he would be back in a few months with the cannon ready to go. Kamehameha had another brainchild. If Russell could build a ship with native labor at Nootka, perhaps he could build one here.

Russell said that might very well work out. But ashore, Kamehameha was secretly faced with the same kind of violent anti-Haole sentiment which had led to Captain Cook's death in 1779.

During Russell's stay at Kawaihae, Kamehameha managed to hold the violent ones among his Alii in check by threats of sheer violence. When Russell shoved off with full provisions, there had been no outbreak against him.

But when he came back the next spring, in 1789, the violent ones plotted for a simple takeover of the Russell ships, the killing of the officers and crew and of course the looting of the ships, and all the cannons and the beautiful goods from the Orient which they carried: the chinaware, the silks, mirrors—and still most attractive, the tools and weapons of the priceless hard substance, ai-lon. Kamehameha was angry: By peaceful methods, trading and diplomacy, he could acquire weapons, keep the friendship of the Haoles, and even get them to build a ship for him.

Before the violent ones could work their plot, the good Captain Russell had traded the muskets, and the mounted swivel-gun. And Kamehameha saw to it that Russell was warned of the plot of the radical violent ones. Russell moved his ships and saved his crew and cargo before any misadventures could befall them. And in Russell's book, Kamehameha became known as a friend to the British.

Kamehameha took advantage of the hiatus before the arrival of the next British trading ships to clean out his radical anti-Haole opposition. Many were sacrificed to the god Ku, and several tried to flee to the large City of Refuge at Honaunau. A few made it to this sanctuary. The wisdom of a course of friendly diplomacy with the powerful Haoles had been confirmed.

But the trader who gave Kamehameha the biggest boost in his campaign of conquest was an American, Captain Simon Metcalfe. The assistance was inadvertent.

Metcalfe, skipper of the square-rigger *Eleanora,* was one of the harshest captains in that day of free-wheeling adventurers operating for maximum profit in a wide (and wild) new frontier.

Simon Metcalfe had reached the Pacific in 1790. His second ship, with which he had lost contact on the west coast (later California), was the smaller schooner, the *Fair American.* Captain of the *Fair American* was Metcalfe's son, Thomas.

Simon was initiated into this vast new and untamed area with a rough dose of frontier medicine. While he was trading on the northwest coast of America, Spanish naval ships seized the *Fair American,* his son the captain, and the crew of six.

They took the vessel to the base at San Blas. Simon managed to make his escape, and sailed with the *Eleanora* to the Hawaiian Islands.

He stopped at Maui, anchoring the *Eleanora* off Honu-aula near the present Lahaina at the end of January, 1790. He began to trade for supplies, and stayed the night at anchor.

That night, knowing the overwhelming cupidity of the natives for any source of iron, he stationed a sailor in the ship's boat tied to the stern.

But in the morning, both boat and sailor were gone. It was the same basic situation which had led to the Cook tragedy: ignorance among the Polynesians of the great value of a ship's boat; and ignorance among the white men of the mores and motivations of the natives. Metcalfe reacted as Cook had, but much more cruelly and violently.

Metcalfe ordered out all the Mauian women who were aboard his ship keeping the sailors company, and ordered some musket fire against some trading canoes, killing and wounding some Hawaiians. One man was caught swimming beneath the ship. Metcalfe wanted to hang him, but his officers opposed the idea, and Metcalfe eventually released him.

Metcalfe sent a shore party to get information and they burned several houses and halawai, or meeting-houses. The hard-nosed captain ordered a punitive bombardment of the town. Several Hawaiians were killed and wounded. But there was no immediate result.

Soon, however, Metcalfe learned from a terrified Mauian that the raiders who stole his boat and abducted the sailor had come from Olowalo, a village down the coast, and gone back there. By this time, Metcalfe had stirred the people of Hono-aula to bonfires and impromptu mobilization. He weighed anchor and sailed to Olowalo.

Here, with the primitive state of communications in those days, the people were friendly and came thronging to the ship in their canoes. Metcalfe met a chief who seemed to have information about the stolen boat and the abducted sailor.

Metcalfe added material inducements when the chief promised to deliver the boat and the sailor. Besides the boat, Metcalfe thought he might now even get the sailor back, alive.

To seal the bargain, Metcalfe promised to give the chief a musket, ammunition, a piece of iron, and a piece of Indian cloth for the boat, and the same reward for the man. But all Metcalfe got in return was a piece of the boat's keel and two thigh bones, bare of flesh. It seemed definite now that the boat had been burned for the bits of ai-lon in it and undoubtedly the sailor's body had been eaten for his mana, the big bones valued for the same reason.

Metcalfe's crew now felt as inclined to violence as he—including

Kamehameha

A view of Kealakekua on Hawaii

Queen Kaahumanu

Men dancing

Women dancing

An offering before Captain James Cook in the Hawaiian Islands

Hawaiian woman

*A night dance
by women
in Hapaee*

Boxing match staged for Captain Cook in Hawaii, 1770

Hawaiian man

Hawaiian canoe, the rowers masked with calabash helmets

A night dance by men in Hapaee

Kalaniopuu bringing presents for Captain Cook

A view of a morai in Hawaii

A view of Hawaii
showing a house
one of the priest
1782

Death of Captain Cook, 1779

Interior of a chief's house

*Hawaiian man
in a calabash
helmet / mask*

A view of huts and a boathouse in Hawaii, 1781

Meeting of Kotzubue and Kamehameha

A view of Kealakekua (also spelled Karakakooa) in Hawaii

Port of Honolulu

Dancing man of the Hawaiian Islands

Young Hawaiian woman

Punishment

Punishment

Hawaiian game

Queen Kaonee

A missionary at Kairua preaching to natives under a screen of plaited coconut leaves, 1826

The Valley of Waipio, from the sand hills on the beach, 1826

A view of the anchorage of French frigates on the island of Maui, 1798

Missionary houses in Byron Bay

A view of part of Lahaina on Maui

A view near Honolulu

Queen Kinau (wife of Kinau) and her ladies-in-waiting returning from the Temple of the Foreigners in Honolulu

his boatswain, the Englishman John Young. John Young, a simple seaman, was soon to become one of the key British personalities who brought Kamehameha his knowhow on White Man's weapons.

This time, the officers were in a hanging mood. They suggested it would be a good disciplinary example to hang several chiefs from the yardarm, so that their subjects could see and learn their lesson.

But Metcalfe had a more insidious plan. He would entice the Hawaiians into coming in their canoes with a view to trading. When the canoes were close in, he would drop his gun ports, fire with his seven main battery guns below and the smaller brass guns on deck, and chop them up properly. The guns would all be loaded and ready to fire on the starboard side, including the deck guns. The load in the cannons would be musket balls and langrage shot, rather than solid cannon balls. Thus the effect would be like canister, a scattering of smaller pellets like shrapnel or antiperson-nel bombs to inflict maximum injury on human targets.

The officers and crew prepared for this revenge while Metcalfe let it be known ashore that he wanted trading canoes to come out with their goods. So a group of fifty to sixty canoes soon clustered around the *Eleanora.* Probably there were 300 to 400 people in the canoes.

Metcalfe had them ordered to the starboard side. The gun crews were ready. They dropped the wood panels which were the gunports. The main battery guns and the deck guns all thundered.

In this close-range fire, many of the canoes were swamped, more than a hundred Mauians killed, many scores were ripped with mangling injuries. Among the canoes, the jewel-clear water was incarnadined with blood.

In a mad scramble, the canoes fell back to the shore, taking as many dead and injured as they could. But many, critically injured, struggled in a strange fate for people who grew up in the water: They drowned.

With the canoe fleet gone in disorder and disaster to the shore,

Metcalfe secured his cannons and prepared to sail. This "Olowalo Massacre" is famous in the copious chronicles of man's inhumanity to man in the Hawaiian Islands.

With the white despoiler gone, the natives put out in their canoes to recover the bodies. They piled the mutilated corpses on the beach, and contemporary bards told of the scene of mayhem. David Malo later chronicled some of these accounts in *Moolelo Hawaii*: "The bodies of the slain were dragged for with fish-hooks, and collected in a heap on the beach, where their brains flowed out of their skulls."

The psychological effect of the massacre was profound upon the locals, and upon the Hawaiians in general when the word spread. One of the Alii living in Olowalo then was Kalola, Kamehameha's former stepmother, later his aunt and the surviving wife of Hawaii's great King Kalaniopuu. With Kalola then was one of her granddaughters, Keopuolani, who later became the "sacred wife" of Kamehameha. Keopuolani was of a very high Alii caste, a Niau-pio, meaning she was the child of a chiefess and her brother. This birth gave her a very elevated "burning kapu," which prescribed among other items that if her shadow fell upon anyone of inferior caste, he would be killed and the body burned.

Another close link with Kamehameha was that the chiefess who was the mother of the sacred Keopuolani was also his half-sister. More of this complicated relationship later. But the net effect in the very tangled skeins of Hawaiian family trees (with multiple marriages on both sides of every tree) was that any child he had with Keopuolani would also be the elevated caste, a Niau-pio.

Poetic justice was not too long in catching up with this penurious and hard-bitten American adventurer Metcalfe. As usual, it worked in an ironic way, a kind of billiard shot of revenge that struck him indirectly, through his son Thomas. And the stroke of death which hit Simon Metcalfe also came in an indirect and ironic way: He was killed by Polynesians in the Tuamotu Islands, far off in the South Pacific, closer to Tahiti.

But meanwhile, Simon continued in his roughshod career of

profit and self-appointed justice. From Maui, he sailed the *Eleanora* to the Big Island and began a trip along the Kona, or west coast.

Among other stops as he worked his way along the coast, he stopped at a village in the northern part of Kona where the high chief was Kameeiamoku, prominent in Kamehameha's court. This chief committed some breach of Metcalfe's quarter-deck discipline. Metcalfe responded with his usual brutality, striking the chief with a rope's end and humiliating him with an angry tirade and expulsion from the ship.

Kameeiamoku swore that when the next trading ship came to his territory, he would have his vengeance. It happened that the next ship was the *Fair American*, captained by Metcalfe's son Thomas.

Thomas had been released by the Spanish at San Blas, and followed his father to the Sandwich Islands. Now he was hoping to find his father's ship and as chance would have it, he was cruising along the north Kona Coast in Kameeiamoku's territory. There he was becalmed.

The vengeful chief came out all smiles on the pretext of trading, and boarded the small schooner with a large contingent of his warriors. He saw that the Haoles were not on guard, and on signal, his warriors jumped Thomas and the five-man crew and tossed them overboard.

But Kameeiamoku was not content to leave it at that. He commanded his men in canoes to finish off the Haoles and they almost did, beating them to death with paddles and clubs as they floundered in the water.

Only one got away. He was Isaac Davis, a British seaman who had an advantage over the other Haoles: He was a strong swimmer.

Davis made his way toward shore, but was chased, and caught, by a canoe-full of Hawaiians who proceeded to give him the same treatment as the others had received: They started to beat him on the head, in the water. Then they decided to get a better purchase. They pulled him into the canoe and were finishing the job by choking him to death. He was by this time half-blind, half-drowned, bruised and bloody. Then their chief, who had more brotherhood in his heart than Kameeiamoku, took pity and saved the Haole's life. The accident of mercy was to redound to Kamehameha's benefit for many years.

Kamehameha was at Kealakekua at the time. He heard by his "coconut wireless" intelligence network (usually, swift-sailing outrigger) that Kameeiamoku had seized the ship and killed all but one of the crew.

While the tragedy of the *Fair American* was happening farther north, another ironic turn of fate brought the elder Metcalfe, Simon, and his ship into Kamehameha's ken at Kealakekua Bay.

The *Eleanora* came to anchor approximately in the spot where Cook had made his last mooring place. By this time Kamehameha had already heard about the seizing of the *Fair American*, the killing of the crew, the capture of the surviving sailor and the seizure of muskets and cannon. Kamehameha declared a kapu on the bay—so that the Haole ship would not know about the piracy, raid and killing. He had also heard about the massacre at Olowalu and he knew it was the *Eleanora* which had done it. He knew Simon Metcalfe's name.

Simon Metcalfe, concerned that there were no trading canoes and visitors, decided to send a group of sailors to Kealakekua, there to seek out the local chiefs, whoever they might be, and make arrangements.

John Young, the personable young bo'sun, went with the shore party, but they were no match for Kamehameha in the devious byways of paramilitary planning. They had no success in finding Kamehameha, or any other responsible chief. The inert, deserted appearance of the beach towns alarmed them. John Young wandered into the green foothills above Kealakekua, and lost contact with his shipmates.

When the fruitless reconnaissance for that day was over, and the shore party was assembled at the ship's boat to go back to the *Eleanora*, Young was still missing.

Back at the ship, Simon Metcalfe was told about the disappearance of Young, and was undecided about whether he had deserted or been captured.

The truth was that Kamehameha had sent warriors to round up a likely Haole crewman. Kamehameha knew that with the exercise of his proper feudal authority over the chief who had seized the *Fair American*, Kameeiamoku, he could take the ship, her cannon and the muskets of the crew. Kameeiamoku was one of Kamehameha's liege lords, and his territory in north Kona an easily controllable part of Kamehameha's realm.

There was no doubt in Kameha's mind that the treasure trove of the muskets and the ship's guns was going to be vastly important to him. But he needed Haoles in his court who could coach him on the use of these new weapons. Kaiana, the new high chief in his court who had come to Kamehameha from the *Iphigenia* and Captain Russell after a trip to Canton, was surprisingly ignorant of the usage of the magical Haole weapons. He barely knew, though many Hawaiians erroneously thought otherwise, that it wasn't the flash which killed.

One crewman had been saved in the *Fair American* raid. But he had been hurt, Kamehameha didn't know how badly. The warriors were told to pick up another Haole sailor who might be separated from the shore party.

And so John Young was isolated and brought to the court of Kamehameha. But he was treated gently, in accordance with instructions from the monarch. Kamehameha had long since learned that Haoles responded strongly to the favorite Polynesian blandishments: good food, the attentions of beautiful golden-skinned females, the luxury of Hawaiian cleanliness, sunshine, lovely scenery and benign climate after months of hardship in the cramped and spartan confinement of an ocean-going ship.

On the *Eleanora* the next day, Metcalfe and his crew were very much on edge: nothing from that idyllic shoreline, very little life or movement visible. Most important, no trading canoes to bring them necessary supplies, and no other canoes to bring curious villagers, men or women.

Metcalfe decided that a few rounds from his ships' guns might bring a change, possibly even a chief who would surrender the deserter or prisoner Young—or his bones. So Metcalfe fired his cannons in a random way toward a couple of villages.

Still there was no reaction from the shore. That night, there were fires ashore and drums, but still no assaults, no canoes, no swimmers attempting to board the *Eleanora*.

The next day was the same. Metcalfe scanned the shore with his telescope, saw only the strange inertness, no reactions at all. And no canoes came alongside.

Indecisive, he fired a few more rounds, finally shoving off to seek a more hospitable anchorage in the Big Island. And when the *Eleanora* sailed, Metcalfe was still ignorant of the fact that his son had been killed and his other ship and crew lost.

Kamehameha moved rapidly to take over the *Fair American*, her cannons and the muskets of her crew. He rebuked Kameeiamoku for his harshness in the raid, piracy, etc.—but ended with the vital booty in his possession.

Part of those spoils, of course, was physical possession of the surviving *Fair American* crewman, Isaac Davis. Thus Davis and Young met and were treated like honored guests at Kamehameha's court.

But they didn't want to stay, despite the bounteous life in this tropical paradise, and of course the attentions of many golden Hawaiian ladies full of curiosity about the Haoles who spoke such a discordant and odd hoo-mali-mali lingo—but were also sturdy, muscular and strong.

With his small schooner, Kamehameha also gained three more cannon. His first had been the swivel-gun from the visit of the *Iphigenia* and Captain Russell in early 1789. The prize from the *Fair American* was a beautiful brass gun which the Kameeiamoku warriors had already christened Lopaka—an attempt to render the Haole name Robert into Hawaiian.

The ship was sailed down to Kealakekua Bay. The Hawaiians, reared on and in the sea, had no trouble handling this white man's schooner-rigged vessel. But before Kamehameha could persuade the two knowledgeable Haole sailors to start teaching him the science of weaponry, Isaac Davis and John Young tried to escape.

They had taken a canoe and were heading for a British ship anchored in Kealakekua Bay. The ship had been trading for a number of days and was preparing to get underway.

Kamehameha, always quick to adapt to circumstance, then decided to adopt a different course of action with his Haole captives. He kept them under closer surveillance, but he also decided that they would be susceptible to the inducements which worked best with the ambitious Hawaiian leaders, perhaps more powerfully than food, sports, women and comfort. Those were power, influence and land.

He continued the regular Polynesian comforts and pleasures, but added the other attractions. Both Haoles were offered the status of royal advisors and lords, and land. And the combination worked. Both British sailors spent the rest of their days in the Hawaiian Islands, as trusted members of Kamehameha's close inner circle. Both were loyal to him, and Davis was to lose his life to insure Kamehameha's survival.

In Kamehameha's impending campaign of conquest, both Haole advisors were more than important, they were instrumental. For Kamehameha, now probably close to forty years old, was driven by a much greater ambition even than his leaders.

He was planning, as usual, to hit and destroy his archenemy, Kahekili. This was a good time to hit his home island of Maui because he was much occupied with cementing his new grip on Oahu and Kauai.

It was clear that Kahekili had emerged as the giant of the islands so far. He was the first king to have a firm grip on the whole of three islands. Maui he had secured by driving Kamehameha out of his beachhead in the extreme eastern tip, the Hana section. Through his son Kalanikupule, he held Oahu. Through his half-brother Kaeo, he held the northern island of Kauai. But now Kahekili was contending with a full-fledged revolt on Oahu. He was also trying by diplomatic means, and military threats and promises as needed, to reinforce his influence over Kaeo.

Kahekili was now very aged. According to most historical estimates, he was seventy to eighty years old, a phenomenal longevity among people of that time, East or West. But he was still mentally in top form and full of driving ambitions. His sardonic humor, his enigmatic wisdom and his mental acuity seemed to be increasing rather than fading. And his lean, half-black-tattooed body was still equal to the rigors of the struggle for empire.

Kamehameha made his plans for another major amphibious assault on Maui. This involved first consulting the kahunas, building the new heiaus they prescribed, and getting promises of war canoes, troops and supplies from his chiefs. By zealous intertribal diplomacy he managed to win the friendship of a former enemy, the aristocratic Keawe-mauhili. Keawe-mauhili was the moi of North Ka'u and Hilo, and he still held sway over about a third of the Big Island. The other third-holder was Keoua of the Red Cloak, a cousin who remained his implacable foe.

With John Young and Isaac Davis to help with the use of muskets and cannon, and with Keawe-mauhili on his side at last, Kamehameha decided that just that moment was the time to start another attack on Maui and Kahekili.

After dutifully consulting with the kahunas, and also incidentally having word that Kahekili and his son and heir Kalanikupule were fully occupied with the revolting factions on Oahu, Kamehameha gathered an invasion force and a fleet of double-hulled war canoes and set off for Maui.

This time, his new ally, Keawe-mauhili, lent him troops and a fleet of canoes. Before his fleet left Hilo, Kamehameha made certain that Keawe had enough troops left at home to keep back the unscrupulous and ambitious Keoua of the Red Cloak in his southern territory of Ka'u and south Hilo.

At least, that was Kamehameha's opinion. And this time, rather than leaving the leadership to a brother he took his royal train, and his imperious and spirited wife Kaahumanu and her servants, and his war council of leaders and his traveling kahunas, and shoved off for Maui and conquest.

His objective this time was his classical target, Hana at the eastern tip of the island. He still smarted over the loss of the territory of Hana, taken from the possession of Kalaniopuu before that old monarch died. Even more, the wound of the harsh defeat inflicted upon his brother on the last attempt at Hana still rankled.

This time, the big brass cannon Lopaka (Robert) went with him. With it came the two British advisors and new nobles in his court, Isaac Davis and John Young, Aikake and Olohana to the Hawaiians. Both were good seamen and handy with the white man's weapons. But as a striking force in comparison with the large armies then current in Europe and America, these arms were a joke. There were only a dozen muskets among the 3,000 men in that invasion force, and half that many among them who knew how to load and fire the weapons, let alone hit anything.

And while Lopaka was mounted on the platform between the two hulls of a sixty-foot war canoe, and Kamehameha's brass swivel-gun followed in the fleet, the best efforts of Kamehameha and Young and Davis had been able to muster only six iron cannonballs from all the trading contact with visiting Haole ships.

Besides Young, Davis and the handful of Hawaiians, the tall, bearded handsome Kaiana, another of his top commanders, would be a large asset in his fight—since he knew something of both the Haoles' and the Polynesians' methods of fighting.

The six-feet-six chief, equal to Kamehameha in height, more than his equal in pedigree and more charming and at home with the Haoles than Kamehameha, Kaiana was outstanding among the nobles of the Hawaiian king's court. He had caught the capricious eye of Kamehameha's favorite queen, the ravishingly beautiful, twenty-two-year-old Kaahumanu. Their spark of attraction was to flare into fire later on.

During the months of preparation for the attack on Maui at Kawaihae, Kaiana had come many times to consult with Kamehameha and his brother Kelii-maikai, and the two solid Englishmen, Aikake and Olohana. Kaiana had seen the lovely Kaahumanu. Kaahumanu loved the conduct of wars and the dashing strong men among the army's leaders always appealed to her.

Kamehameha, despite his preoccupation with conquest, frequently was jealous of this or that noble warrior—and, it should be noted, with good reason. She was an arch-Polynesian practitioner of the feminine arts of driving men mad with desire and infatuation, and she was supremely aware of both her unusual, imperial-sized physical charm and the power it gave her over them.

Yet Kamehameha was firm and frequently rough and forceful with her. It was the kind of strong masculine hand which a woman as capricious, proud and desirable as she needed to keep her in check and convince her that momentarily at least she needed him.

There were frequent scenes of rancor already, of love and rage, between the king-sized ruler and his consort, especially in the libidinous game of Kilu which the nobles played and Kaahumanu adored. And in the surf, where the statuesque, nude figures of Kaiana and Kaahumanu were frequently seen riding their long and heavy boards in the curling, thundering white and wind-whipped waves.

Already, Kamehameha had several times flown into towering rages at the vampery and strong-willed amorous intrigues of Kaahumanu and other attractive Alii. Already, these rages had led him several times to batter her in fits of jealous rage. And Kaahumanu, professing desperation and probably meaning it, had evolved the high-spirited revenge of threatening to throw herself to the sharks, or jumping from the rocks into a man-devouring current or drift. No doubt, given her pride and her flashing flame of spirit, she had meant it when she threatened to destroy herself as revenge for his frequently unreasoned jealousy and violence against her.

Again, her fiery femininity craved his jealousy as the greatest compliment to her attractiveness. There was no doubt that this athletic, assertive and still utterly feminine ruler loved this big, formidable and indomitable leader of men—and in his way, which was powerful, he started it by loving her passionately.

It was always thus through their lives that Kamehameha and Kaahumanu lived in violent and instant love-hate of each other. He loved Kaahumanu most of all women even though she failed to bring him the Alii heirs he craved so intently. She had no children. But she was all he wanted in womankind, in the romantic sense. And yet Kaiana was undoubtedly one of the major threats to her marriage and probably the man she thought most of among a life-long slew of paramours.

Kamehameha's fleet came along the south shore of Maui and landed mostly to the south of Hana, but the fleet covered the entire eastern tip of Maui. Legend has it that the beached canoes blanketed the sand from Hamoa to Kawaipapa, a distance of five miles.

And this time, with Kamehameha himself in command and the threat of the White Man's cannons and muskets (very little more than a threat at this point), the Hana defenders fell back—except from the Kauwiki fort on the point of Hana.

Instead of again laying siege to Kauwiki—that had been a trap in previous assaults—Kamehameha bypassed it and began a major amphibious campaign which might well have served General Douglas MacArthur as a model for his "island hopping" sweep through the southwest Pacific in World War II—that is, it might have if MacArthur had known of it, which he didn't.

Kamehameha this time worked his way along the northern coast of Maui rather than the southern. In Kalaniopuu's previous large effort the strategy had been to conquer the southern coast and then assault the capital, Wailuku, from the south.

In the last major effort to assault Kahekili in Wailuku, Kalaniopuu's forces, since they attacked from low ground to the south toward the rolling hills of the north which Kahekili held, were at a disadvantage. It was the classic military handicap of any force which assaults high ground from below.

This time, Kamehameha was going to attack Wailuku from the north, and take advantage of the full mobility of his canoes to "island hop" along the north coast—rolling up resistance ahead of his huge amphibious force.

Kahekili's capital was still Wailuku, and Kahekili's son Kalanikupule was governing Maui from there. Kahekili, still holding the recalcitrant elements in check on the new acquisition, Oahu, was staying at his capital in Waikiki and had sent Kalanikupule to govern Maui.

Now, Kamehameha's sizable army worked along the north Maui coast from inlet to inlet, heading toward Wailuku and picking up such supplies and food as needed. Like any fast-moving modern assemblage of troops, he left his heaviest elements, like the cannon Lopaka, to the rear—the striking force at the head of the formations traveled light. And of course, on such a fast-moving campaign as this, the womenfolk were left behind with the cannons.

Kalanikupule, at his capital in Wailuku, heard disheartening reports of Kamehameha's progress along the north coast. Not only was he moving fast, successfully and in great strength, he was winning support for his cause against Kahekili and Kalanikupule by tact, diplomacy and an assiduous cultivation of the local chiefs. He was taking this one leaf from the book of his brother Kelii-maikai. Kelii-maikai's diplomacy and sense of popular support had been good, although his military judgment and strategy were inferior. Of course, it had been Kelii-maikai's sense of public relations, his popularity with the people, which had saved him from death after his large military defeat in the last Hana campaign.

Kalanikupule sent his most dashing and gifted chief, Kapakahili, posthaste to attack Kamehameha in the north coast district of Hamakualoa. The army moved fast across Hamakuapoko and came close to the Kamehameha force near Halehaku Bay, about fifteen miles west of Wailuku.

The exact spot is a hill called Puukoa (it means a reddish brown sedge growing in marshland, or a bird the same color, later known as the bo'sun's mate bird).

Here Kamehameha and a large force met the vanguard of the Kapakahili forces, turning them back to the west. But Kamehameha's scouts told him that the enemy was being heavily reinforced.

Kamehameha hesitated. The bulk of his forces was still strung in canoes along the north coast of Maui. Deliberately, he set up a camp near the village of Halehaku. Intensely, he consulted the kahunas who traveled with him. They paraded the war god Ku through the camp that night among the warriors' bonfires.

Kamehameha, standing with the great chief Kameeiamoku, watched the solemn parade among the bonfires with the heavy, sonorous beating of the pahu while they chanted their invocations to his principal god Ku-kaili-moku. Kamehameha waited patiently when the chief kahuna, the gaunt, white-bearded Kalima, came to him to report, three others standing respectfully behind him.

Kamehameha did not have to search the aged face for a clue. Kalima pointed to the red feathers of the hideous, crouching warrior god.

"Exalted Majesty," he said. "I need not say more. The God's feathers are bristling like spears in the direction of the crown feathers of Hina-wai-kolii on Ku's head. The omens for conquest are good—if Kamehameha sees the gleam, red fire flashing through the hala trees beyond Puu-maile, the outcome is assured."

Kamehameha knew that the hala trees grew in a grove beyond Puu-maile. They were in the bottom of a valley. It would make military good sense if he could catch Kapakahili here with an attack from high ground, at Puu-maile.

Kameeiamoku had the same thought: "The red fire in the hala trees could be the red cloaks of the enemy. If we could catch him here with spears and stones, we can finish him." Kamehameha nodded.

Kamehameha had faith in the magic, the hidden secrets, the curses and powers which the kahunas could invoke. So often, they had made readings which later turned out to make the most sense in a military way. So often, their predictions had seemed at first to tax good military logic, but when the battle was over, their recommendations had been right. They had magical foreknowledge and he had faith too in the vindictive powers of the gods. That vengeance came when mere men, even Alii descended from the gods, had the effrontery to oppose the revealed will of the supernatural powers. Kamehameha told Kalima to prepare a sacrifice and prayers for the great god Ku-kaili-moku.

That night, he alerted his commanders to move in to Puu-maile the next day. He planned a scouting expedition to Puu-maile to explore the enemy strength there. He sent Koa-kanu, one of the sons of Keawe-mauhili, back along the coast to the east with a force of canoes to find out how soon they could reinforce him. The conduct of the battle tomorrow would depend on the events of the scouting expedition in the morning—and the readings of the omens Kalima might manage—and, of course, the on-the-spot developments that would emerge in the heat of the fight.

That night, the two giants, Kamehameha and Kaiana, talked over these prospects in the au-oro, or thatch-roofed command post, his men had put up near Puu-maile.

Kamehameha and Kaiana talked about the impending confrontation with Kapakahili. Kaiana knew that Kamehameha was determined to win this time—even if he had to abandon the classic and traditional form of a Hawaiian battle: with the opposing armies drawn up, and the usual formal preliminaries. Those preliminaries included not only many readings from the kahunas, which Kamehameha approved strongly, but also loud oratory and threats by the leading chiefs of both sides, giving notice of their intentions. Thus the enemy was fully prepared for the battle, the crescent-shaped forces colliding head-on with the victory generally going to the side that heavily outnumbered the other.

But Kamehameha had learned a fundamental lesson from archenemy Kahekili. He knew that Kaiana, with his familiarity with foreign ways, understood his new eagerness to try the unconventional—anything that might bring him victory. Nearly forty years old now, Kamehameha was stricken with impatience for quick victory.

Kahekili the Thunderer, when it came to military tactics, had never been afraid to use surprise and unconventional methods, anything that would yield victory.

Kamehameha was not given to communication as a habit. He had a warrior's reverence for action and less respect for talkers. But Kaiana knew that he now needed a chance to talk, and the reassurance that talking with a friend can bring.

"Pai'ea," he said, using his battle nickname, "will the big guns be coming up to help?"

Kamehameha seemed relieved to hear the question. "The guns are heavy. They move slowly."

Kamehameha walked to the door where a kukui light flickered yellow. He looked out at the camp-fires.

"If we have them outnumbered tomorrow, we will surprise them and win—without the cannons."

He stalked back to Kaiana. "Send scouts tonight to tell us how many enemy camp-fires can be seen to the west. Whatever happens, we will surprise them."

He took a well polished short ihe spear from a corner of the hale and checked the sharpness of the double-pronged point with one long finger.

"If the god Ku is with us tomorrow, the old weapons will do well for Kapakahili. Ke-kei-nani o Kapa-kahili—how glorious is Kapakahili's pride. His name 'Almost Royal' is the man himself. His pride is his sore thumb."

"You will use his pride against him, Pai'ea?"

Kamehameha carefully propped the spear in the corner. On the edge of the red and white tapa mat stood his lei-o-mano battle club, studded with shark's teeth. Lei-o-mano was usually translated to mean "shy away from a shark," and this formidable club, veteran weapon of many battles, was studded with the largest shark teeth he had seen.

"Kapakahili is the strength of the enemy. He was the choice of King Kahekili to give backbone to this army."

He picked up the battle club, dodged as if ducking a spear, and swung the heavy club in a short, hooking swing.

"Kahekili's son, Kalanikupule, is olo-wai, a pleasant, but weak man. Without a leader like Kapakahili, he and his troops are nothing."

Kaiana laughed. "And so? And then?"

Kamehameha smiled. "If I can confront Kapakahili himself and challenge him, they will be finished. If Ku is with me tomorrow."

CHAPTER 10

Hector vs. Achilles— Hawaiian Style

WITH THE FIRST light of day, Kamehameha put on his warrior's malo, the short loin cloth which would be his fighting costume if it came to the combat he expected and hoped for. If he found and fought Kapakahili, the "Almost a King," he would shed his gold-feathered war cloak and fight to the death in the minimum of costume of mokomoko, the fist-fighting game. Carefully he put his head through the human hair necklace of his niho palaoa, his badge of Alii rank with its large, upturned whale tooth.

Kamehameha's old orderly, Kamae, helped him with his war cloak and helmet. He strapped on his heavy belt of olona fiber, stuck his treasured meki, or iron dagger, from the time of Cook, into it, and tied on his lei-o-mano war club. Kamae handed him his short ihe fighting spear.

"Ku go with you, Majesty," the old man said.

"Mahalo," Kamehameha said. "This may be my last single combat."

"I hope not, Majesty," Kamae said.

When he left the hale, Kamehameha gathered his advance guard, the Alapa. They started down the slope of Puukoa toward the west, the rising sun behind them. Kamehameha carefully left behind his kahili bearers, his badges of kingly rank, and his pahu beaters, those other noisy servers-of-notice that royalty was approaching. With him he took Kaiana, Kalima, the kahuna and a staff of leaders—but only his selected shock troops, his own Alapa or vanguard. They went toward the draw which Kalima had indicated in his prophecy where the hau trees grew thick. Beyond this draw rose a long coastal hill called Opae-pilau (literally "Rotten Shrimp").

Kamehameha went ahead of the body of his Alapa, taking with him Kaiana and his vigorous kahuna, Kalima, and two kahunas carrying the sacred, angry red feather image of Ku, on a tall pole. Kalima, being fit and aggressive, was almost a warrior. He wanted always to be near the scene of maximum action. The kahunas were most aggressive and daring. Even the oldest of them, like the late-lamented Holoae, father of Kekuhaupio, were often reckless in exposing themselves—which took considerable faith and daring, even though ordinarily a kahuna was supposed to be sacrosanct, off-limits as a target. Still, they were often killed —and Kalima was the most fearless of the kahunas Kamehameha had seen.

So this day, Kalima went ahead with Kamehameha on the scouting foray—far ahead of even the Alapa. But Kamehameha insisted as they moved forward that Kalima leave the image of the great god Ku behind, with the two subkahunas and the body of the Alapa.

They moved quietly through the hala trees, heading toward the beach. The ground was still high, but through the trees they could see a long column of troops, with an echelon of vermillion at the head.

"The prophecy, Pai'ea!" Kaiana said softly. "We see the red flame through the hala trees—the battle cloaks!"

Kamehameha's purplish black eyes focused hard on that leading echelon. He held out his hand to halt the column. "Perhaps Kapakahili himself is leading them. And if he is, we must take him now. Whether or not the reinforcements reach us soon."

Kaiana was an apt military pupil of the master. "I can send a runner back to our camp to see if Koa-kanu has come back with his canoes from the scouting expedition."

"Maikai," Kamehameha grunted. "Good. Do it wiki-wiki. Don't waste time. And in the meantime we'll scout them thoroughly, to see how strong they are. And quietly!"

Kaiana went back to secure a runner, and Kamehameha led the way along the ridge through the trees. Here a thick undergrowth of bushes grew, nourished by the trade winds which came here to bring rain from the northeast, the direction of Kai and Hema—the direction from which the sun rose, Kai, and as he faced it, his left hand, the north, Hema.

Kalima came up proudly, knowing that Kamehameha and Kaiana had been mentioning the accuracy of his prophecy. Kamehameha was more expansive and open during a military action, as now, and he acknowledged the kahuna with a nod and a pleasant attempt at a smile.

"Mahalo, Kalima," he said. "What omens do you read now?"

"The great god Ku, the god of bristling war feathers, is not here to advise us or lead us."

"When we establish contact and the fight begins, we must bring his mana to bless us."

Kalima nodded. "Until then, I will read the god signs in the clouds and the sky."

"Good," said Kamehameha. "And what do you see in the heavens now?"

Kalima squinted at the tall masses of white clouds moving in the high sky from the north. He raised his hand to shield his eyes from the sun. The local guide, Ahua, whom Kamehameha brought from the beachhead at Waipio Bay to show them the trails, came up at the same moment.

Kalima said in his deep and solemn voice: "From the direction of the sun, we will kill them, every one."

He looked toward the jungly slope of Pii-holo, rising toward the southwest. "But the final blow will be not here, but in the house where the light is done."

Ahua, moved by the solemnity of Kalima's tone, spoke abruptly: "Majesty, could the great kahuna mean the slope of Kokomo, where they will be killed?"

But Kalima moved off, as if in a trance. Kamehameha turned to Ahua, the guide. "Are they heading for the beach?"

"No, Majesty, the path they are following leads to a low area on this side of Kokomo."

The giant Kaiana had come trotting back with a runner trailing him. The runner seemed minute by comparison, and his body gleamed with sweat. Kaiana seemed cool, huge and unexercised.

"This runner has come up all the way from Honomanu," he said. "He says that Ke-e-au-moku has arrived there with Olohana, John Young, and Lopaka, the red-mouthed Speaker of Destruction."

"Maikai, we need that cannon," Kamehameha said. "But what of the troops? How many have reached Honomanu?" Something like a smile lifted his wide mouth at the outer edges.

"If they have come that far, only a half-day's paddle and they will be here."

Kaiana was pleased. "If you could see the numbers of them, you would be happy. There are as many as the people of Hilo."

"Never mind the poetic comparisons," said Kamehameha. "Tell me in Haole language. How many kakani? How many hanale?"

"You are right," he laughed. "I must say it in thousands and hundreds. The Haoles have to teach us how to count beyond lima, the five fingers, and four, the number of the family. There were at least, I would say, a kakani, a whole thousand, and some hundreds. At least eha lima, twenty large war canoes full—more than a full kakani."

Now it was Kamehameha's turn to chuckle. "Kilohana, Kilohana! As the white Lono, Kapitan Kuka, liked to say, 'Ex-cellent!'"

Kamehameha led the way to a small patch of sand and beckoned to Kaiana to follow him. He bent over the sand and stuck one large finger into the ground.

"The mountain of Pii-holo here. If we climb the slopes with our Alapa, we will be above the enemy and behind him. Most important, we will be between him and his home base at Wailuku."

"But our reinforcements come up with Olohana and Ke-e-au-moku. How will they be able to reach us?"

"We will attack the enemy from his rear. Ke-e-au-moku and Olohana will be able to tackle him from the other side. That is, if my message reaches the reinforcements."

"This runner, Kewalo, is the best and fastest in the islands."

"Good. Send him with the message to Ke-e-au-moku and Olohana. And I will move my Alapa to the slope of Pii-holo. They can move very fast, very wiki-wiki."

"They are the best shock troops I have ever seen." Kamehameha was silent. Kaiana went on: "Worthy of the best traditions of the great Alapa of Kalaniopuu."

Kamehameha's black eyes flashed. "No! *Those* Alapa were beaten on Maui—wiped out." He looked up the wooded slope toward Kokomo. "These Alapa—will win."

Kaiana was heading back with the runner. Kamehameha had one last order for him: "Tell Ke-e-au-moku of the plan. Tell him where to hit the enemy."

Kalima the head kahuna came forward, an erect, exclamation mark of a man, to stand by Kamehameha. He seemed a slight figure, tiny next to the bulk of Kamehameha in his golden warrior's cloak and towering coxcomb-shaped helmet.

"Kalima, speaker of the charmed tongue, my general in all but name, do this for me: Go back, speak to the Alapa. Bring them back, running wiki-wiki!"

"Great Chief, I will."

"I will wait here for them. No pilikia. Right here."

Kamehameha had seen enough. A sizable force of the enemy had penetrated along this flank, along the slope down to the rocky cliffs and the tiny beach where Halehaku came to the ocean at Halehaku Bay. No matter what else happened, if he led his Alapa up the slope of Pii-holo to a commanding position, he could dominate them, and then—if his reinforcements came up from Honomanu with Ke-e-au-moku and Olohana—he could annihilate them.

Whether he would meet and fight Kapakahili personally was a moot question—in the hands of the gods. But there was a very good gambler's chance that Kapakahili would be with the very forefront of his troops. He was that kind of an awini leader, sharp-pointed and bold.

Kamehameha was never a man to waste time when his mind was made up, whatever dangers and discomforts might be involved. Now he sought the local guide, Ahua. One mention to the six chiefs attending Kamehameha in their red and yellow cloaks, and Ahua came running.

There followed a lengthy questioning session, where Kamehameha pursued the most minute details of the terrain all the way from Halehaku stream and the ocean up to the summit of Pii-holo.

By the time Kaiana and Kalima came back from their respective errands, he was well briefed on the features of the territory: all the rills and the arroyos running down from Honopou, Peahi and Hoolawa, their heights and dimensions, all the way up to Ulalena, the eastern peak nearly as high as Pii-holo.

Kamehameha, elated far beyond his usual phlegmatic disposition (phlegmatic, at least, up to the exploding point of his hot temper), remarked on the geographical omens.

"Kaiana," he said, "if we climb the slopes of Pii-holo, and menace the enemy from up there, he will be afraid, maka'u—full of hesitation."

Kaiana smiled. "And suppose he outnumbers us?"

"We can beat him until our reinforcements come up."

"And will you fight Kapakahili man-to-man?"

"At the best time. And that is soon."

And soon it was. The Alapa came up at the quick dogtrot which Kamehameha had ordered, with Kalima at their head. Kamehameha spread them up the slopes of Halehaku stream, in the big hala trees, and they waited for his command.

From here, on a sparsely-treed height in the northern rain forest of Maui, along the festoons of the ridge, they were a magnificent spectacle of red and gold, their towering red feather and tapa god images looming above them on spearlike poles.

And from here they could look down on the equally impressive column of Kapakahili's red and yellow cloaked warriors moving along the northern coast of Maui, the Hamakua coast where the heavy ocean waves beat on black lava cliffs, with only occasional shreds of tawny (or darker) sand where the streams like Halehaku cascaded to the sea.

It was steaming hot in the morning sun, although heavy white clouds were rolling in from the northern horizon on the same trade winds which blew constantly to bring the Haole merchantmen with their miraculous new inventions.

Kamehameha, Kaiana and Kalima stood on a bare knoll overlooking the two armies, and Kamehameha made his final preparations for the encounter, both military and religious.

First, the religious. "Kalima, great general and great kahuna, we will sound the pahu loudly and long now—to let them know we are ready and to strike fear into them. And we will tell them that *I* am ready to do battle with Kapakahili."

"Majesty," said Kalima, "let there be a sounding of the pahu such as will make the most violent thunderstorms a mere whisper. Then I will deliver the challenge."

Kamehameha said: "Even if I kill him, they will be slow to accept defeat, surrender, perhaps death. We must be prepared for a fight afterward."

Kaiana said: "Yes, Majesty, but you will have destroyed their

will to fight. In its place, maka'u: They will be full of hesitation, and that—"

"Is death," said Kamehameha, with the faint shadow of a smile
on his wide lips.

Down on the Kipahulu shore, Kapakahili the Hotspur, commanding the enemy King Kahekili's legions, had seen the red and
yellow festooning of troops marking Kamehameha's advent.
Kamehameha had wisely chosen the high ground to start. He had
the instant advantage of position above the grove of hala treees
which was going to be a battle scene.

Kapakahili had prepared himself mentally for the day and the
exigency, like any distinguished chieftain who has fought his share
of desperate battles, and especially like a warrior chieftain widely
known for his fearlessness. He was mentally prepared to fight
for his life with his last desperate edge of strength, and prepared
if necessary to die if events turned against him. In this he was
remarkably like Kamehameha.

Now, walking close to the head of his column as they trudged
along the rough ground near the Kipahulu cliffs, he had stopped
with another high chief, Kamohomoho, to make an estimate of
the situation, and a battle plan.

Kamohomoho, a high military counselor to Kalanikupule
(and his foster father at one time), was also a friend and close
associate of the aged king of Maui, Kahekili. Kamohomoho,
meaning approximately "The Candidate," was the younger half-
brother of Kahekili and therefore Kalanikupule's uncle. Now he
was an elder statesman and advisor to Kalanikupule. An eager and
aggressive chief, though aged, he had come down the rough
northern coast of Maui with Kapakahili, mostly by canoe. He
had left his nephew back at Wailuku, with about half of the
armies to whom Kahekili had entrusted the job of engaging
Kamehameha. Now Kamohomoho, a vigorous warrior chief in
his late years, was tired from a long and rough hike from Maliko
Bay, where they had landed in the predawn hours of this morning
with about 900 men, an advance guard to engage Kamehameha's

fast-moving forces until reinforcements could be brought up from Wailuku to finish the job of wiping out the upstart.

Now Kamohomoho, whose lean figure marked the fact that he was still an active military leader and aggressive, turned to face the Kauwa who wielded his fan, and his fly-switch. He stood in the extra breeze of the fan and looked around for the young Alii warrior who carried his spitoon. He hocked and spat, then turned to Kapakahili. Kapa was ahead of him as they had been walking. Kapa had an annoying habit of staying at least a pace ahead of any person with whom he walked. If Kamohomoho was tired, one of the large reasons was that Kapakahili had walked with him from the beginning of the march almost as if they were racing.

Now Kamohomoho said: "A word of caution, Ula [the word meant "Red" and it was a nickname referring to a small red birthmark on Kapakahili's left heel]. Remember that what we see of the enemy's force may or may not be all of it. Don't make a rash attack until we find out more."

Kapakahili spoke rapidly. "I would wager Kamehameha is spreading out his forces on the ridge this way because they are small. He wants to make them seem larger, and to frighten us with the fact that they dominate us from higher ground."

"Never mind," said Kamohomoho. "We will know soon enough what their strength is." He indicated a group of Alii, perhaps forty, with the red god images of Ku towering over them on spearlike poles. They were moving down a winding path from the ridge down toward the Kapakahili force. At the head of the column, surrounded by snarling, crouching red images of Ku, moved the slight, intense figure of Kalima, Kameha's chief kahuna.

Behind him, now that the Alapa had arrived, there followed a host of subkahunas in red tapa cloaks—and a wide percussion section of pahu drums in an assortment of sizes. Also the higher-toned knee drums, puniu, strapped to the upper legs of the warriors; and the intermediate ipu hula, or gourd drums. A rattling accompaniment of hula sticks and uli uli, the nervous sounds of small gourds and the bamboo-branch pu-ili, or rustle-makers, made the noises of rain falling on a variety of surfaces.

Then a herald or crier came up with a large kipahulu shell, sounded a decisive blast, and Kalima strode forward to a rocky knoll, clearly to make a pronouncement. He stood there, the drums sounding their most compelling introductory thunder, and when they stopped, the silence was all Kalima's.

"Kamohomoho, son to the noble chief Ke-kau-like and Kapa-kahili, valiant fighter and leader of men, we are come to fight.

"Kamehameha, descendant of the immortal line of Uli, challenges you to mortal combat. Since Kamohomoho is older, our King specifies he will fight the more vigorous of the two, Kapa-kahili. To the death. The outcome to determine the outcome of the day."

Kapakahili was quick to react to the invitation: "At least," he said to Kamohomoho with a wry grin, "they are polite so far. Next come the insults. They are polite in asking me to risk my life in a battle-to-the-death."

Kamohomoho, the cynic, said: "Yes. Now the insults. Probably delivered by the Upstart himself. Intended—of course—to provoke you to blind rage."

Kapakahili smiled. "Not necessary. I am already greatly curious to fight Kamehameha."

At that moment, another distant pahu chorus became audible. It was growing rapidly louder, and soon from the hala trees another column descended to the rock where Kalima stood. At the head moved the harbingers of royalty, the kahili bearers with their staffs of authority, the flower scepters made of wide wedges of plumeria blossoms.

Kamehameha was coming after the god figures, the kahilis, and the royal spitoon-bearers, as they appeared from the hala trees and moved along the ridge. Then came the giant figure in gold, towering over seven feet with his high yellow helmet.

He moved like a big cat or a great heavyweight boxer, with all the instinctive, self-contained grace and cautious strength of a dancer—or a habitual spear-dodger. As he moved, the pahu chorus thudded and rumbled louder, to a crescendo and abrupt halt the moment before he was to speak.

There was dead silence for a few seconds—no one of those thousand souls moved or stirred. Then he bellowed, in the best battlefield, thunderous voice of the habitual leader on the field:

"Kapakahili," he called. "Almost a king! I, Kamehameha, a king in birth and deed and not merely an imitation like you, will fight you to the death.

"You, who pick fights with inexperienced youngsters like my brother, now will fight with a fighter who knows what he is doing. That you will realize before you die, in terror, squealing like a pig."

Kapakahili spoke softly, with the flicker of a smile on his lips. "Let us see how far he will go on with this train of insults."

Kamehameha was going on. "You are known for having defeated my brother and his armies, here in Maui. From this you gain fame as a warrior. But like your name, it is fame which is not real, but kapa. Almost—but not quite! That is the kind of fighter you are!"

He halted, and a wave of cheering and jeers swept across the red and yellow festoon of the Alapa.

Kamehameha said: "So let us fight, you and I will fight to the death. Let the outcome determine the end of today's battle."

Kapakahili moved forward and upward to a large, open rock where he could be clearly seen by both sides. It was the moment for him to act—the soldiers there expected it. And he momentarily was relieved that it had come, although he was also tired, bone-tired, from the long hike through rough country.

He stood, a graceful, erect warrior chief's figure in red and gold helmet and cloak. He spoke to Kamehameha in a firm, clear voice, but his body angled so that all could hear.

"Your majesty—to use the common (and mistaken) form of address," he said. "You have said that my name means 'Almost Royal'—this is true, although my lineage is clear—and stems from famous (and legitimate) lines of warrior Alii.

"But you have no such claim, not even to *half*-royalty. From the beginning you have been a drop, an upstart, only a pretender."

Kapakahili, the veteran of many such individual combats as this, waited for the reaction to the insult, the most grievous and offensive kind of innuendo to an Alii warrior.

The impact was considerable. A surge of sound, like the cresting rumble of a breaker, swept through the crowd—sharp laughter and jeers on one side, oaths on the other. The overall sound was a hissing, liquid, glottal wall of reaction. Then it stopped, almost as if it were programmed. The pause was expectation, the waiting for Kamehameha's response.

Kamehameha's giant figure strode rapidly to a craggy peak overlooking the mass of warriors. His dark face suddenly looked black with the rage that had filled him. Like Kapakahili, he was practiced in battlefield invective, and the vehemence and strength which grew from the crackling fire of combat. He shouted, and his shout came like the roar of the volcano pit when Goddess Pele, goddess and devil of the Halemaumau Fire Pit, is enraged and speaking with all her stunning supernatural power.

"Ke kupu! Upstart!" He spat out the words. "You have the effrontery to call *me* a drop, illegitimate! I will make you eat those words.

"You! The best you could claim is to be a kaukau-Alii, a hanger-on who sings for his supper in the Chief's kitchen. And worse than that, the unrecognized, behind-the-wall child of kamalu, the secret shadows. And in those shadows, your secret father, another upstart, an unknown warrior without Alii blood."

Kapakahili snorted like a wounded bull. "I a ke kupu! That's the biggest joke of all, coming from you." Expert in such calculated provocations, he waited long enough for the wave of the crowd reaction to subside. Then he spoke at the proper moment with the final insult.

"*You* are the most secret child of the shadows. And the secret father is not King Kahekili, as you would have us believe. But a commoner, a slave, a Kauwa. Even as a drop, you are still only the child of a commoner. And the secret child of a Kauwa with your mother Kekui-apo-iwa. Not even the secret drop of King Kahekili."

A loud wave of outcry and cheers swept across the crowd. And as Kapakahili had estimated, Kamehameha was genuinely enraged.

Kapakahili could almost see the impact of his insult on Kamehameha from the moment of his words. The giant turned abruptly and, moving nervously as a shark at feeding time, he snapped back into full view with his long pololu spear in his right hand, and his barbed and bristling war club in the left.

"You, upstart, speak hehena, madness. But the wrong is done; crazy as you may be, I, Kamehameha, the son of a great Kalani, Keoua and Kekui-apo-iwa, will make you eat that insult. However hehena it may be, you will eat it! And drink your own blood until you drown."

Kamehameha raised his pololu spear. It was a giant of a weapon, a good fourteen feet long, and as thick at the butt end and out to the middle, as a child's wrist. But against his height and the bulk of his upper torso, it seemed light and slender, a graceful toy.

Not permitting himself the luxury and indignity of the usual run to launch such a heavy weapon, Kamehameha balanced it in his grip, backed up a few steps, crouched and flung it on a high flight, propelled by massive long muscles powered now by a genuine rage. No insult could have been better calculated to get this effect than Kapakahili's. But probably Kapakahili, had he known the pride and towering strength which the insult would jam into Kamehameha's sorest wound, and the giant natural strength and skill in which that insult had begun to explode, would have thought twice before he flung it. Yet both great chiefs, no matter what the caliber of insults they might hurl at each other to start the argument, had determined far in advance that they were going to fight to the death this day if they had the luck to meet.

The long pololu flew high and true, straight in the direction where Kapakahili and Kamohomoho stood. They measured the flight with the warrior's eye, saw that it was going to land short of them, and accordingly did not duck or move.

The long spear hit the ground in a clump of makou fern and skidded through the underbrush almost to the two waiting chiefs. It was a magnificent throw, because the spear came to rest only fifteen or twenty feet from the personages. It was a beautifully aimed and executed move to herald Kamehameha's final challenge. Kamehameha made that announcement in a firm loud voice so that all could hear:

"Let the fight begin—now! To the death! In the open place below!"

Kamehameha moved deliberately down the slope toward a small field of buffalo grass, aki aki haole. Kaiana, his kahuna Kalima and others of his royal train followed closely. His enemies, Kapakahili, Kamohomoho and their closest supporters, were moving to the clearing from below. The pahus of both camps started immediately with a nervous, expectant hammering. The masses of brown fighting men in red and black malos, with a scattering of the red, gold and black ahuula cloaks and helmets, the marks of the chiefs, closed around the clearing.

Above the clearing, Kamehameha and his train of chiefs appeared from the trees. Now the great chief again was armed with a fresh pololu spear, as long and heavy as the one he had thrown in challenge. In his left hand, he carried his massive war club, studded with shark teeth; and, looped around his wrist, a sling of hau tree or linden inner bark. A sack of large pebbles, ammunition for the sling, was looped over one shoulder. Clearly, the great warrior was not going to forget his advantage as a nonpareil wielder of the sling—in his hands, a terrifying long-range weapon.

Now, as Kapakahili appeared on the lower end of the clearing, Kamehameha's sling arm whipped into action. The throw was neither overhand nor underhand, but the shorter, more rapid course three-quarters of the way to the top. It was a fling that seemed to be the fastest and most lightning-like projection of effort in a short compass.

The stone whipped like a bullet toward Kapakahili. But he had seen it coming, his warrior's eye catching it almost the instant it left the sling. Now he dodged adroitly. The stone thudded into a hala tree, bouncing from one aerial root to the next.

Kapakahili struck back in kind. His sling movement seemed as rapid as Kamehameha's. The projectile arc seemed nearly as flat and bulletlike as his giant opponent's.

But the giant Hard Shell Crab, Pae'ia, was not bothering to dodge. He was at that moment in the midst of another venture into small-compass violence, a throw at Kapakahili when the enemy was still off balance from his own throw. And this time, the stone found a vital mark. It glanced from the wide arch of the left cheekbone. The impact, though not a flush blow, knocked Kapakahili's head back and blood ran down his cheek. He staggered back, then came weaving forward. He bent over and came up from the ground with a short ihe spear. In that same movement, despite the force of the blow he had taken, he had launched that short spear in another flat, direct flight toward Kamehameha. The giant Hard Shell Crab dodged again, using his own pololu long spear to deflect the shorter weapon from its low trajectory.

The spear slid harmlessly into the buffalo grass. Now, with a hoarse shout, Kamehameha came charging toward Kapakahili with his long, heavy pololu spear jammed out like a projectile attached to him. From Kapakahili's direction came a barrage of sling stones: one, two, three, four zipped toward the charging giant, the pistonlike arm of Kapakahili aiming, firing and powering the human battery in an incredibly swift warrior's exercise. Kamehameha, charging spear and all, somehow managed to dodge and slip the swift stones. And now he had the advantage: his great charging bulk, the long point of the spear ahead of him, and the whole power-package of force and strength now almost as close as another length of a pololu. Kapakahili's ihe spear and his bombardment of sling stones had failed.

Now another ihe spear was in Kapakahili's hand. Probably he had picked it up from the ground. And truly, like a dagger or Roman sword parrying a pike thrust, the spear moved in an expert, spiking movement to divert the drive of the longer weapon and the powerful warrior behind it.

In that split second, Kamehameha snapped the weapon back toward the target, but Kapakahili instinctively struck again with his spear to knock the pololu toward the other side—the normal second stroke of the expert parry movement.

So the charging spear was jammed upward and to Kapakahili's right. The pololu slid up the length of the rigid ihe spear of Kapakahili, and the charging mass and bulk of Kamehameha collided with the also formidable bulk and strength of Kapakahili— their spears jackknifed between them.

For a moment, the sweating, straining bodies of the two champion warriors were jammed face to face. Kamehameha had the satisfaction of seeing that Kapakahili's face was bleeding and swollen from the glancing impact of the sling stone: an advantage. Kamehameha hastened to pursue it. He bounced back a half step, wrenching his spear down. But Kapakahili flipped his handier short weapon free, caught the long spear on the other side, and held it. His purchase was better with that angle and his closer grip and leverage with the ihe equalized Kamehameha's greater might applied to the longer leverage of the pololu.

Abruptly, Kamehameha dropped the long weapon. He and his foe were still practically face to face and he flung his heavy war club into action. Here at close quarters, his greater strength could smash his enemy with sheer brute force. The range was still shorter than the length of the short ihe spear. He swung hard, a short uppercut blow that caught Kapakahili flush across the chest and flung his short spear upward clean out of his grasp. It flew straight up and the force of the blow sent Kapakahili staggering backward, his chest ripped by the shark's teeth. But he did not fall. Kamehameha was on him like a tiger, the war club swinging back in a wide arc.

The blow caught Kapakahili squarely on the shoulder. He was already stunned by the stone in the face; that impact had dulled his precision enough so that he missed with his stones slung at Kamehameha—unusual for him to miss three successive efforts. And now the rending shock of knowing that his guts were ripped by the shark's teeth. He was stunned to know that he was all gone inside. And only dully did he feel that final war club blow.

The blow was like a volcano in force. He staggered to the side. But he was still capable of thinking. Vaguely he thought: "The time for pahoas! *Where* is my pahoa?"

In a second, still standing, he somehow had his long pahoa dagger in his hand and he was moving in to use it quickly before the next dreadful stroke of the shark-tooth war club. He knew his guts and his shoulder were ripped and wet with blood. He had been badly hurt many times before this and come back with an expert pahoa stroke to turn it the other way, into a victory. But he must be fast. All this in a split second of half-consciousness in a stunned psyche. The warrior instincts to fight and win were still there, still driving him. *The dagger is faster than the war club!* His old kahu's favorite saying.

He thrust his wide-bladed long pahoa of ele-ele wood, a heavy ebony shaft, toward the looming size of Kamehameha, the yellow feather war cloak all gone from those torso muscles slick with sweat. He glimpsed the narrow red warrior's malo below the heaving brown back muscles, and he thrust. His blade struck something, something resistant that seemed to give with it.

Then the white flash of another great blow struck Kapakahili. It hit him like a lightning bolt in the head. The light filled him with force and a metallic feeling like an iron dagger instantly to the edges of all of him, stronger than his will. He felt his legs going from under him, and sinking, sinking into darkness.

Kamehameha felt the strike as his war club hit Kapakahili again, the third time, now, on the skull, crumpling and crushing the foe down, down to the ground. In his own middle, the white-hot strike of a dagger. He knew it well.

Yet he did not go down. It could not be too bad or he would go. He focused on Kapakahili, down in the grass, the muscular brown body on its side, the skull smashed in blood, the coconut lolo of those brains pushed out. Very still. Finished. Then Kamehameha felt his own legs begin to go. Someone was supporting him, Kalima, and—and Kaiana! No mistaking Kaiana's equal height.

He heard the great roar of the thousands of soldiers around him, the long shout, it seemed, not rejoicing, nor an auwe of distress. Just a shout, and long.

"It's not so deep, the side, not the insides, that muscle." But the muscle of his flank was burning now, the flank muscle just above his waist, the sleek muscle of swimmers. That muscle was afire now with creeping flames. Still, he could stand, he thought. Kapakahili was dead. He must summon all his strength and tell the world, noisy as they might be. He drew his wind, all he could get.

"Slain by Pipili," he trumpeted. "The sticky plant, Kamehameha, killed him in close quarters." His voice seemed to echo. Then his left leg did begin to go; Kaiana held him up. He seemed to be looking the wrong way. He asked Kaiana, "Are they fighting? Or retreating?"

"Fighting, Pai'ea."

"I guessed they might."

"Tell them that Kapakahili is slain by Pipili."

"Too late, Majesty. They are already fighting."

Kamehameha heard Kalima say: "I hear noise behind us. And below. The reinforcements! Are they?"

Now Kamehameha realized. Kaiana had come back with reinforcements. He would know. "Are the reinforcements with us, Kaiana?"

"Some of them, Pai'ea. The others will be here before too long. And we will win." Kamehameha said:

"Maikai! Now—get me to a hala root so that I may sit while Kalima takes care of this wound. I must get up to fight again today. And see this victory. I agree with you, Kaiana. We will win today. And push on to Wailuku."

"We will carry you to the hala tree."

"No. No one will see me being carried. The enemy must be confirmed in his fear of defeat."

He turned and looked at the battlefield below. His Alapa were pushing down toward the Kapakahili forces below. Fortunately, his generals and his Alii had followed his instructions and kept their forces on the high side of the slope, even during the fight between Kamehameha and Kapakahili. Now the Alapa were driving the enemy down toward the water. And he could see the reinforcements coming across the battlefield from the east, the morning bed of the sun, kakikole. They were fresh troops in their fighting red malos, among the helmets of red, black and yellow of the Alii. And there was a cry, like a cry of distress, that rose from the enemy as they saw the new troops coming onto the slope to take their flank. The red and brown long crescent of the enemy lines began to bend and give.

"Maikai!" Kamehameha exulted. "They know they are going to be beaten. Their line is breaking!"

He turned toward the trees on the high side of the clearing. "Take me to the roots, Kalima, and fix this wound. I will fight again today."

But not that day. His troops finished off most of Kapakahili's legions that day on the uplands above Halehaku Bay. A few hundred managed to escape over the rough badlands to Kahalui on the way back to Wailuku. They carried the word that Kamehameha's armies came in waves of thousands, and that back in Hana there were still more thousands and the magical killing invention of the Haoles, the Red-Mouthed guns. These tattered survivors carried the powerful virus of fear to Kalanikupule's reserve forces, more than 2,000 of them still. But when the survivors of Kapakahili's force had told their stories, the reserve forces at Wailuku were generally convinced that they were now vastly outnumbered and outweaponed by Kamehameha.

Kalanikupule believed this too; he was easily convinced that he was far from the greatest leader of armies. But he kept a brave face, and held a council of war with his chiefs, including the durable Kamohomoho, who had managed to shepherd the disordered hundreds of survivors back to Wailuku. Also active in the planning was Kalanikupule's brother Kao-lau-kani. They also sent messengers by canoe to the patriarch, and Kalanikupule's father and Kamehameha's archenemy, Kahekili. Kahekili was still in his governmental seat at Waikiki on Oahu.

Meanwhile, Kalima's kahunas took the wounded Kamehameha to Halehaku Bay to treat his wound. They washed his injuries with salt water and dressed them with aloe poultices, and kept him at rest in the usual half-house of the sick Alii, or hale hau, made from ironwood branches. Kalima chanted prayers as he brought raw yam juice, to keep down any incipient fever.

The battle-trained Kalima made a careful study of the wound. Knowing Kamehameha's relentless thirst for facts, he reported concisely to his prone king: "The god Ku was on your side. That thrust by the kau-ila hit into a heavy part of your sling belt. So it glanced from there into your waist. There is pain because the dagger struck a scar from an old wound."

Kamehameha grimaced: "An old wound from a fighting practice on the Big Island. Is it deep?"

"No. But the King should stay in his hale hau at least one more day. The scar should heal faster because of the old wound. But you will have the pain."

"Will I have the pain whether I lie or get up?"

"Probably."

"Then I must get up."

"No, Great Chief. You can have your war councils here in the hale as you lie. If the omens of the gods are good tonight, then perhaps tomorrow you can get up."

"Then sacrifice a pig to Ku this afternoon. And I will wish and pray that we will not have the bad omen of a rain tonight."

And that evening the war councils went on by the light of burning kukui nut oil, under the stars. Kaiana came back from the pursuit of the remnants of Kapakahili's army. And coming up from the rear, with a large force in war canoes, came Kamehameha's old friend and father-in-law, Ke-e-au-moku. With the group came Koa-kanu, the son of Kamehameha's new high born ally from the Big Island, his uncle, Keawe-mauhili. But the bulk of the forces, and the two Haole practitioners of the cannonading art, Isaac Davis (Aikake) and John Young (Olohana), had not yet arrived with their big gun Lopaka. Nor had Ke-e-au-moku's beautiful daughter and Kamehameha's light, Kaahumanu.

First came the plans. Kamehameha, Ke-e-au-moku and Kaiana agreed that they would wait at hale hau—since Kamehameha needed to build strength anyhow—until more of the forces and the cannon and the squad of musketmen arrived. They would move as rapidly as they could, to take advantage of the defeat of Kapakahili's legion. That night Kamehameha was cheered by the omens: It did not rain.

It was three days before the bulk of the forces had caught up and they were ready to move on to Kahalui. The second day, Kamehameha was up and walking with a gnarled galoa, a tall cane.

It was pain to walk or move, but Kamehameha strolled along the high ground overlooking Halehaku Bay with Ke-e-au-moku. When they were alone, Kamehameha motioned his old friend to sit with him on a rock. From here, they could see the long, swinging surf smashing in showers of white spray against black cliffs.

Kamehameha came right to the point: "No hoo-mali-mali, no nonsense, Moku: I tell you my truth always. First, we must finish Kalanikupule's army. If we both survive this, then we must finish Kahekili. But one more step. I must have children, children of Niau-pio rank."

Ke-e-au-moku's craggy, lean face broke into a half-smile. "Yes, I understand. You are hehena with love for Kaahumanu, but she has been unable to have children, in five years of marriage."

"Yes." Kamehameha picked up a stone and tossed it down the slope. "Kalima has said that I will reign like a king over all the islands. This will be good because then there will be peace at last."

Kamehameha's dark face seemed even darker with the shade of a mood that seemed to have dominated him this day. "There are ways to build a control of men and land more than fighting."

The mercurial Ke-e-au-moku laughed. "So—Pai'ea, I understand you. So you will make arrangements to marry Keopuolani. You will arrange it with Kalola, her grandmother, Kalola also being your aunt and at one time your stepmother as well."

Kamehameha got up, making a face at the pain it was costing him, and walked down the slope a few feet. Then he turned back to Ke-e-au-moku. He was disturbed by Ke-e-au-moku's instant understanding.

"Yes. Kalola is with Kalanikupule right now, I am told, at Wailuku. I must arrange to catch up with Kalola and—"

"And this will arrange your marriage to her daughter, Keopuolani. And by her you will have a Niau-pio child or several, because of the closeness of the blood line, since Kalola is your stepmother and Keopuolani's mother too."

Kamehameha was astounded. "Yes, your guesses are right." He was concerned now that Ke-e-au-moku's well-known hot temper would flare. But it didn't. Ke-e-au-moku still smiled.

"You have been thinking hard during this pilikia with the wound. But I also have been thinking."

Now Kamehameha smiled. "Your mind is quick. Wiki-wiki. As always."

Ke-e-au-moku was still smiling when he said: "Sometimes, son-in-law, you are so clever in your planning that I could gladly kill you."

Kamehameha said: "As long as you tell me about it, you won't do that."

Then he said: "To speak of clever planning, this time, Moku, we will reverse the battle of the Sand Hills, where Kalaniopuu's great defeat lay. This time we will attack the remnants of the enemy forces here from the north and the high ground. As Kahekili did to us before. And this time we will have the great Haole weapons to turn their fear into a flight."

This time Ke-e-au-moku used the Captain Cook phrase which they both knew well. "Excellent! Maikai!"

But Kamehameha's rapid mentality sensed an edge of incompleteness and tension in his close friend. "No matter how many wives, Moku," he said, "Kaahumanu, with all her temper, will always be the light—my queen." And Kamehameha read in his friend's face now that all was well.

CHAPTER 11
A Dazzling Future?

THE Battle of Kepaniwai, which followed at Kamehameha's instigation and engineering in about a week, is hailed in Hawaiian legend (and by Fornander) as "one of the hardest contested on Hawaiian record." Ke-pani-wai means literally "the damming of water" and as Fornander says, "the corpses of the slain were so many as to choke up the waters of the stream of Iao."

But the real defeat of the hosts of Kalanikupule and his father, Kahekili, had been administered at the battle to the death, Hector and Achilles style, between Kamehameha and Kapakahili at Halehaku Bay and Pii-holo mountain. There, and in the accompanying defeat of the forces of Kahekili's best general, the outcome of the Damming of Water was determined. It was nailed down by the arrival of heavy troop reinforcements, the white men's weapons in workable quantity, and Kamehameha's as usual astute generalship.

The so-called battle was in the Iao Valley, beginning in the sand hills of the Maui capital of Wailuku and working west into the high green peaks of the Iao River valley. If a fiction writer were looking for a dramatic locale for a historic battle, he would have to go far to beat the Iao Valley. The green peaks and rainbow-shrouded slopes are a set decorator's ideal of beauty, mystery and danger.

According to the guidebook legend, the Kamehameha forces drove the Kahekili army along the Iao stream and they were annihilated as they were forced higher and higher into the foothills of the Mountains of the Moon. These sharp-edged extinct-crater peaks rise to 4,000 to 5,000 feet high. Even today they are wild and unroaded.

Kamehameha brought his force of large war canoes and amphibious soldiers across the north shore of Maui the fifteen or eighteen miles from Halehaku Bay to Kahalui Bay. This time, knowing he had the great advantages of better position, more men and the Haole weapons of cannon and muskets—plus, of course, the psychological advantage of the great defeat he had inflicted on Kapakahili at Halehaku—he moved surely. The only surprise his foe Kahekili might manage would be to run a fleet of reinforcements in from his new capital at Waikiki, Oahu.

So Kamehameha did not waste time. But he made sure that this time his two military advisors, the sailors Olohana and Aikake (John Young and Isaac Davis), and plenty of men to move and fire their weapons, were with the main body of the attacking forces.

On Kahalui Bay shore, Kamehameha mustered a special force of soldiers, that might have been as numerous as 100, with the job of moving Lopaka, the brass cannon, from the *Fair American,* Isaac Davis's ship.

The older of the two Haole advisors, John Young (he was the bo'sun, in his forties, from the *Eleanora*), had rigged a cart with homemade wooden wheels to carry the big weapon into action.

Also, a platoon of soldiers had been assigned and trained by both Aikake and Olohana to load, aim and fire the dozen muskets (a formidable force in Hawaiian terms) secured from the *Fair American* and from Kaiana's captain, Douglas. As the army prepared for the march upon Wailuku, Kamehameha was doing his best to get John Young to construct yet one more homemade gun wagon. This would be a crude gun-carriage for the swivel cannon which Captain Douglas had given Kamehameha, in 1788 when Kaiana came to Kealakekua Bay to join with Kamehameha. As of that time, it was still mounted on a double war canoe.

As that week progressed and all of Kamehameha's forces had come to reinforce his position at Kahalui, the second gun wagon was still on the canoe. Despite the best intentions of both Haole advisors and the undoubted carpentry skills of Olohana, the second cart was still in sections. The wheel and the geometry of its construction, and the carpentry and steel work methods of the Western world (and tools, too), were too new and too scarce.

But Aikake led the twenty men of the musket platoon in daily drill with their weapons, with the mechanism of loading and aiming. And even a little practice with scarce powder and ball supplies was afforded.

Finally, Kamehameha made a decision and ordered both Olohana and Aikake to concentrate their efforts on beginning to move Lopaka, the single brass cannon, to position on the higher ground overlooking Wailuku. And they made sure that the gun wagon with its giant wheels was moveable and that at least eighty men were standing by to load, fire and move it.

Kamehameha's more than 1,200 men and more than 200 helmeted Alii marched in the usual crescent-shaped battle formation from Kahalui to Wailuku. With their banners streaming and the pahus beating, nearly a hundred men were pushing and pulling the brass cannon at the center, and a square of men marched with the steel gleam of twenty muskets in a platoon sergeanted by Olohana ahead of the brass gun Lopaka. They were a fearful sight to the beaten army of Kalanikupule.

The defenders, particularly the defending Alii under Kalanikupule and Kamohomoho, hung back and failed to move into the attack.

"The defensive," Kamakau writes, "was drawn up in a narrow pass in Iao, and the offensive advanced from below and drew up the cannon as far as Kawel-owelo-ula and shot from there into Iao and the hills about, and the men were routed. The victors pursued them and slew the vanquished as they scrambled up the cliffs. There was great slaughter, but mostly among the commoners: No important chief was killed in this battle."

The unique aspect of this Damming of the Waters battle in Hawaiian history is one never noted so far by any of the historians: that it was the first use by Hawaiians of the great Haole weapon, the cannon. The general who managed it appropriately was Kamehameha the First. And his vision here and in the remainder of his conquests in using it and expanding its use and other of the White Man's skills is certainly one of the large reasons for his being called Kamehameha the Great.

After the Battle of the Damming of the Waters, Kalanikupule and his remaining chiefs—Kamohomoho, Kao-lau-kani and the chiefesses in Kalola's train—were hurried over the high peaks of the Mountains of the Moon to join Kalola at her once-favorite beach place, Olowalu.

The pristine memory of Olowalu in Kalola's mind had been sullied by the brutal massacre conducted by the infamous Captain Simon Metcalfe, earlier that year of 1790. Kalola's prize and highest-caste granddaughter, the eleven-year-old Keopuolani, had probably been with her at that time too, and that dreadful memory was much a part of her psyche.

But for the moment, bad memories or not, Kalola was joined by her daughters and granddaughters and they made ready for a further flight, to Molokai as Kamehameha's wave of victory swept closer. Now Kalola was an old woman. Once Kamehameha's stepmother and probably his first lover, Kalola had been running scared these days as the conqueror moved from victory to victory over her father, Kahekili.

In the dreadful bloody scene of the Damming of the Waters in the Iao Valley, Kalola and the other Kahekili high chiefesses had been taken to the hills above the valley before the battle began, and had seen the defeat by the Red-Mouth Big Gun and the Muskets. She was sick and terrified.

Now, as the war canoes prepared to take the womenfolk to Molokai, she grew seriously ill. Relays of Kahekili's and Kalanikupule's kahunas kept constant watch—and chants and poultices—over her as the huge war canoe sailed that morning.

The night before, the night of defeat for Kalola, Kamehameha had of course celebrated as a victory, back in the old-time capital of his archenemy Kahekili. In the almost palatial hale where Kahekili had lived as king and most recently son Kalanikupule had held court, he held a long and intent council of war with his kahunas and his chiefs. By this time his imperial, imperious and fantastically beautiful favorite young queen, Kaahumanu, had joined her train to her husband's camp. Even the capricious Kaahumanu did not dare to inject herself into the kukui-nut-lit councils of the chiefs. But through her father, Ke-e-au-moku, she had already learned the best part of his conversation with Kamehameha on the rocks at Halehaku. And thus far she had not thought fit to object to Kamehameha's new determination to marry Keopuolani, Kalola's granddaughter. Kaahumanu knew well, as Ke-e-au-moku did, that to secure marriage with Keopuolani was one way Kamehameha could secure a son of the heavenly Niau-pio caste.

But Kaahumanu, though she was only twenty-two years old, was wise in the ways of men, and she knew that when the day's long battle and the council of war were over, Kamehameha would come to her hale, the hale of Kahekili's queens close to his own.

When he came to her, she could hear his still-limping footfall approaching. He still walked with an adhesion from the wound souvenir (pukana aloha, or memoir of love, he called it ironically). And that pukana had marked his already lined face with new creases of suffering.

She dismissed her chattering and giggling court girls of this night well before the mahina piha, the full moon. The full moon was fullest at about this time of the night, the time which the Haoles called "midnight."

She wore a short malo of white kapa (paper) intricately worked with a fine red pattern, and a red-and-white cape dyed with noni roots. She had chosen this cape very carefully with the aid of the court girls before she sent them away. They had giggled hilariously as she tried various drapes and folds of several capes, striving for the most intriguing combinations of breast curves. The attractions of her long and athletic legs, she knew, would take care of themselves from almost any posture into which she might fall. And Kamehameha would respond the way he almost always did—except on very rare occasions when he was too distracted by heavy kaumaha, the weight of silent worry. That could always happen and spoil everything.

She could not help a happy grin when she saw his battered face peeking around the corner of her hale. "Ipo Manu," she greeted him with her favorite pet name, "Sweetheart Shark." She touched her short, tip-tilted nose against his generous one, and smoothly converted that movement into the caress which the Haoles seemed to love so much, the kiss. Since the kiss was already such a central part of the Hawaiian game of Kilu, Kamehameha could not have accused her of having learned the kiss, or honi, from the handsome Kaiana. She knew that her ipo manu, Kamehameha, was already jealous of Kaiana. Sometimes, if her ipo manu were in too good a mood, she would taunt him with the fact that Kaiana was fun to have for a partner in Kilu. That was acceptable as a favorite game of the Alii, but one had to be careful how many honi one asked for when playing Kilu with somebody all the women admired like Kaiana, or how far one let those honi go when she had lost the game of bowls with the Kilu gourd and had to pay the forfeit.

Now Kamehameha looked pleased. "Maikai! As Kapitan Kuka used to say about other things, Excellent! Your honi—makes me young again."

"I hope I will always be able to do that. Besides, especially these days, you need to be young again. You should be very tired."

"A few fights. The worst one was with Kapakahili."

"I know. Does your side still hurt, like toothache, pakoni?"

Kamehameha almost smiled. Then he grumbled: "The trouble is: too many old wounds." Gently, her slender long fingers touched his right flank.

"Almost," he said, "you make it better by touching it." He sat on a woven mat and she carefully sprawled her long-legged figure next to him. Through the open door they could see the bright full moon.

"And where, Ipo Manu, do you plan your next victory over Kalanikupule?"

He thought. "Not him, but his father. Kahekili is the strong one still. If necessary, I will beat him in Oahu and finish him off. That is, if the god Ku is with me."

She had a strong practical streak. "Kikane, who knows the way to Kahekili, is here in Wailuku. Did you know, Ipo Manu, he could carry the message; maybe a black stone and a white one, so Kahekili could choose."

He walked over to the door. "Hmm. A good idea." He turned to face her. "But—Ipo Nani—there is something which must be done first."

She knew very well what it was. "Judging from the line in your face, it bothers you a lot."

Then he said it. "Nani. I told your father. I have a plan. Before I send a message to Kahekili." He realized he was beginning to sound idiotic.

"I must see Kalola." He blurted it out.

She was still smiling, now devilishly. "Why not? Yes, your stepmother and first lover, Kalola, has a granddaughter who has the proper bloodline to give you a Niau-pio son. A child of the high burning kapu, one so sacred that if his shadow falls on anyone of lower caste, that person must be burned. That is because two of Kalola's children had two daughters, and Keopuolani. So she fits as the proper mother for your son—of exalted caste."

Kaahumanu's dazzling smile grew wider. "Yes, I have brought you no children. You want to have a son and heir for those future victories which you are planning even now, Little Ipo Manu, Little Sweetheart Shark."

Kamehameha could see the anger rising within that brilliant smile. "Ipo Nani," he said desperately, "didn't your father tell you what I said to him about you on the rocks at Halehaku?"

Now she knew she had him going and the streak of meanness in her was determined to twist the knife a little more, to wring a little misery from him before the matter was settled—her way, of course.

"Yes, he said something. About your wanting to marry Keopuolani. Is that it?"

He was beginning to grow angered. "That is all he said?"

She was growing defensive. "Very little more."

And he was growing surly. He began to turn away. "Maybe we should just leave it at that. I am a grown man, a chief and a king."

She saw some of her ground slipping away from her. She hastened to retrench. "My Ipo, who grows angry so fast! What did you say that he did not tell me?"

"Never mind. I have said enough. Kalola was close to me and has always meant a lot to me, even when she has been an enemy in the camp of Kahekili. I am going to see her on Molokai—where she is going. That is enough."

Kaahumanu recouped with a favorite feminine technique. She smoothed his cheek with her palm. "Ipo, you have had some dreadful days. While the moon is full, let us go and swim—you and I, in our happiest place: Mother Ocean. Now. And forget everything in the moonlight. It's an easy walk down to the bay at Paukokaulo."

She turned on him such a dazzling smile, and the spontaneous drape of her cape over her smooth shoulders and breast was so overpowering to him that he grinned his particular and distinctive excuse for a grin, and kissed her. And he said as they went out the door: "You will always be my Queen. The Foremost, Mua Loa." It was what she wanted to hear.

Kaahumanu was amazingly like Kamehameha in her mental penetration and power and had, as he did, a rare drive and determination. Of course, her methods were more subtle and feminine. She knew well that he would probably use Kikane, the messenger and herald so familiar to Kahekili, not only for the message to Kahekili, but as the messenger to Kahekili's daughter Kalola on the way. Kikane could be told to stop off at Molokai on the way to Oahu, and to see Kalola—who trusted him as Kahekili did—and arrange for Kamehameha to see her.

That was exactly what Kamehameha did. He found Kikane, arranged for him to sail with three of his most imposing war canoes and an impressive contingent of kahunas, to stop at Molokai and go on to Waikiki and Kahekili. At Molokai, he would visit with the high grand-dame Kalola and ask her to stay there and wait for the visit of Kamehameha, rather than running back to the court of Kahekili at Waikiki on Oahu. He commanded Kikane to assure Kalola, who had been so close to Kamehameha as stepmother, aunt and lover for so many years, that he had an unending aloha, devotion and respect for her. Then Kikane was to sail on across the heavy seas of the Molokai channel to Waikiki and the mountain sentinel beside it, the crouching lion shape which he later called Leahi, or Diamond Head.

Kikane was carrying the white stone and the black basalt stone for Kahekili. Before that mission, he successfully arranged the visit to Kalola. So Kamehameha, taking with him his powerful war fleet of more than thirty-five large canoes, came to Molokai to see his great lady.

He landed at Kaunakakai, the largest settlement, his canoes spread along the shore for miles inside the reef. But there was no need for force. Kikane had done his work well; a splendid deputation of tall-helmeted local chiefs, without fighting men, were there to meet and welcome him. Included were many chiefesses from Kalola's royal party.

The chiefesses told Kamehameha that Kalola was mortally ill, that the kahunas believed she had not long to live, so he hurried to see her at Kala-maula. In her elaborate village ironwood hale she was struggling hard for air. The place had a hush about it as if others were afraid to make a sound that might intrude on death, while her stentorian gasps filled the room. Her large, ordinarily smooth body seemed to have sunken. It was a shell now for one of the great Hawaiian beauties and one of the great ladies. Even in her infirmity, there was an air of grandeur about her that came with her being a full-blooded descendant of the line of Ke-kau-like, Ulu and Nanaulu. Like our own most exalted elected office, this station of the highest-caste Polynesian blood carried its own aura of magnetism and strength, and in this case, beauty as well—even now in terminal sickness.

Because of the extreme and deliberate biological selection process practiced for and by the Alii chiefesses, including infanticide if the children were physically inferior, the noblest Alii were beautiful specimens in a large, selected tribe of athletes. And because the Alii women were in many ways the freest of all women in history, a woman like Kalola had been through many more affairs of the heart and many more childbirths and family complications than the most highly practiced and experienced livers of life in the royal families of the European world, including such adventuresses as Catherine the Great of Russia and the Empress Poppea. And now, when her death was expected, the richness, zest and proudness of beauty of the Alii chiefs were felt in the room like an essence.

Kamehameha, in honor to that essence, and to show his grief and respect for this woman who had been more to him personally than any other, removed his yellow feather cloak and came to her bare-chested, bare-headed and bowing.

"Kalola, Light of my Life for the Longest Span of Years and Aloha, Dearest to me of All Women, I ask you a final favor."

From the large husk of womankind in the swaddling of white and pink tapa came a sound within the breathing.

"Au," the voice said, "I—." And after another breath, "hani." That meant "to know something very well." She had a bright Alii brain. He had made the same request before, and she had denied it. He knew that and so did she.

Now, again between gasps for air: "You—want my daughters —and my granddaughters—for your wards." She turned to struggle for more air. Her breathing now had a hacking edge of roughness, as if these could be her final efforts to keep the heart going.

He looked straight into those large brown seas of softness which he had known when he was a boy, on occasional visits to his father's hale at Hilo. He remembered her beauty from those days, the warmth of those eyes, the incredible perfection of her smooth skin, the loveliness of her breasts, her long legs. But she had been only one of his father's wives, this stepmother, almost a stranger. Then, he saw her only rarely, and he remembered mainly the kindness of those eyes and her childish smile. In those days, it had been too early for him to know the meaning of her beauty in man's terms.

Then, when he had all the loves and miseries of a dawning man-strength, when he was concentrating every nerve to be a great warrior, and she had become foremost of King Kalaniopuu's wives (therefore his aunt), her soft brown oceans of eyes had a different meaning to him. Then they had taught him the meaning of woman: Those brown seas had spilled the hugest heart, the heart of lovers, over him in fulsomeness and complete generosity.

And she and another of Kalaniopuu's wives, Kane-kapo-lei, had taught him the meaning of the giving that women have with their bodies for one they love when childbirth comes; the kind of fulfillment it is for them that men cannot know directly. How that can be enough for women, but that then men want the child —and suffer something like what women suffer in childbirth if it cannot genuinely be theirs. One of the greatest regrets of his younger years had been that as a young and untried warrior, a stripling, he could not marry Kane-kapo-lei, like Kalola, his lover, his queen and his aunt, and claim the child and son, Kao-lei-oku, as more than a drop. That "drop" was tolerated and loved by Kane-kapo-lei and even acknowledged by King Kalaniopuu. But it was because he could not marry Kane-kapo-lei then and make the child really his own that he now wanted to marry Kalola's granddaughter, Keopuolani.

It was odd that Polynesian society, the freest society in history when it came to the affairs of the heart carried on by men and women, should have some conventions left, like that of the kingships and chiefdoms, which did restrict the freedom of even the least inhibited women in history, the Alii chiefesses. So now, to have a proper Niau-pio son and heir, he would marry Keopuolani.

He would have asked her, but she knew. Now, with some of the last gasps her body seemed to be capable of, she was saying so. And now, those brown seas of kindness had a glimmer of that love and warmth, even in that sunken shadow of a face and body.

Now Kalola came to it. "You—may take—my two daughters and—my granddaughters too—as your own." She reached out to touch his forearm and he wrapped his long fingers around her wrist. "But only when I am dead."

She gasped for air, struggled to manage a shadow of a smile, and added: "That, Pai'ea—will not be long. And—when you defeat my father—be gentle with him. As I have always been—gentle with you."

He looked once more into the soft seas of her eyes, and saw an ocean of the kindness which was glimpsed there beneath the other overocean of discomfort and struggle. He brought his cheek close to hers and touched as much of their faces together as he could. It was a time when, according to good Hawaiian form, he should wail and shout in grief at the expected loss.

But he did not. He stood up, trying this time *not* to sob, and felt a tear build in his eyelid. Because it was Kalola, he did not want the tear to break loose and run down his cheek. Yet it did, as he was leaving that room with its heaving, expiring shell of beauty.

On the way out, he spoke to Kalola's chief kahuna. "Is there nothing you can do to make her breathing easier?"

The kahuna was spare and ascetic, with a graying beard. "I am sorry, Your Majesty. There is not much time before lewa nu'u, the heavenly spaces."

Kamehameha turned abruptly. "Send a runner to me immediately. I will prepare for her departure from this world and from us."

His preparations were decided, as they had been these recent years of his maturity and power. He sought Kaiana and told him:

"When Kalola dies, there will be great lamenting. I will lose someone closest to me in blood and Aloha."

Kaiana said: "Many of the womenfolk in her train have already made plans for mo-epu-u, to have themselves disfigured in mourning her. Some only tattooed."

"Have any offered to have themselves strangled, to accompany her in death?"

"None I know of."

"Nor will I. But I want you to promise to do this for me: I will suffer for her in the fashion of our fathers."

"Your eye teeth?"

"Yes. You must promise to knock them out."

Kaiana was troubled. "Pai'ea, you have good, strong teeth. They cannot be replaced. You will need them every day in life."

"I must suffer much for her. It must be for long."

Kamehameha was leaving. "You must promise me that you will do it."

"I will, Pai'ea. When she dies. Maybe she will not. I am hoping."

"She does not want to live longer. I will try to talk to her again. Perhaps you will come with me. You are always a cheerful man and somehow you encourage people to live."

"I will come, Pai'ea." But before they could see her, Kalola had departed this life.

There followed a great rash of mo-epu-u, and other vehement mourning. Kaiana and Kamehameha's chief kahuna, Kalima, worked over the great chief, with chants and an iron woodworking tool and a wooden mallet. He lay quietly with no complaint and held himself motionless while they banged out two of his teeth.

The keeper of the royal spittoon was there to catch the blood and debris, and then Kamehameha planned with the relatives to send the daughters and the granddaughter, Keopuolani, on to the Big Island, to the security of Kailua-Kona.

Since he was close to Kalola and a male, and the rest of her entourage were females, he took charge, with the kahunas, of the preparation of the body. He went alone to hide the treasured bones and their great chiefess's mana in a cave in the hills of Molokai. He trudged up alone with the tapa package and came back two hours later, his face drawn with pain and deprivation.

And then, since he was Kamehameha, and deeply disturbed by the loss of Kalola and his own uncertain future, he sought out a lady in the train of women who was Ha-alou, Kaahumanu's grandmother. He had not seen Kaahumanu during this busy time, except in the kahuna's rites for Kalola. Nor, as yet, had he moved to see Keopuolani, now destined to be another of his brides and his sacred wife.

The mission of Kaahumanu's grandmother, Ha-alou, was to go all the way to the northernmost of the large Hawaiian islands, Kauai, to search for a renowned soothsayer, Kapou-kahi. Kapou-kahi, besides being one of the most famous of the Hawaiian seers, was a cousin of Ha-alou.

Once she found him, she was to make representations that Kamehameha was deeply troubled, and wanted divine guidance, particularly in the line of bringing final peace to his home island of Hawaii and the rest of the islands.

Meanwhile, his other messenger, Kikane, had traveled to Oahu and reached King Kahekili at his capital in Waikiki.

Kahekili's good-natured but unwarlike son Kalanikupule and his beaten chiefs had just returned from their great defeat at the hands of Kamehameha, and Kahekili had given Kikane an attentive audience.

Kikane had presented his two bowling stones, the two stones from the bowling game Maika, one black and one white. Kahekili, according to Kikane's report to Kamehameha when he got back to Molokai, said:

"This one [the white stone] stands for fishing, farming and the prosperity of the government. That one [the black] stands for war and death. Does Kamehameha want to go to war with Kahekili, and Oahu?"

Kikane had been carefully briefed by Kamehameha, and he said that Kamehameha had such a plan if necessary, that his fleet of war canoes and his army in it were very powerful and his intentions were serious.

Kahekili listened while Kikane laid out Kamehameha's plan that Oahu should be a part of a Hawaiian Islands kingdom, and that Kahekili should live under Kamehameha's reign in that larger kingdom. And that otherwise Kamehameha would come with his war canoes and his armies and do battle to the death.

Kahekili's answer was surprising. He said, according to Fornander: "Go, tell Kamehameha to return to Hawaii. And when he learns that the black kapa covers the body of Kapakahili and the sacrificial rites have been performed at his funeral, then Hawaii shall be the Maika-stone that will sweep the course from here to Tahiti: let him then come and possess the country."

But the devious Kahekili, never a man to be taken at his face value, was even then engaged in a plan which was aimed at undermining Kamehameha's power in the Big Island of Hawaii.

Back in the Big Island, one of Kahekili's allies in previous efforts against Kamehameha, Keoua of the Red Cloak, with Kahekili's knowledge and support, had taken advantage of Kamehameha's absence on Maui and Molokai, and mounted a military expedition into Hilo. He hit the territory adjoining the land he claimed as his in Puna, in the southern part of the Big Island.

Keoua of the Red Cloak, Kamehameha's cousin and the youngest son of the late King Kalaniopuu, had not only invaded Keawemauhili's territory of Hilo (allied, remember, with Kamehameha), but had fought and won a large battle against Keawemauhili at the town of Alae. And worse still, Keawe-mauhili,

Kamehameha's uncle, had been killed in the fighting and Keoua had taken over all of Hilo.

From Hilo, Keoua and his army had crossed over into Kamehameha's adjoining territory of Hamakua. He had overrun all of Hamakua and was destroying fish ponds and taro patches still deeper in Kamehameha's heartland, in Waipio Valley.

Kamehameha had this news in Molokai, and immediately he assembled his fleet and his army for the trip back to the Big Island. Before he left, Ha-alou, his messenger to the Kauai soothsayer, came back to Molokai and had a positive report to make.

She had saved time by finding the soothsayer, Kapou-kahi, on Oahu and avoiding the long further voyage to Kauai. And Kapou-kahi had responded with a detailed plan to insure Kamehameha's future on the Big Island. He told her Kamehameha must build a large heiau for his god Ku-kaili-moku, exactly next to the old heiau of Maile-kini near Kauai-hae. Then, said Kapou-kahi, he would quickly become supreme over all of Hawaii without losing any more lives.

So Kamehameha, Ke-e-au-moku, Kaiana and the sons of Keawe-mauhili had a council of war at Kaunakakai on Molokai and determined on two strong resolves: one to go back to the Big Island and wreak vengeance on Keoua the Miscreant before all else; and at the same time to make sure that the new heiau should be built on generous terms at Kauai-hae, for the god Ku.

Only then, as the fleet of giant war canoes were beginning to get underway, did Kamehameha go to see the ten-year-old princess Keopuolani. He went to see the little girl with her mother Lilila. He arranged to sail on the same large double war canoe with Lilila and the other daughter of Kalola, Kalani-akua, and, of course, his new betrothed, Keopuolani.

With the prevailing winds on the quarter, it was a sail of only about a day and a half from Kaunakakai to Kauai-hae on the Big Island. But it was a difficult exercise in diplomacy. He shepherded the two grieving princesses and their train of female adherents aboard this huge Wa-akaulua canoe, biggest of the fleet.

He managed to bring aboard also Kaahumanu and her father, his old comrade Ke-e-au-moku. He also essayed another major diplomatic effort by including his friend (and perhaps his rival, he guessed, for the favors of Kaahumanu), Kaiana, as one of the passengers for the trip. With Kaahumanu, Ke-e-au-moku and Kaiana aboard, he would be insulated from some of the shocks of bringing his future bride and her mother and aunt back to the Big Island.

It was always like being in a box of gunpowder to be on the same craft with Kaahumanu, let alone her hot-tempered father and the warrior whom she seemed to find so attractive—besides, of course, the ten-year-old girl who was going to be his next bride.

But one easing factor was the undeniable truth that the little girl was *not* beautiful. She was small and slight, Kamehameha thought, seeing her as she played with her mother on the center platform of the big pahi. It had been a persistent story that when the little girl was very small, her nursemaid had tried to make a secret change of her for another, healthier and more beautiful child. But—so ran the story—a wild dog of the kind used for food broke into the adjoining cribs and bit the beautiful baby quite badly, so that the change could not be made.

In a way, Kamehameha was not too unhappy with the fact that Keopuolani was *not* turning out to be a large and beautiful girl like Kaahumanu. Life was complicated enough without that; he thought of it as his empty tooth sockets ached. His heart still ached, too, over Kalola's death. And he hoped that Keopuolani would prove to be well enough to bear those children of Niau-pio caste that he wanted so desperately.

This night he sat on the steersman's platform with Ke-e-au-moku and Kaiana, and his chief kahuna, Kalima, under the rising stars of the Three Sisters. The men made ambitious plans for building the largest platform on the largest heiau for the god Ku that had ever been known in the islands.

CHAPTER 12

Bloody Keys to Conquest

WHEN KAMEHAMEHA reached Kauai-hae, his runners told him that Keoua of the Red Cloak and his advance-guard troops were in Waimea. That was the village a dozen miles up the slope from Kauai-hae. Kamehameha did not stop then to build the new heiau. He mustered his forces, including the cannon Lopaka on its big-wheel carriage, and Olohana and Aikake with their musketeers, and a force of nearly a thousand fighting men.

And Keoua, somewhat intimidated by the reports he had been hearing of Kamehameha's new invincibility, withdrew his forces from Waimea (the older name for Kamuela). He shifted his fast-moving advance guard back east to Honokaa to join up with his more sizable main army.

Kamehameha had trouble moving the big cannon, and the larger force of riflemen he now took with him from Kauai-hae and

Kealakekua Bay. Now there were at least a platoon of riflemen and more than two dozen flintlocks, scrapings of the best he and his chiefs had been able to get together from the ships which had come trading.

Keoua's runners reported back to their chief that with the cannon and the weight of the rifles and ammunition to slow the parade over the rough terrain, Kamehameha was slow in moving. Keoua took his time, and made elaborate plans with raiding parties who would attack the gunners and seize the cannon and the flintlocks.

But the slowness of Kamehameha's progress with the heavy Haole weapons worked eventually to his advantage over Keoua. With the extra time Keoua waited, Kamehameha was able to bring up an overpowering force of army. When Keoua's forces, spread out on the high plateau of Honokaa, saw the vast Kamehameha army arriving in sight with the brass cannon and the square of marching men with flintlocks, a wave of alarm spread.

However, the fiery Keoua had chosen his raiding battalion carefully and they were determined men. Keoua had a fevered consultation with Uhai, one of the leaders of the group, and they decided to fall back still further to Koa-papa, and let the cannon pushers tire themselves further. Koa-papa was close to the east coast of the Big Island, an open, sloping plain with a grove of coconut trees on the high ground at the south. Had they known more about modern arms and been more thoughtful, the Keoua army would have made their attack earlier. Earlier, they could have caught the cannon crew while they were still trying to manhandle their cumbersome weapon up a slope. At Koa-papa the Kamehameha army was moving down this slope toward the east coast and the Keoua legions were being driven back toward a cliff and the sea. Furthermore, the field at Koa-papa was perfect for the cannon. It was an open field of fire. The cannon could be set up in the edge of the grove of trees, where the cannon crew would be somewhat shielded from the spears and sling stones of the Keoua troops while they could pour cannonballs and shot on the Keoua army in the openness of the Koa-papa plain.

And that was the way it went. The host of the Kamehameha force came in a wide crescent-shaped mass, as on the Maui attack, with the Red-Mouthed Speaker of Destruction at the center. Just ahead of it marched the two squares of riflemen—by now a fairly bedraggled assemblage of sweating, brown-skinned warriors stripped down to fighting malos. Despite the best efforts of Aikake and Olohana, their marching by now left a lot to be desired by comparison with the precision of a British Square of Army or Royal Marine troops. But at least they had managed to convey their weapons to the battle site and in general, they were ready to fight.

Keoua foolishly had arrayed his troops in the classic wide Hawaiian crescent formation, across the bottom of the Koa-papa plain. They were a nice target. And Kamehameha, as at Wailuku, Maui, the first use of cannon by Hawaiians, dispensed with the usual form and did not go through the usual hurling of insults, challenges and provocations before the fighting began. Instead, at the urgings of Aikake and Olohana, he used the time to prepare the cannon for firing and to make sure, he thought, that the riflemen were charged and ready.

Without further ado, Olohana's loud bo'sun's voice barked out command to the riflemen drawn up in a rough double line, the first kneeling, the second aiming the long barrels over the heads of the first rank. "Ready—Aim—Fiah!" (This Royal Marine form, by the way, was soon rejected by the Hawaiians. The first rank did not like being showered with the firing debris of the second rank shooting over their heads.)

The plan was that the two ranks should fall back and go through the lengthy process of ramming and reloading their pieces, while the cannon crew fired their first rounds. Henceforth, the two ranks of riflemen would line up one on each flank of the cannon so that the firing could go on more or less continuously. Olohana's theory was that the one-two punch of the rifles and the cannon would undermine the morale of the enemy, and the simultaneous firing afterward would crumple it completely.

This theory did not work exactly as planned. It was true that the first punches were devastating: the rifle fire striking from such great distance and the mayhem of the grapeshot ripping so many bodies in Keoua's close-packed ranks. It was black magic, and at first, the whole crescent formation of Keoua's troops fell back, torn with the strike of remote power, the line ripped with the sudden downing of a scattering of malo-clad warriors all along the line—and occasionally a fallen red or yellow helmet or cloak marking an Alii among them.

The wide wedge of men did fall back at first. Then there was a shout from the center of the Keoua line. A large group from the center of that line was breaking loose, with war cries, charging up the slope toward the grove of trees from which the firing had come.

And as if in quick sympathy, from the rest of that line a horizontal rain shower of ihe spears and stones rose and sailed toward the grove where the cannon and rifles had fired. Like a cloud, the spears and stones sailed, while the attackers of the raiding group were starting up the slope. But unfortunately for Keoua, the range, while easy for rifles and cannon shot, was too long for the manual kind of weapon. All but a few of the spears and stones hit the ground well before the beginning of the poinsettia-shaped coconut trees.

And in the meanwhile, the cannon had pounded its distinctive kind of thunder again and grapeshot struck again into the ragged crescent of the Keoua line. But the group of raiders led by Uhai had detached themselves from that main body and were racing toward the grove, shouting and waving spears and battle clubs.

Kamehameha's nondescript riflemen were ready by this time to fire again. So were the cannon crew under Olohana. Both groups fired again, and again there was a ragged selection of carnage striking through the wedge of the Keoua main force. Yet the raiding party kept charging up the slope toward the coconut grove, their momentum unimpeded. They had not yet been hurt by the volley.

And a critical situation was developing there at the edge of the grove. After the first two volleys, the Hawaiians (and their

Haole advisers) were being reminded forcibly of an urgent reality in European war making: that the impedimenta of Western-type war, like ammunition and gunpowder, are heavy and cumbersome and must be provided by some kind of logistic system.

Kamehameha, Kaiana, Olohana and Aikake, though they should have known by now, were even then being shocked at the realization of the problem. Kamehameha and Kaiana had found their way to the Lopaka gun position and the two ranks of riflemen and found it a scene of desperation.

A hailstorm of spears and sling stones were beginning to bounce among the coconut trees, thrown by the advancing raiding party. Brown-faced John Young (Olohana), in tattered linen shirt and trousers, was bawling to Aikake and the cannon train:

"Aikake! What happened to the grapeshot and the gunpowder? I thought we had it with us."

Isaac Davis sprinted to him. The gun crew, brown, sweaty and malo-clad, lounged around the big-wheeled brass weapon carriage. So did the pushers, some naked and mud-streaked, their hair dishevelled, bodies wracked by the horselike efforts to drive the ponderous weapon along muddy trails into this, the rainy side of the Big Island.

Some of the Hawaiians, looking down the slope of Koa-papa, saw and heard the commotion of the raiding party, now growing close. Some had to dodge the occasional ihe spears and more frequent sling stones bouncing among the trees. And the wide wedge of conventional Hawaiian fighting men, malo-clad with a scattering of Alii in feather cloaks and helmets, were beginning to throw spears and stones now at the advancing echelon of enemy. Commands to throw, and the inevitable back talk of the troops, were ringing through the trees. Now some of the Kamehameha spears and stones were finding their mark among the raiding party. Many of them were falling, but they came on. The assemblage of Kamehameha warriors were realizing now, without a superior command from their chief, that something had broken down with the cannon and the other Haole weapons. They knew they had better fall back quickly on the older Hawaiian type of weapons if they wanted to survive the next few minutes.

At that moment, Kamehameha and Kaiana reached the Olohana gun position and so did Aikake. Aikake said: "Olohana—there is no more gunpowder in the back of the army! It must be there, but I can't find any!"

"Kalima is supposed to be bringing along the porters. Where is he?"

"I don't know." The din of the war cries of both sides was loud now around them, and the men's bodies were contorted everywhere with the effort and noise of throwing spears and stones. Stones and some spears were hitting into the position of the gun between two tall palms and there were grunts and thuds and protest sounds as men were struck and fell.

Kamehameha was demanding of Olohana: "Has the cannon broken?"

Kaiana wanted to know: "Are you out of ammunition?"

Now there came a shout and uproar and impacts and the surf roar of a fight as the raiding party struck the Kamehameha troops close to the position of big-wheeled Lopaka. The fierce hand-to-hand fight, impacting of bodies and war clubs, grunts with dagger thrusts and impacts, the swinging, bending and breaking of bodies and the lines of men, were suddenly raging only a few score steps from the chiefs. And it looked to Olohana as if the Kamehameha wedge of fighting men was bending and yielding at the edge.

He shouted to Kamehameha, in Hawaiian: "Better go fast, Sire. Wiki-wiki! Now! Before they get here."

Kaiana had the same view. "Pai'ea, they will be upon us in a moment."

Kamehameha flung off his yellow feather cloak and it was re-trieved in flight by his spitoon bearer. "No! We can beat them easily. This is only a small group! Very few!" He had his ihe spear and his shark-tooth war club in hand now.

And it looked as if he were right. Perhaps his example in forti-tude helped too. At any rate, the mass of his troops between him and the enemy buckled the other way, the desperate sounds of hand-to-hand were going on still, but the mass of bodies of the attackers was being bent and forced and jammed back down the slope. Kamehameha had been through many such situations before and although thoroughly war-scarred, he knew well that extra desperate reservoir of strength, punch and resolve that comes to a good fighter when it looks as if the opponent is winning. Experience had taught him that often in a time like this the enemy seems stronger than he really is: that he too may be making a desperate, last-ditch effort. And that it is the final will of the fighter that wins. Now Kamehameha moved forward, his momentum taking Kaiana with him. That moment, Kalima, the chief kahuna, came up, harried and sweaty, but somehow reflecting confidence.

He danced along beside the two giants. "Majesty. More gunpowder and shot are coming up! The cart had been broken in a ditch. Men are carrying the bags on their backs! If your soldiers can hold off the attackers!"

But that was not to be. Ahead of Kamehameha, another sigh, another impact of fresh fighting. More troops had run in from somewhere down the hill to reinforce the raiders. Now the Kamehameha line was being bent back again, toward the gun. And the riflemen, the line of them on each side of the gun, were only standing idly by, reduced to wondering what to do without ammunition. Had they been better trained and equipped, they might have fixed bayonets and used their long-barrelled weapons as pikes. But they were indecisive, inexperienced.

And Kamehameha by main force was carrying his knot of commanders toward the impact line, where the scrimmage of the hand-to-hand fighting flexed the participating bodies violently back and forth.

Now the fighting knot rolled toward the gun again. And Kamehameha and the others were caught up in its periphery. In seconds they were a mass of swinging war clubs, jabbing spears and uppercutting daggers. Kamehameha chopped down one opponent with his spear, fought off a second with his war club.

The fighting bulged back around the gun as more of the raiders jammed into the assault. Kamehameha was fighting for his life as a large warrior, wearing only a red malo, and bleeding from a number of wounds, clawed his way toward the gun. Kamehameha came bearing in toward him, swinging his spear to parry the strokes of the wide-shouldered foe. In the fighting, Kamehameha had lost track of Kaiana and Kalima, and Olohana and Aikake had also disappeared. He found himself alone with the big foe and another enemy who was jabbing with spear thrusts. This man was equally large.

It dawned on Kamehameha that these two leaders of the enemy raid might be Uhai and Kaia, two famous warriors of Keoua. But that moment, he also saw an Alii figure in an all-red feather cloak and towering red helmet, an enemy with an echelon of followers, who was familiar, painfully familiar, to him. It was Keoua of the Red Cloak and he and his followers were fighting well beyond the gun, deeper into the coconut grove, on the left flank.

And Kaiana came up too, from nowhere, close behind Kamehameha, the giant Hard Shell Crab, Pai'ea. Pai'ea saw the tall shape wielding ihe spear and battle club expertly, brushing Uhai and his friend to one side so he could stand by Kamehameha's side.

"Pai'ea," Kaiana said as they thrust aside a less distinguished warrior who was blocking their path. The two thrusts by ihe spears drove the enemy into retreat. "Good news—Olohana has found the carriers of the powder and shot. They will be up soon."

It was one of those gaps that always happen in a fight, reasons usually not known until some later analysis can make them clear. That analysis was that the raiding party were concentrating all their energies on seizing the Haole weapon, the cannon Lopaka. The sudden fact remained: Kaiana and Kamehameha were for the moment unopposed. To their right, a dense knot of fighting raged around the cannon Lopaka.

Kamehameha had another, much higher-priority target in mind, to his left. He pointed him out. "Kaiana—look—I see our enemy —Keoua—over there. Let's jump him."

Kaiana nodded. And in the quick look-around he noted one

other pertinent fact. "Something else good: the powder bag and shot carriers are coming up in the back! In a few minutes, we will have rifle and cannon support!"

Some of the wounded were still creeping and crying out in their agonies. They were being crushed out by Keoua raiders with battle clubs and daggers.

Kamehameha saw it all and changed his plan on the spot. "Let's get the Haole weapons back in action wiki-wiki. Now! With the cannon and the rifles we can finish them off."

Kaiana was already moving toward the rear, where the powder-bag carriers were dumping their heavy loads beside the two ranks of riflemen. The hand-to-hand fighting still swirled around Lopaka, the cannon.

But now a sudden disaster seemed to be happening in that fighting: The Keoua raiders were winning around the gun and the ground around it was strewn with mangled bodies, the ugly fruit of that fierce hand-to-hand struggle. Even now, the Keoua raiders were heaving at the gun to manhandle it around so it could bear on the Kamehameha forces.

"Let's get back to the riflemen and get them firing! Where are Olohana and Aikake? The riflemen can finish off Keoua's raiders wiki-wiki! Right now!"

Kaiana was already moving back that way. "They can't use the cannon on us!" he said. "They don't have any ammunition!"

Olohana, his usually calm, sun-browned face now sweating heavily, had appeared near the powder-bag carriers. He was pitching in to help them unload now for the riflemen. Kamehameha hailed him in haste: "Olohana! The riflemen must fire quickly! Now! Wiki-wiki!"

"Now! Great Chief! They can fire now."

"Quickly then! Hurry." Kamehameha could see that the raiding party had turned the gun nearly all the way around.

Kaiana said: "Pai'ea! They are ready!"

And Olohana's command rang out: "Ready—aim—fiah!"

One rank fired, more or less as a unit. Close in like this, within the grove, their fire was sharp, ear-splitting. Near the gun, in this point-blank range, a handful of the raiding party were suddenly thrown to the ground, as if by magic—the magic of the red-mouthed death.

Now the second rank was firing—raggedly. More men fell around the gun, and the first rank was loading again. And equally important, Kamehameha's conventional warriors had awakened from their wonder; they were attacking the ragged remainders of the raiders with spears, war clubs and daggers. The raiding party was ripped, torn and falling back now. The remnants were falling back, running down the hill, away from the grove. And the first rank of riflemen had moved up in a fairly orderly line and fired at the raiders who had detached themselves from the melee. Again, four or five fell. And the second rank, heartened by the success of the magic weapon in their hands, fired, too, and killed some more at a distance.

Kamehameha's conventional warriors, who had fallen on the raiders with such vigor when the firing started, hesitated once more. They stood again and were frozen with the wonder of the weapon. Then the cannon was charged and Olohana called the command: "Ready! Fiah!" The thunder of the gun boomed and echoed in the grove. And the grape-shot ripped ragged holes in the mass of the Keoua main line, just as the first of the pitiful remnants of the raiding party were beginning to reach it. Now the whole mass of that main line was beginning to give way, some men running in a sprawling mass toward the bottom of the Koa-papa slope and the trees there before the cliff.

Kamehameha was about to bawl a command to his conventional or old-fashioned troops to charge after the routed Keoua main body, but Olohana reached him first. "Majesty! We have very little more gunpowder and shot! You know, we are short!"

Kamehameha reacted quickly to the problem like the akamai field commander he was. "Fire as much as you can now. While they are running! Rip them! Make sure they remember their terror, their weli-weli. And Keoua must remember too. Remember so it shakes his heart! If he is still alive."

Kaiana reported: "He is not among the dead up here. He must have got away."

Kamehameha barked another command, to Kaiana: "Tell the spearsmen and sling-throwers to stay here. Let the red-mouthed death kill the enemy. Quickly. Olohana! Have the riflemen and cannoneers fire as fast as they can while the enemy retreats. Until the ammunition is gone!"

Olohana said: "It is wise, Majesty, to keep our people away. In this way we will not kill our own."

Kamehameha added as Olohana turned away. "Next time we will have nui powder and shot. Plenty!"

The once-proud host of Keoua was disappearing from the Koa-papa battlefield, except for the wrecked remnants of the dead and wounded farther up on the slope.

"Keoua," said Kamehameha, "will remember today for a long time. Until we finish him off. Let him think about it for a while, and perhaps he will come to us for peace."

He looked sharply around. "Where is Kalima?"

The words fell on a curious silence. It was Kaiana who broke it. He said gently: "Majesty, Kalima is dead."

The impact of the words shook Kamehameha almost visibly. "Take me to him," he said. "And I pledge to the god Ku-kaili-moku that I will build the heiau now, right now. For him. Before we fight again."

The ammunition was rapidly exhausted and more casualties ripped into the Keoua host, and the battlefield was mopped up as Keoua scurried away with his remnants in his canoes. Then, immediately, Kamehameha led his army back to Kauai-hae and started building the heiau for Ku. So urgent was the building operation that all of the Alii chiefs carried stones and poi glue for that massive temple—including Kamehameha himself.

Kamehameha's belief in the powers of his gods, and particularly mighty Ku, was strongly confirmed by the events of the next few weeks.

The temple was constructed in record time, and Kapou-kahi, the seer who had originally prescribed the building operation, was brought over from Oahu to consult on the work. And before this first part of the work was done, an awesome concomitant in chance had occurred. Of course, the devout ones like Pai'ea ascribed this success to the religious effort on their part and the intervention of the gods.

That intervention, a strange coincidence at the least, happened to the remnants of Keoua's army as they were marching across the interior of the Big Island. They were still retreating to the south, returning almost in a panic to his home in the southernmost district of the island of Hawaii, Ka'u.

Pele, the Hawaiian goddess of volcanos, is thought to be an independent force and a mighty (and seductive) deity in the Hawaiian pantheon. But in this case she moved as if she were a close ally of the war god Ku and Kamehameha, too. Keoua's army was crossing the volcano area near Kilauea, the army straggling across the gray volcanic ash and moonlike cinder cones of the Fire Pit, when Pele began to speak.

First, the hollow, harsh voice of the earth rumbled from the steaming craters. Then, tremendous columns of fire and molten rock exploded from the ground. According to Kamakau they rose higher than the summits of both Mauna Loa and Mauna Kea, both well over 13,000 feet high. A new hill of sand and rock, molten rock pushing more solid pieces, rose almost underneath the Keoua column. Scores of the soldiers were thrown down, burned to death or asphyxiated, and some were sucked into the fiery rents in the earth. The loss was catastrophic, and it included scores of women and children, the camp followers, wives and families following at the end of the train of warriors.

The eruptions did not end with the initial violent outburst. The heavings of the earth continued, lava columns erupted, ash and stone and sulfurous gases were violently thrown out for several days. And for many of the marchers, there seemed to be no escape. The whole area was rocked and ripped by Pele's fierce activity. Keoua and many of his Alii, at the head of the column, were lucky to escape alive. But the lesson of the volcanic forces, the power of the gods, was hammered into his head as into Kamehameha's.

Keoua was so depressed by this show of disfavor that he was reduced to a state of quasi-resignation to his fate of being extinguished and defeated. He gathered together the remnants of his army and made fresh levies of troops from the chiefs of Ka'u and Puna. Skirmishes went on between Keoua's forces and those of Kamehameha. But these continued to end in victories for Kamehameha and Kaiana, at Kalae and Kama-oa.

These were only skirmishes. The forces were small. As yet Kamehameha was without any major reinforcements of cannon, muskets and ammunition. Back at Kealakekua Bay on the west side of the Big Island, he continued to trade assiduously with all visiting Haole sea captains for muskets and gunpowder. He built his army and canoe fleet slowly and methodically while reports continued to come to him that Kahekili was mounting a large amphibious force to invade the Big Island and come to the aid of his beaten ally there, Keoua of the Red Cloak.

It was a busy time for Kamehameha. But there was time also for surfing and swimming and the other marvelously regenerative Hawaiian sports—much of the sport undertaken with his imperial-sized and beautiful queen, Kaahumanu. It was a happy time of preparation, hurry—and love. He said that much later, when he had grown old.

Kahekili would not leave him alone, however. Reports reached Kamehameha that Kahekili and Kahekili's half-brother Kaeo, whom he had helped to get control of the island of Kauai, had joined their fleets and amphibious troops on the island of Maui and were heading for the Big Island.

Kamehameha spurred his construction of canoes and the enlarging of his army, and he also reactivated his pious work of finishing the heiau at Kauai-hae (the temple now called Puukohola). The seer who had come to assist in the work, Kapoukahi, was given almost everything he wanted to make this the most splendid heiau in the islands.

And Kamehameha prepared for a major sea battle against the forces of Kahekili and Kaeo. This time he was better prepared with gunpowder and cannon: Now he had readied the *Fair American*, the sloop which had become his at the time he acquired Isaac Davis, or Aikake, as an ally, in early 1790. That was the time he had also acquired the brass cannon, Lopaka.

This time he could use the ship and all its cannons (including Lopaka, now taken from its big-wheeled carriage and put back aboard). Also included in the fleet were several large double canoes armed with cannons. Kamehameha was not going to be caught this time without all the mighty Haole weapons he could muster.

But the wily Kahekili responded in kind. This time he had secured several cannons on double canoes and some Haoles to handle them (it is not clear how many war canoes or cannons they had, but they certainly had no larger ships like the *Fair American* with multiple cannon armament). They did, however, have a Haole chief gunner who was called by the romantic-sounding name Mare Amara. Mare Amara was a semi- or hapa-Haole name compounded from Ocean and Armorer for perhaps "Murray the Armorer," and the gunner in question was evidently a sailor whom Kaeo and Kahekili managed to inherit. Nothing is known of him.

However, his talents were in vain in the sea battle which raged between the two fleets near Waipio, off the northeast coast of Hawaii. The superior firepower of the Kamehameha fleet, marshaled and directed by Olohana and Aikake, emerged triumphant.

There is an appalling lack of information among the chroniclers about this sea encounter. Fornander's account is characteristic:

No particulars of this battle have been handed down: no chief of any prominence lost his life in this engagement.

It is said, however, to have been sanguinary, and many lives and not a few canoes on either side were lost of whom Hawaiian fame had made no note; the artillery of Kamehameha seems to have been too heavy or too well served for his foes, as he remained master of the situation; and Kahekili and Kaeokulani (Kaeo) returned to Hana in Maui with their shattered fleet, and with no farther thoughts of invading Hawaii, fortunate if they might be able to defend Maui from retaliatory invasion by Kamehameha, which they certainly expected, and which they are known to have strained all their resources to frustrate.

Kamakau, the other old chronicler who was a contemporary of Fornander (half-way to three-quarters of the way through the nineteenth century), was even sketchier. He covered the events of the battle in a short paragraph. He sums it up by saying that it was indecisive, that Kahekili's and Kaeo's warriors all returned to Maui, and that it was Kahekili's last battle.

All historians agree, however, that the battle was called "The Red-Mouthed Gun" or Kepu-wala-ula or Kepu-wala-ula-ula. Also that Kahekili and Kaeo left with all evidences of defeat.

And the effect of that defeat was profound, on the Big Island. Added to his other reversals and the evident disfavor of the gods toward his cause, it confirmed Keoua's general depression and despair.

Kamehameha's military intelligence (or informers) continued to be good and he heard that his cousin and rival on the Big Island, Keoua of the Red Cloak, might be interested in talking peace. In fact, that he was so desperate he might even try omu-o, or cutting off the end of his penis, in recognition of the fact that there was no hope and he was about to die. This final desperate rite was also called "the Death of Uli" (Uli being the tutelary goddess of the priesthood who worked this evil on males by sorcery).

Kamehameha, emerging as a better and better diplomat, sent two emissaries to Keoua. They were prominent chiefs, Kamanawa and Keawe Aheulu. They went to Keoua and told him that if he would go to Kauai-hae to meet with Kamehameha, peace could be arranged. At the same time, "You two [Kamehameha and Keoua] shall then be the rulers," according to Kamakau.

Keoua agreed to go with the two chiefs, but evidently with a good deal more than misgivings. For he stopped with his war canoes en route at Kekaha (near Kailua on the Kona or west coast of the Big Island) and there, when he went to bathe, did perform the Death of Uli rite.

At this time, his counsellors (notably the durable raider Uhai who had survived the Battle of Koa-papa) urged him to kill the emissary chiefs and break off the mission.

But Keoua refused, and carefully sorted out his accompanying Alii and picked out those who would be "correct companions in death," or mo-epu-u. These he gathered in his most splendid double war canoes, and those Alii who he thought would survive he placed in another large canoe led by a chief whom Kamehameha would be certain to spare. That chief was Kao-lei-oku, or Pauli, Kamehameha's first child by Kane-kapo-lei, his aunt and the wife of King Alapai.

This child of Kamehameha's "beardless youth" had a special place in Kamehameha's heart, even though Pauli never could be given official status as an heir to his rank and title. In the odd give-and-take that occurred in the continuing hostilities between Kameha and Keoua, Pauli had moved to Ka'u and had come with Keoua on this mission of supposed peace.

When the Keoua canoes reached Kauai-hae, Keoua's worst forebodings were realized. When the Keoua party, in their most splendid feather capes and helmets, rounded the south point of Kauai-hae Bay, they saw the regal party of Kamehameha waiting for them on the beach. Prominent was the impressive and physically dominant figure of the Great Chief, further distinguished by his all-golden cloak and tall yellow helmet.

But the really disturbing sight, in the lee of the majestic mass of the new heiau of Puu-kohola, was a wide circle of war canoes, full of armed men. Some of these warriors were armed with flintlock rifles, and many of the canoes were armed with cannon.

As Keoua's canoes moved toward the shore, a group of Kamehameha's canoes surrounded Keoua's own craft and escorted it to the beach. The many conflicting accounts generally agree that a group of Kamehameha canoes evidently did have a special plan to isolate the canoe in which Keoua was riding, and take it in.

From then on, what happened could have been planned by

Kamehameha, or it could have been a spontaneous deed of the hot-tempered Ke-e-au-moku and some of the other top counselors to the giant monarch.

Much debate, written and verbal, has occurred about the morality of what transpired. But Keoua and Kamehameha had been at war for nine years, Keoua was a bitter foe of Kameha and a staunch ally of Kahekili, and the Hawaiians had a very liberal view of crimes of passion, even murder; provided, of course, that the kapus were observed.

At any rate, as Keoua's canoe came closer to the shore, Keoua called out to Kamehameha on the shore: "Here I am."

To this Kameha replied: "Stand and come forward so that we can recognize each other."

Keoua came forward in the canoe and started to leap from it into the shallow water. But Ke-e-au-moku, Kameha's close friend, right hand and relative, was there at the water's edge and with a short ihe spear.

With no warning, he thrust it toward Keoua; Keoua dodged, but Ke-e-au-moku got the weapon into its target and Keoua fell.

In a flash Ke-e-au-moku's followers fell upon the others in the canoe. Riflemen fired at them from the beach, then moved in with closer weapons. All in the canoe were killed, except for two. They were Keoua's kahuna, Kua-kahela, and a chief called Laa-nui.

Kamehameha apparently remained silent during this killing. But he noted the canoe of Pauli, the "child of his beardless youth," a little farther out, and called out to assure him that he would be safe.

However, Pauli was cautious, and perhaps rightfully so. His father was a fierce warrior with no trepidation about killing. Kameha accordingly, as reported by Kamakau, said: "Why should our child die, the child of our youth? . . . He shall be saved this day."

And to one of his chiefs (Kalani-mamahu) he said: "Proclaim the law and save our child."

So the chief called out: "Let live! Let live! No one is to die.

Let the captives live! The Law of the Broken Paddle is proclaimed!"

After that, Pauli's canoe was allowed to land, as were the other canoes of Keoua's entourage. And all the warriors and chiefs were allowed to live—as were the two men who had managed to escape from Keoua's canoe and hidden in two of the hales on the beach at Kauai-hae.

Kamehameha's party took the body of Keoua and carried it up to the heiau at Puu-kohola. There it was offered as a sacrifice to the god Ku. The seer of Kauai, Kapou-kahi, who had counseled and superintended the building of the heiau, amplified his prophecy of peace after the building was done: "War shall cease on Hawaii when one shall come and shall be laid above on the altar of Puu-kohola, the house of god."

But Kamehameha was not satisfied, whatever Kapou-kahi had said. He was busily building his canoe force and his army—cultivating the help of whatever European traders came to the Big Island to build his strength in cannon and rifles so that he could destroy Kahekili and really bring peace to all the islands. Meanwhile, he somehow found time to love and feud bitterly with Kaahumanu, largely because of her attachment for the handsome Kaiana and her other favorite playmates in the Alii kissing game of Kilu.

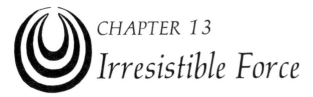

CHAPTER 13

Irresistible Force

THE ISSUE of jealousy over Kaiana and the other Alii gallants had arisen well before Kamehameha met the second great British explorer to the Sandwich (Hawaiian) Islands, Captain George Vancouver, in 1793. Vancouver was to play a part in mollifying some of Kamehameha's domestic troubles. He also tried hard to be a peace-maker in the Hawaii king's larger quarrel with Kahekili.

Vancouver had touched briefly at Kealakekua Bay in 1792, with two ships, the *Discovery* and the *Chatham*. But Kamehameha was not there during the few days the ships stopped. He was probably in the Hilo area, cementing his new domain.

Vancouver, however, did talk to Kaiana at Kealakekua Bay, on that 1792 visit, and as he moved along the coast of Hawaii, to Ke-e-au-moku at Kawaihae. The two chiefs gave Vancouver quite differing accounts of the war between Kamehameha and Kahekili. Vancouver distrusted Kaiana, but probably because Kaiana and his chiefs were very curious about the numbers of men Vancouver kept on deck watch at night. The *Discovery*, by the way, was not the same old ship Cook had commanded, but a new one.

Vancouver remembered well the troubles Cook and the other visiting sea captains had with marauding Hawaiian natives during the night hours, and he suspected Kaiana might be planning some mischief, like seizing the ship. Vancouver had served as a young officer during the Cook visits here and his mission was similar to that of the first great explorer of the Pacific. This time, he was ordered to pay particular attention to surveying the northwest coast of North America, but also to explore the Pacific islands, as Cook had.

That first visit to the Hawaiian Islands on this assignment, in March of 1792, involved stops at the Big Island, Oahu, Kauai and Niihau. But the whole visit covered only two weeks, including all the stops and the slow sailing between them.

At Waikiki, Kahekili's capital, Vancouver found the monarch was absent. His son and heir, Kalanikupule, explained that Kahekili and many of the chiefs were on Molokai, planning countermoves against an expected invasion of Oahu by Kamehameha.

Vancouver left for the west coast of North America. One of his great concerns on this visit was to find word of the whereabouts of his supply ship *Daedalus*. He had expected to meet the ship on the Big Island. But as of the time he left the Hawaiian Islands that March of 1792, there had been no sign of the vessel.

Thereby hangs a tale that shows how anxious Kalanikupule, like Kamehameha, was to secure more of the Haoles' magic long-distance weapons. The *Daedalus* reached Oahu in May, at last, and put into Waimea Bay on the island's north shore. Waimea, by the way, is a place name found on the Big Island, Oahu and Kauai. It means "Reddish Water" and refers to a river in flow colored by red earth. A shore party led by Lieutenant Hergest, the commanding officer, and the astronomer, Mr. Gooch, went to the beach to fill water casks.

Kalanikupule had told his chiefs that Haole weapons would be appreciated and their acquisition would be rewarded, whatever means were required to secure them. A local chief, Koi, saw his chance for distinction. The small party of Haoles looked like fair game.

But Koi's tactics of ambush were perhaps too timid. He and his henchmen decided to separate Lieutenant Hergest and Gooch from the rest by some beguiling talk of good trading arrangements for pork and yams. Two seamen went with the two Haole leaders. But the rest of the watering party was left at the spring, filling their casks.

When Hergest's party was somewhat separated, the mob of local Hawaiians began stoning them. They were knocked down. So was one of the sailors, but the second sailor got away. Meanwhile, the watering party broke off the job, ran to the boats and began firing at the natives.

The natives retired, dragging Hergest and Gooch with them, and bombarded the remainder of the watering party with a barrage of stones from the high ground. The Haoles had to leave, and when they came back the next day, they were told that Hergest and Gooch had been killed and their bodies divided among seven chiefs. Then another set-to developed as another stone barrage came, the Haoles fired their rifles, and the stoning grew so heavy that they had to leave.

The *Daedalus* sailed back to the North American West Coast and there reported to Vancouver. The episode increased Vancouver's already considerable distrust of the Hawaiians and particularly of Kalanikupule. From the Hawaiian point of view the venture was impolitic and netted only two rifles.

When Vancouver came back to the Sandwich Islands the next year (February, 1793), he came directly to Kamehameha's domain, and anchored in Kauai-hae Bay. Among his objectives was to bring the killers of the men from the *Daedalus* to justice. He was prepared to be very nice to Kamehameha, the foe of Kahekili and Kalanikupule.

And Kamehameha, becoming more diplomatic (and also even more determined) as the years went by, rolled out a sumptuous Polynesian version of the red carpet for the visitors. When the

Discovery and *Chatham* anchored at Kauai-hae, Kamehameha hurried to get aboard and deliver a personal invitation to Vancouver to come to Kauai-hae for an official welcome.

That welcome was impressive, with the same kind of precise canoe maneuvers Vancouver remembered from Cook's visit, but even more splendid and precise. And the presents of feather helmets and cloaks and hogs and other comestibles were equally lavish. There was so much food that Vancouver could not take it all aboard.

But Vancouver's presents were also lavish. He brought the first cattle to Hawaii—seven altogether—and Kamehameha was happy with the "large hogs."

Kamehameha was amiable. Vancouver found him mellowed from the last visit with Cook. "I was agreeably surprised in finding that his riper years had softened that stern ferocity which his younger years had exhibited, and had changed his general deportment to an address characteristic of an open, cheerful, sensible mind; combined with great generosity, and goodness of disposition."

Vancouver also met Kaahumanu, and at this point saw no signs of any enmity between Kamehameha and his favorite wife. Vancouver found her to be "about 16," although she must have been 24 or 25 then. He was also much impressed with her beauty. She "undoubtedly did credit to the choice and taste of Tamaahmaah [contemporary British rendition of that spelling], being one of the finest women we had yet seen on any of the islands."

Vancouver had no suspicion at this time of any jealousy or strife between Kamehameha and his favorite wife over Kaiana. When the British explorer came back in 1794, however, that jealousy had flared into violence. Of that, more later.

Meanwhile, Vancouver saw an apparently loving relationship between the big warrior and his *femme fatale* wife: "It was pleasing to observe the kindness and fond attention, with which on all occasions they seemed to regard each other."

At the first Vancouver anchorage in Kauai-hae Bay, Kamehameha took along on his visit not only Kaahumanu, but also a young lad whom Vancouver did not identify except as Kamehameha's eldest son, nine years old. Probably it was a younger son, Kinau, child of another wife, Hoa-pili. Obviously Vancouver's reference is a mistake, because Kamehameha's oldest son was Pauli, the "child of his beardless youth," who had rejoined him at the time of the recent killing of Keoua on Kauai-hae beach. By this time Pauli must have been twenty-five to twenty-eight years old—and it is interesting that he had dropped out of sight so soon after the killing of Keoua. He reemerged in the Kamehameha household later, but under a cloud always, partly because of the shadow of his birth to King Kalaniopuu's wife, and mainly because of having gone over to Keoua during Kamehameha's wars.

It is a significant sidelight on the marital and sexual permissiveness of the Hawaiian society that by this time, when he was about forty, Kamehameha had accumulated eight wives and uncounted lovers—not counting, of course, Pauli's mother, King Kalaniopuu's wife Kane-kapo-lei. Eventually, Kamehameha was to accumulate a total of twenty-one wives, and of course, more than fifty children, most of whom died. His sacred wife, Keopuolani, who brought him his highest-caste, Niau-pio children, had eleven children, but only three survived into adulthood. So high were the scores of disease and accident, in that environment and in those days—when the Haoles' diseases (even common colds) began to take heavy tolls.

As of this moment, Kamehameha had not yet married Keopuolani, though she was probably the "captive daughter of Kahekili" whom Vancouver observed when he saw Kamehameha's court. That "sacred marriage" was not performed until two years after Vancouver's 1793 visit.

Kamehameha entertained Vancouver sumptuously—and missed no opportunity to request firearms and Haole-type ships. Vancouver's supplies of arms came very grudgingly. He had been beseiged by Kalanikupule on Oahu and by almost all of the well-informed chiefs he met, for firearms, and he had steadfastly refused. Already he had lost one commander, Lieutenant Hergest, to the natives' cupidity for arms.

But Kamehameha, the diplomat, made a point of introducing John Young and Isaac Davis to Vancouver, and he made it clear that both of these British seamen had been well treated and emerged as noblemen in the Kamehameha court.

Kamehameha had already impressed Vancouver with his "great generosity, and goodness of disposition." And so far, Vancouver's experience in the domain of Kamehameha's enemy, Kahekili, had been anything but reassuring.

So eventually, Vancouver supplied some arms and helped Olohana and Aikake (John Young and Isaac Davis) to drill their musketeers. He also promised (and supplied) masts and sails, metal fittings, and expert help in building a Western-style ship, later constructed and called *Britannia*. Vancouver also seems to have promised to supply a man-of-war complete with brass cannon.

In return for all this, Vancouver had his own set of demands and negotiation points. He seems to have had a strong mental (and ideal) image of himself as a peace-maker in the Hawaiian Islands, and more important, the man who would arrange for the islands to become a colonial possession or at least a local ally of England.

Accordingly, he held a conclave of Kamehameha and his chiefs and according to the journal of Thomas Manby, the naturalist of the expedition: "Captain Vancouver was very urgent with Kamehameha to take this opportunity of declaring himself and his subjects, together with the whole island, under the dominion of Great Britain, but this he positively declined doing unless Captain Vancouver would promise to leave one of the vessels behind at the island to assist in defending him and his people against the inroads of their enemies, which was certainly a very strong and reasonable argument." But no agreement for a cession or deal with Great Britain was arranged until 1794, when Vancouver came back for his last visit.

That year, in February, Vancouver claimed a "cession" to the sovereignty of Great Britain had been made. He raised the Union Jack at Kealakekua and taught some of the chiefs to shout

"Kanaka no Beretani," "We are men of Britain." Exactly how much sovereignty Kamehameha thought he had given up, however, is another matter. Mainly, he wanted the British man-of-war which Vancouver promised him. But it never came, and the British government never recognized the "cession."

Meanwhile, Vancouver felt it incumbent upon himself to undertake a peace mission in 1793 to bring an end to the continuing hostilities between Kamehameha and the opposing camp of Kahekili and Kaeo.

First, he had long conversations about peace and ways of achieving it with Kameha. Nothing much was accomplished, except that Kameha, Ke-e-au-moku and Kaiana told the British captain what rough and despicable villains Kahekili and Kaeo were.

Then Vancouver went to Maui and conferred with Kahekili and Kaeo. They returned the compliment in kind. Kahekili and Kaeo and Kameha all seemed to agree, momentarily, that they would talk about making peace. Yet when the peace emissaries went from Maui to the Big Island, they were thought to be a raiding party and they were killed.

On the score of his supply ship *Daedalus* and the two murdered officers thereof, Vancouver had a somewhat more satisfactory result.

Kahekili had originally executed three members of the Koi group which had taken part in the killing of the two *Daedalus* officers. Now, at the insistence of Vancouver, he executed three more Oahuans. There was a trial on a double canoe moored next to the *Discovery* in Waikiki Bay, in the lee of Diamond Head.

Vancouver took much stock in the testimony of an Oahuan whom he calls Tohoobooarto, whom he believed especially reliable because he had made a voyage to China with some British traders and spoke a little English.

The three accused men stoutly denied the accusation, but Vancouver, who was in charge in the absence of Kalanikupule (he was ill), was satisfied that justice had been done.

Vancouver, when the accused men protested they were not guilty, wrote:

"This very assertion amounted almost to self-conviction, as it is not easy to believe that the execution of their comrades by Titeeree's (Kahekili's) orders for the same offense with which they had been charged had not come to their knowledge, or that it could have escaped their recollection."

So on March 22, 1793, the three men were executed with a pistol by a chief whom Vancouver calls Tennavee. The execution was carried out amidst the double canoes spread across the bay. This execution satisfied Vancouver, although Kamakau, who talked to several survivors of the *Daedalus* episode, writes that none of the parties who committed the murders of the two English officers was punished.

"Kalanikupule," he writes, "consented to put to death those who had committed the crime, but Kamomoho, whose man Koi committed the crime, refused to have Koi and his men killed for the foreigners. . . . Some other men were brought and put to death."

Before Vancouver left the islands, he saw Kahekili, Kaeo and Kalanikupule, and found them all in bad health, a condition which augured ill for their future before the onslaughts of the determined Kamehameha.

Of Kahekili, Vancouver wrote: "He came boldly alongside, but entered the ship with a sort of partial confidence, accompanied by several chiefs who constantly attended him.

"His age, I suppose, must have exceeded 60. He was greatly debilitated and emaciated, and from the color of his skin I judged his feebleness to have been brought on by an excessive use of the ava. His faltering voice bespoke the decline of life, and his countenance, though furrowed by his years and irregularities, still preserved marks of his having been in his juvenile days a man of cheerful and pleasing manners, with a considerable degree of sensibility, which the iron hand of time had not entirely obliterated."

Kaeo's poor health Vancouver also attributes in part to the use of awa. Vancouver remembered him from the days of Captain Cook's visits as a young chief. "But to my great surprise, on his entering the cabin, I beheld him far advanced in years, seemingly about 50, and though evidently a much younger man than Titeeree (Kahekili) yet nearly reduced to the same state of debility.

"If he were really the person I had considered him to have been I must have been much mistaken with respect to his age on our previous acquaintance, or the intemperate use of that pernicious intoxicating plant, the ava, which he took in great quantities, had combined to bring upon him a premature old age."

Of Kalanikupule, Kahekili's heir apparent, Vancouver wrote:

"Try-too-boory (sic) appeared to be about 33 years of age; his countenance was fallen and reduced, his emaciated frame was in a most debilitated condition, and he was so totally deprived of the use of his legs, that he was under the necessity of being carried about like an infant; to these infirmities was added a considerable degree of fever, probably increased by the hurry and fatigue of his visit."

All three of these rulers of the Windward Islands—Oahu, Maui, Kauai, Lanai, Molokai, Niihau—were to die within three years. The lesser two men, Kalanikupule and Kaeo, fell in the wake of the giant among them, Kahekili.

Kahekili died in July of 1794, at Waikiki. Undoubtedly his ailment was old age, somewhat aided and abetted by his fondness for awa, as Vancouver said.

In a development which seems odd today, Kamehameha allowed his two trusted chieftains, Kameeiamoku and his twin brother Kamanawa, to go to Oahu to take care of the last rites (and bone-disposal) of the dead chief. Kameeiamoku and Kamanawa were the two half-brothers of Kahekili whom Kahekili had earlier sent to Kamehameha's court as ambassadors-cum-kahus.

In view of the simmering hostilities which continued between Kameha and Kahekili, and the fact that Kameha was then building a vast army and war-canoe fleet to attack Kahekili, we with today's standards might be hard pressed to understand this kind of proceeding. But old Hawaiian custom and tradition would sanction it. The behavior of Kameeiamoku and his twin brother in going to Oahu to receive and hide the bones of Kahekili, and also the behavior of Kamehameha and Kalanikupule in permitting this—that was pious, by contemporary Hawaiian standards.

So Kameeiamoku and Kamanawa carried out their mission. They carried the bones of Kahekili to the Big Island and hid them in a cave at Kaloko, in the northern part of the Kona (west) coast.

By all rights, and Hawaiian tradition, Kamehameha also should have taken part in the hiding of the bones, since there was considerable reason to think that Kahekili was his father. But as of this date, Kameha had not heard sufficient reason to believe it.

As it was, Kameha went ahead full blast with preparations to invade Oahu and depose or destroy Kalanikupule. By 1795, he had assembled a fleet of about 500 canoes and an army of more than 15,000 men for the job. He had accumulated a battalion of riflemen drilled by John Young and Isaac Davis. Through skillful trading with visiting captains, he had formed a battery of cannon. He had appointed a British seaman, Peter Anderson, who had some experience as a gunnery officer, to command the cannons. And in return for ceding the island of Hawaii to Britain, Vancouver had built for him a British-style sloop which could serve as his flagship, the *Britannia*.

Incidentally, before he left the Big Island, Vancouver had successfully patched up the fight then going on between Kamehameha and the moon of his delight, Kaahumanu. Vancouver was scandalized to hear the court gossip about Kaiana's affair with Kaahumanu. It was odd that Vancouver should find it such a shock, for he had been exposed to the free-wheeling customs of the Polynesians in matters of sex and the love life for many years.

But following the ideal of the eighteenth-century gentleman of sensibility, and his own vision of himself as a diplomat and British patriot in the Age of Reason, Vancouver devised a surprise meeting of Kaahumanu and Kamehameha in the Master's cabin of the *Discovery*. With the connivance of Kamehameha, he lured Kaahumanu on board the ship, then brought Kamehameha into the cabin with her.

"They faced each other first with embarrassment, then agitation, for a moment not saying a word—then they fell into each other's arms, weeping, caressing and murmuring endearments."

On Oahu, in the wake of Kahekili's death, his heirs, Kalaniku-pule and Kaeo, had already fallen into squabbling over their shares of the spoils.

The trouble started when a prosperous British trading captain, William Brown, began to take his ships into Honolulu harbor, in 1793.

Brown was a man of great ambition, not too severely troubled, like many of his compatriots in the trading game, by conscience. Brown also had vision and imagination, and he was struck with the excellence of Honolulu harbor as a natural deep-water port.

Brown led his ships between the reefs of the south coast of Oahu, exploring a natural deep channel, and found inside a sheltered harbor with deep water, where as many as 100 ships could ride at anchor.

He made several successful trading ventures into this new harbor, which he called Fair Haven. Honolulu (Hono, or bay, and Lulu, calm) was the Polynesian name.

After Kahekili's death in July of 1794, Kaeo decided to go back to Kauai to see how his kingdom there was faring. But on his way there from Maui, he stopped with his assembled army and his war canoes at Waimanalo, Oahu. And Kalanikupule's generals distrustfully opened fire at the fleet and held them off shore.

Kaeo's riflemen, still led by his Haole gunnery officer, Mare Amara, fired back. And Mare Amara, who was quite a sharp-shooter, picked off one of Kalanikupule's top generals with an expert rifle shot.

In the interchange of firing that followed, the two sides killed a few more. Then Kalanikupule called for an end to hostilities. He came to the beach, at Kalapawai, Kailua, met with Kaeo, and they seemed to have patched everything up.

But as he prepared to leave from the west coast of Oahu, Kaeo heard of a revolt against him being hatched by several of his leading chiefs. To unite his armies behind him, he mounted a surprise attack on Kalanikupule.

He launched his assault from the Ewa side and his chiefs and army, attracted by the prospect of loot in the fertile valleys, responded enthusiastically.

Kalanikupule, outnumbered and outgunned, turned in his moment of extremity to Captain Brown and his two ships, the *Prince Lee Boo* and the *Jackall*, at anchor in Honolulu harbor.

Brown's ships were impressively gunned, and he made it a point to arm his sailors with the latest in flintlock rifles. Brown was a canny horse-trader, and before negotiations were over, Kalanikupule had ceded something—his chiefs seemed not to know exactly what it was—in return for the active military support of Brown and his sailor-army.

The vanguard of Kaeo's army reached the Aiea district, about where the huge Pearl Harbor installation of the U.S. Navy was built later, and there they met the temporarily larger force of Kalanikupule, reinforced by a platoon of Captain Brown's do-it-yourself marine troops and several of Brown's boats full of rifle-equipped sailors.

The mate of the *Jackall*, William Lamport, led the eight sailors scattered in small boats in the Puuloa arm of Pearl Harbor bay.

The Kalanikupule forces in the Puuloa vicinity and the water-borne sharpshooters of Captain Brown's navy harassed Kaeo. This time Kaeo's Haole gunnery officer, Mare Amara, was unable to work any sharpshooting miracles.

Instead, the Kalanikupule forces crowded the invaders toward the sea and chopped them up. Some of the Kaeo forces, led by Kaeo himself, escaped to the high ground. But Lamport's sharpshooters spotted his brilliant yellow feather cloak and helmet and fired at him, and the slower-moving conventional forces closed in on him and killed him and seven of his leading chiefs, and captured some of his wives.

Now, Kalanikupule was blinded by a sudden rapacious cupidity for possession of the array of cannons and rifles in Captain Brown's private army and navy.

On January 1, 1795, Kalanikupule's warriors struck on board the two Brown ships. They killed Brown, his second-in-command, Captain Gordon, and several sailors. They seized the small arms and ammunition stores of the *Jackall* and the *Prince Lee Boo*, and strung Captain Brown's naked body on a pole. At gunpoint, they forced the mates of the two ships, George Lamport and William Bonallack, to get underway.

By this time, Kalanikupule, with his wife and a reinforcement of warriors (bringing the total to about forty), had come aboard the two ships. Kalanikupule ordered the two mates to sail down the coast to Waikiki. His army would follow in their war canoes. At Waikiki, he planned, he would provision for a major expedition against Hawaii and Kamehameha. And with the advantage of more than thirty cannon, an arsenal of rifles and two formidable Haole ships, he would teach his rival a final lesson.

But he had not reckoned with the resourcefulness and fighting spirit of Lamport and Bonallack. Lamport found a sailorman's excuse for heading out to sea (he had to tack against the trades). Then he and his surviving crewmen, armed with rifles and differing from the natives in that they knew how to use them, drove the natives overboard. They retook control of the ship. Bonallack did the same, and now they commanded the situation because they had their cannons and their rifles again.

They embarked Kalanikupule and his favorite wife and leading courtiers in a canoe and set sail for the Big Island.

Then, arriving at Kealakekua Bay, they traded some of their arms to Kamehameha, left a terse note for John Young and Isaac Davis, and sailed for Canton.

Kamehameha knew that the time was ripe for him to strike against Kalanikupule. Kameha was at his strongest and Kalanikupule had been reversed and humiliated.

In early February of 1795, with the usual logistics bustle attending such a mobilization of men, Haole arms, canoe-power, and small European-type ships, the Kamehameha fleet embarked from the Kona shores, the bays and beaches between Kealakekua and Kauai-hae. They headed for Lahaina and Kaanapali on the

West Maui seaside. In the fleet, Kameha took the usual assortment of favorite wives—including Kaahumanu and his bride-to-be, the fifteen-year-old Keopuolani, and her mother, Lilila.

The invasion fleet darkened the rim of Lahaina Bay with its sheer size, and the lieutenant whom Kalanikupule had appointed to defend the island rapidly received the clear visual input signal. Without ceremony, this worthy, named Koa-lau-kane, took off with his leaders for Oahu.

From there, this last conquest at Maui was a walk-through for Kamehameha's overwhelming force. The invading army took what provisions they wanted and swept on to Molokai.

This too was a bloodless conquest. Kamehameha paused to map a plan for the conquest of Oahu and Kalanikupule. And here, his once staunch friend and ally, Kaiana, made secret and dangerous plans to defect. Kaiana, the bold, sophisticated and handsome lover of Kaahumanu, had noted that he and his closest friends were being studiously left out when Kameha held his top war councils. It was clear that many of Kameha's oldest and most trusted chiefs (viz., Ke-e-au-moku, Kameeiamoku and Kamanawa) were Kaiana's bitter enemies.

Not only did they distrust him because he was an outsider (from Kauai), but they disliked him and were intensely jealous because he was so handsome and dashing (a dandy, in fact) and because he so easily attracted and won over whatever females he met. Also, the enemy chiefs were vastly jealous because he spoke the Haole language, had traveled with the Haoles to China, and because he got on so well and easily with the Haoles (and understood their weapons too).

So Kaiana marshaled his leadership in secret meetings in a grass hale near Kealakekua, and they agreed that on the last lap of the conquest of Oahu, the route across the rough Molokai channel, they would be separated, and sail to Kailua on Oahu. There they would turn over to Kalanikupule their forces—which they reckoned at a fifth to a quarter of Kamehameha's army.

It was a major project to spread the word to all the subcommanders—and a touchy one too, because if a word leaked to

Kameha they would all be dead. Kaiana's leaders therefore trusted only those who were impeccable in their loyalty. And thus, when they purposely got lost in the Molokai channel and steered away from the rest (stormy weather in the channel was a good cover-up), they ended with a good deal less than a fifth of Kamehameha's massive army.

Kaiana did not know the intricate details of Kameha's battle plan. But he did understand the general outline: that the invasion fleet was to land on Waimanalo Bay, on the east side of Oahu, and from there make a flanking attack on Kalanikupule's capital at Waikiki, about eighteen miles to the west.

The Kaiana force was properly lost in the Molokai channel span; they reached the beach at Kailua just about the time Kameha's main force landed at Kaupo. Kaupo was a neophyte surfers' beach in the Waimanalo strip, seven miles to the south of Kailua.

Kalanikupule rapidly heard of the arrival of Kamehameha's vast invasion fleet at Waimanalo. He also heard that Kameha this time had a formidable force of riflemen, and many cannons mounted on wheeled carriages.

Kalanikupule, a friendly (and perfidious) personality, had never been a valiant or accomplished leader in war. As a matter of fact, in previous encounters with Kameha, he had always sent some other chief to lead his armies, and each time Kameha had beaten him badly. Accordingly, he put off any counterattack against the landing of the Hard Shell Crab, Pai'ea.

And he welcomed the defector, Kaiana, and his troops, with as regal a welcome as he could manage. He was disappointed to find that Kaiana had not appropriated many of the Haoles' golden weapons from Kameha's store. But the fighting men Kaiana had brought would be very valuable in the face of Kameha's overwhelming force. Probably there were more than 1,500 troops and Alii chiefs in Kaiana's force, and he had brought at least a handful of the much-desired red-mouthed rifles.

None of Kameha's Haole advisors with whom Kaiana was supposed to be so friendly had come with him. By this time, Kalanikupule had heard that Kameha had sixteen Haole military advisors attending him. Actually, when his armada sailed from the Big Island in that February of 1795, Kameha had twenty-nine Haoles living at his court. He had given them lands and the privileges of the Alii (including Hawaiian wives and sweethearts). And it was certain that he made use of all of their knowhow on military matters which his eager brain could perceive. For example, he had gained enough knowhow to have rigged a battery of mobile cannon on hand-hewn wagons or carriages. He had correctly estimated that the sheer size of his invasion force would bowl over the remaining slight opposition at Maui and Molokai.

Now Kameha took his time about preparations for the final assault on Kalanikupule. His forces set up a wide network of camps at Waimanalo. He correctly estimated that Kalanikupule's warrior's heart would be of the chicken variety. And he rapidly learned that in his defection, Kaiana had not made off with more than eight or ten rifles—and no cannon.

As a safety measure, he manhandled a couple of his cannon ashore, but left the rest of his battery in his thirty-six-foot flagship *Britannia* and in a couple of large double canoes. His expectation evidently was that the fastest and easiest way to move these heavy weapons to Waikiki would be by sea. A concomitant assumption was that if Kalanikupule should offer a battle before Waikiki, on the rough trails along the south coast of Oahu, he would be able to run his cannons ashore at what is now called Sandy Beach or at Hanauma or Maunalua Bays on the way.

But the Hard Shell Crab's estimate was correct. His invasion force encountered no resistance at Waimanalo and they moved by sea to a large-scale landing at Maunalua Bay and Wailupe, to the east of Diamond Head and Waikiki.

Then they moved boldly on to Waikiki, and oddly enough, Kalanikupule did not defend his capital. He withdrew inland, probably waiting for Kaiana to come over the Nuuanu Pali Pass from Kailua, and join him.

Kamehameha did not stop to enjoy the luxury of Kalanikupule's capital at Waikiki. Instead, he drove on against the retreating forces of his enemy—up the slope rising toward the Nuuanu Pali Pass. That gateway to the windward side of the island, to Kailua and Kaneohe, was the trail up the Nuuanu Highland.

This time, Kalanikupule was planning well—possibly because Kaiana was now advising him. And Kamohomoho too was an astute general. Kalanikupule's plan was to leave Waikiki in Kameha's hands, and retire up the steep slope toward the windy Nuuanu Pali Pass. His thinking evidently was that Kameha's great weapon advantage, his cart-mounted cannons, would disappear as his warriors had to transport the massive weapons up the rough Nuuanu trails.

But Kalanikupule evidently undervalued three essentials in his calculations: first, Kameha's well-trained platoon of riflemen with their long-distance, terrifying and portable killing capacity; second, the thorough preparations—double-size work crews—detailed to keep on moving the cannons no matter how rough the trail grew; and third, the sheer, overwhelming numerical superiority of Kamehameha's conventional army.

Another factor which Kalanikupule might have underestimated was the ultimate consideration of what might happen to him and his troops if Kameha's juggernaut did drive them up the Nuuanu slope to the Pali Pass. Because here, where there is a breathtaking view of the jagged green volcanic peaks of Kaneohe and Kailua to the north, there is also a long and very steep precipice tumbling to the lowlands. Beaten troops in panic might not find time to search for the hairpin trails around the cliff—especially if they were terrified by expert rifle fire, and demoralized by defeat amid the howling winds of Nuuanu Pass.

Yet in the exigency of the assault, Kalanikupule adhered to his plan. On the way up the green Nuuanu slope, he and Kaiana had hurriedly built several stone walls where they might have some protection against the red-mouthed rifles of Kamehameha. And he deployed his forces in a wide and thick crescent, the conventional Hawaiian military formation, across the span of foothills rising to the north of Waikiki and Honolulu.

But the Kamehameha juggernaut would not be denied; up

through the rich valleys with their lush green crops of taro, bananas and sugarcane they surged. And Kameha cleverly drove hard on his right flank to compress the enemy into the Nuuanu valley. There the legion of Olahana's and Aikake's sharpshooters easily drove their enemy into a panic. The rich lowlands—rich with what Kamakau called "the fat things of the land"—were strewn with the bloody human wreckage left by the red-mouthed rifles and the spears and stones of Kamehameha. And the bulk of his artillery—probably no more than four or five cannons on carts as Peter Anderson's battery struggled up the slope—were fortunately or perhaps by Kameha's design concentrated in the narrowing Nuuanu draw that led up to the precipitous Pali Pass.

By the time the bulk of the Kameha force had reached what is now the vicinity of Old Pali Road, their enemy was falling back, a disordered, shouting, bloody host, in almost a rout.

At one of Kalanikupule's improvised stone walls, near the present Old Pali Road, Kaiana and Kalanikupule, and a sizable echelon of troops and commanders, chose to make a determined stand. They did not know that it was going to be their last.

Kamehameha's main body of troops, with two cannons, was moving up the Nuuanu Pali draw. And as the Kaiana-Kalanikupule high command dug in behind the stone redoubt, the Kamehameha force had to slow down while 200 dusky, malo-clad warriors sweated and struggled to move a cannon up the center of the trail. It was the veteran brass weapon Lopaka. For five years it had been kept in functional order through the efforts of John Young, who had secured powder solvent, brass polish and other necessities through trading efforts with visiting sea-captains. Now, although the weapon was spotted with the April mud of the trail, it still shone like a brass uniform button.

Now Young and Peter Anderson directed their struggling, shouting gun crew as they muscled Lopaka on its big-wheeled carriage into position. As before at the battle of Koa-papa on the Big Island, there were a large group of cannon-pushers who moved the weapon about and a smaller, trained gun crew to do the tamping, loading, aiming and firing.

This time, however, the gun-moving crew was twice as large as before, and the gun-firing detachment better trained. Accordingly, the shining weapon moved and operated with more speed. Now it was a center jewel in a wide, straining mass of muscular brown bodies. John Young and Peter Anderson superintended as the weapon was trimmed and oriented on a level place in the trail. Above them, 200 yards away on the same trail, they could see the irregular wide wall of dark volcanic rocks in a grove of koa trees. Behind the wall, a large crowd of Oahu soldiers clustered, and they bulged behind, up the slope and raggedly beyond both ends.

This distance was well beyond the range of the Oahuans' spears, but an easy reach for the four-pounder load of the brass cannon Lopaka. Young took his time. In a sense the enemy were sitting ducks for him—if they did not decide to attack—or if they did not have rifles. He was concerned now about his rifles.

"Peter, did you see where our rifle platoon is now?"

Anderson, a raw-boned, lean man with sandy hair, said: "Olohana, I saw a squad of them a half-mile back, on the trail."

Olohana said: "Good. They should be here soon. It would be easy killing range for my long-barrelled flintlocks."

Anderson grinned. "Doubly easy for Lopaka."

He barked at the gun crew: "Are you loaded and aimed?"

A huge Polynesian gun-crew chief smiled a brilliant white grin. "Ready to make plenty pilikia over there."

Olohana said: "Better have them aim for the center of the wall. Probably that is where the highest ranking Alii will be. Perhaps Kalanikupule himself."

Anderson said: "And while we are at it, let us hope for Kaiana, Kaiana's brother, and all of Kalanikupule's leading generals."

It was odd that his off-hand estimate was nearly correct. Behind that section of wall at that moment were Kaiana, his brother Nahi-olea, and Kalanikupule and his brother Kao-lau-kani. It was a good thing for the fortunes of Kamehameha, perhaps, that Olohana and Anderson did not know what big-game bullseyes they were preparing to target, or they might have hurried too much.

By the time the gun crew had charged and aimed their weapon, the missing squad of riflemen had appeared near it. Olohana took charge of them and ordered them to load their pieces.

He carefully scanned the rocky redoubt, looking for any sign of the bright feather cloak or helmet of an Alii above the wall. But Kamehameha with his infatuation for the long-kill Haole weapons had taught the Kalanikupule high command that concealment is the better part of valor when facing the long strike of a rifle. The agglomerations of people protruding beyond and to the sides of the stone wall were ordinary fighting men in the brief malos of kanakas, or commoners.

"Fire at the kanakas you can see in your sights. Remember, fire at one man at a time."

He saw that they were ready, and called out: "Ready. Aim. Fi-ah!"

The ten rifles barked almost as one, and above the rim of the wall where the slope of the hill rose, a handful of Oahu soldiers fell. The crowd buckled where the men tumbled, in a kind of eddy in the wake of the striking bullets. And the air carried the faint shouts and moans of the wounded.

"Reload!" Olohana commanded. And he said to Anderson: "As marksmen, they have improved greatly."

"Almost military," said the sardonic Anderson. But he was at that moment concerned with his own military enterprise. He hurried to the brass barrel of the field piece, bent to squint at the sights, and stood to command:

"Ready! Fiah!"

The big weapon beat out its local thunderclap, and with a blast of orange fire sent it echoing in the corners of the narrowing Nuuanu valley. The charge of grape shot ripped the sweet air of the valley. Smoke and the smell of powder rolled among the gun crew. And among the visible mass of people on the slope above the wall, the crowd surged with the impact. Men had fallen and this time the shouts and screams afterward were more insistent.

"That charge hit 100 feet beyond the wall," Olahana said.

"You'd better come down a mil or two and you can breach the wall—with solid cannon ball."

The sounds—wails and shouts—in the wake of casualties were still reaching them from the wall. The mob of brown bodies bulging around the wall had been broken into knots of excitement agglomerating around the wounded and dead. The first charge fired into the vicinity of the wall had raised havoc. Since it struck, the decibel level of the outcries and shouts had stayed up. The cannon and its sudden wide devastation had struck rampant fear into the Oahuans. There was no escaping it and without cannon of their own, they were hopeless and frantic. Since Kamehameha had landed with his cannons and rifles, and they had none with which to fight back, their fear had grown to terror.

"Load with ball this time," Anderson told his gun crew. They carried a solid cannonball to the muzzle of the gun and rammed it home in the barrel. And Olohana's rifle squad had loaded their pieces. "Ready to fire, Olohana," said Moki, the big lance corporal appointed by Olohana who led them.

That moment, a new sound reached them from lower in the valley. It was the distant, reverberating thunder of pahus. The two Haole commanders looked down the valley and saw a wide host of marching men, spread across the green expanse of fields, yams, trees and sugarcane. The banners and the towering god images of the kahunas moved at the center. Near them, the lumbering shapes of two cannons on large-wheeled carts, and a mob of cannon pushers moving them.

But a kind of advance flood of these reinforcements were already reaching them: more soldiers in small red malos, with spears and slings, and Alii with red, yellow and black feather capes and helmets.

"Kamehameha always comes through with overwhelming force," said Anderson.

"The Oahuans could have overrun us just now."

"If they hadn't been so demoralized."

Moki, with brown, wide shoulders and tapered small waist, the characteristic build of the swimmer-surfer, stood beside Olohana.

"Ready to fire, sir."

Olohana faced the rank. They were on one knee, rifles ready. "Aim at one man! Fiah!"

The volley blasted. Anderson jumped to the cannon, bent over and squinted through the sights. He pushed at the ratchet controlling elevation, struggled with it, looked through the sights again. The crew watched him respectfully.

"Ready to fire!" he barked out.

The fuse was lit. The cannon blasted with an earth-shaking din that made the crack of the rifles seem picayune. The crash of the cannon echoed in the valley and the gun crew was flooded with the usual sudden inundation of smoke, the smell of sulphur.

Olohana and Anderson peered through the dissipating smoke cloud. "This time we really smashed it," Anderson said. The boulders near the center of the wall had been tossed agley as by a big iron fist. Again there were a handful of people in that mob who had been thrown to the ground and ripped by the flying rock fragments. Beyond the rent in the wall, the mob of brown bodies this time was falling back, moving up the slope. And their outcry was like the last, struggling gasp of a dying man.

That moment, the towering, regal figure of Kamehameha appeared beside the cannon. With him stood the still athletic figure of Ke-e-au-moku. Now, Ke-e-au-moku's responsive face had grown more seamy with age, his reddish-tinted black hair seemed to have picked up a grayish cast. And Kamehameha, still quick-moving in his tigerlike warrior grace and strength, walked with a slight limp. Like most Hawaiians', his skin, although he was in his early forties, showed remarkable health and elasticity.

His driving energy seemed undiminished. He squinted up the hill, shading his eyes in the sun. "Olohana," he said. "A few more shots and they will be pau. They will run."

"I think so, Sire."

"Good. Fire as much as you can. Make them makau—afraid of our hardness."

By the cannon, Anderson called out to his gun crew. "Ready. Fiah!" The cannon blast shook the earth. The gun belched orange fire and smoke and violently jerked back on its carriage. And smoke and the pungent smell of burned gunpowder rolled over those around it.

"I like the smell of the gunpowder," said Kamehameha. "And I give thanks to Ku-kaili-moku for the Haole weapons."

Ke-e-au-moku squinted through the dissipating smoke toward the stone redoubt up the slope. "There is a pass through the middle of the wall," he said. "We have broken it."

Kameha too surveyed the wall. "Yes, Popo-ahi," he said, using his nickname for his combustible father-in-law, meaning approximately "Fireball." He went on. "But before you charge it— wait until the bulk of the army has caught up with us. Then, perhaps the enemy will have fallen back and left his dead. And there will be fewer dead on our side."

"Pai'ea," said the Fireball, "you are growing cautious in your old age."

Only an old friend, close relative and brave man like Ke-e-au-moku would have tried such a dangerous joke with the greatest warrior of the islands.

But Kamehameha answered him in good nature, like the long-time crony he was. "Not old yet. But old enough to know that ten men can always beat one," he said. "Especially if the ten also have Haole weapons."

Ke-e-au-moku's dazzling, white smile flashed. His grin, like that of his beautiful daughter, came like lightning to illuminate his face. Like the teeth of most Hawaiians, his were nearly perfect. Most Hawaiians had beautiful teeth, unless they had been bashed out in war or accidents, or self-inflicted mortification in grief over the death of a loved one. Kameha's eyeteeth were gone since his self-destruction over the death of Kalola.

"So be it," he said, using one of the phrases of the famous Kapitan Kuka. "We will wait for reinforcements and save lives." He squinted toward the smashed wall. "But I will bet you that in the wreckage of that wall, you will find Kalanikupule, dead or alive."

CHAPTER 14
Triumph—and Doubt

K E-E-AU-MOKU was almost right. Among the disordered stones and bodies of that barricade, not Kalanikupule but Kaiana and his younger brother Nahi-olea already lay dead.

And among the dead along that wall were more than a dozen of Kalanikupule's courtiers and leading generals. But under the onslaught of the cannon and rifles, all the rifles and the overwhelming mass of Kameha's conventional forces, the bulk of Kalanikupule's forces had left—including Kalanikupule.

But the withdrawal was not under control. It was much more a rout than a withdrawal. Kamehameha's war machine almost with ease was driving the survivors up the narrowing valley of Nuuanu toward the pass.

The Kamehameha bulldozer had no wide contention at all as they pushed toward the windy Pali peak—only pockets of resistance where a local commander could spark a fight until his group was wiped out.

Some of the soldiers—including Kalanikupule—took off individually or in small groups, struggling up the heavily forested narrow trails over the jagged Koolau peaks. The bulk of Kalanikupule's forces, a disordered but sizable mob, was driven into narrow Nuuanu Pass. And here, with little heart left to fight, the Kalanikupule remnant was driven in panic back toward the edge of a 200-foot precipice overlooking the windward side of the island, Kailua and Kaneohe.

Here, too, many were cool enough to slip away to the sides, up tiny paths over the high peaks. But a wedge of Oahu troops was still jammed between two steep slopes to the east and west sides of the pass. On the down slope of the Nuuanu grade descending to Honolulu (the south), Kamehameha's army stretched for more than two miles.

Because of the narrowness of the pass, the Alapa, the assault elements, the selected shock troops, stretched back for a mile. But with the foremost elements, Kameha had kept at least one field piece, the polished, aggressive shape of the brass cannon Lopaka.

Now, just past Wai-puhia Falls (literally "Blown Water")—the famous Upside Down Falls where the wind whips so fiercely sometimes that the water flows up, not down—the prominent shape of the cannon was ready to fire.

But the Kamehameha vanguard was pressing them so fiercely farther up the slope, they were locked in such unrelenting hand-to-hand combat on the rim of the Pali precipice, that Kamehameha gave the order he liked least of all when he was winning: Do not fire the cannons, and tell the riflemen not to fire their pu laipala (rifle weapons).

He passed on that unwanted command to John Young and knew that if he didn't, Young would suggest it. Young had done so, many times before; it was for the obvious reason that he would kill friendly troops in the hand-to-hand combat ahead, as well as enemy.

At the very rim of the Pali, the push of the Kamehameha forces drove scores of Oahu soldiers over the cliff. Fighting for their lives, many fell off that jagged edge, and in the fighting, some of the Kameha host tumbled with them. On the jagged outcrops of the cliff face dead bodies were clustered. And at the bottom, where at last the steep drop ended and the more gradual slope down to Kailua started, hundreds of bodies had accumulated.

It was at least three months before Kalanikupule was caught by the Kamehameha forces. He wandered in the obscure mountain trails of the Koolau rain forest, while the hot breath of a pursuing Pai'ea kept him on the run. He was as close to being a wretched fugitive as is possible in the happy Hawaiian climate. Finally he was caught, and Kamehameha sacrificed him to the war god Ku.

Meanwhile, Kameha had moved his court to Kalanikupule's (and Kahekili's) former capital on the Waikiki shore. Here, he and Kaahumanu could frolic in the eight surfs of the great beach strip.

On their heavy, long boards, and free as the wind in their nakedness, they met the challenge of the big waves at First Break, way out to sea. And close to the shore, in the small breakers now called the Malihini or Beginner surf, they played on their boards. Here they ran up and down on their heavy slabs of koa wood, in the same evolutions which young surfers were to discover as "hanging 10" and "hot dogging" 150 years later, when surfing became an international sport, and with Hawaii still its world capital.

And in the aquamarine-clear water of the Waikiki strand, they enjoyed the ultimate Hawaiian luxury, swimming. They relaxed by themselves in the always-swimmable, warm and lucent waters of Waikiki. They enjoyed the Hawaiian sport of making love in the water, a sport most enjoyed by those to whom water is a second element and nearly as easy to move in and enjoy as air.

There, in the jewellike, always-changing belts of water inside the lines of white surf and the reefs, they played at hono-ipu, the healthy Polynesian sport of love. Waikiki today and always is a monument to the love of these two tall and handsome super-beings—and to the thousands of other lovers who have delighted in the clear natural fulfillment of love and other beautiful sports in the water.

But Kamehameha also had the unrelenting curse or blessing of driving ambition. The same flame of ambition which had burned in him since he was a boy now pushed him harder and hotter than ever.

Kaahumanu had her times with him in the pale-jade shallows in the lee of the crouching lion of Leahi, Diamond Head. But his other hours were filled with urgent consultations with his leading chiefs—Ke-e-au-moku, Kameeiamoku, Kamanawa—and urgent plans to finish his road of conquest.

One of the largest jobs was to keep his vast army and canoe fleet in being so that he could mount a massive assault on the only major Hawaiian island which had so far eluded his grasp, Kauai.

In this, the northernmost of the main Sandwich or Hawaiian Islands, the late Kaeo's son, Kaumu-alii, had taken the reins of power. And Kaumu-alii intelligently—in view of Kamehameha's lethal behavior before this with rivals for power—had a profound disinclination to meet with the Great Warrior to talk about making peace.

So while he was at a high level of military strength, Kameha was determined to lead his armada in a full-scale assault on the northern neighbor and Kaumu-alii.

And another purpose drove Kameha hard. Despite his blissful sessions of swimming, surfing and hono-ipu with Kaahumanu off the Waikiki strand, there remained his driving urge to have truly regal, high-caste sons. This meant one thing. He would marry Keopuolani. He had brought her along, with her mother, so that it could be done as the climax of his great conquest of Oahu, in the capital of his rival.

Kaahumanu did not actively resist the addition of yet another female to Kamehameha's roster of wives. As long as Kamehameha assured her that she was his queen and his love, and acted that part, she was willing to settle for her status. In the meantime, she relished her regal position as leading female in the Kamehameha household. She had outgrown in rank the privilege of Alii women: choosing as many husbands and lovers as she might arrange.

Now that her husband was the preeminent male of all the islands, she presumably would not want to marry again; still, she could arrange lovers as might fit her convenience and interest, and the tolerance of Kamehameha. The latter item, the openmindedness of Kamehameha, was a tricky affair. Yet she had managed lovers before and would have many more as the years and her life cycles progressed. She was a sensuous and lusty woman and her frankly amorous appetites were a part of the traditional Hawaiian character and custom. The main inequality between male and female when they became monarchs was that the queen would not marry again, while the king could marry as many women as he chose.

So in Kahekili's capital village on the Waikiki sands, in July of 1795, Kamehameha and Keopuolani were married. She was now sixteen years old. The preparations were elaborate, because of Keopuolani's Niau-pio caste, and also because she brought to Kamehameha's household a new goddess—an akua mo-o, or water god.

That goddess was Kiha-wahine. The legend was that Kiha-wahine was an ancestor of Keopuolani in the Keawe line. Kiha-wahine—meaning approximately "diving (like a porpoise) woman" —was a chiefess deified into a water sprite. The Maui chiefs who were her contemporaries in antique days had given her the kapus and kapu-sticks of a god.

From the marriage on, Kamehameha carried the Kiha-wahine image with him—with, of course, the exalted Ku-kaili-moku. Kameha, presuming somewhat on his intended marriage, had taken Kiha-wahine with him on the final battle in the Nuuanu Pali. But from here on, it was all to be official, with the total knowledge and consent of the kahunas.

The preparations for the marriage at Waikiki were elaborate, but the ceremony itself was the regular, simple sort favored by the Polynesians. After the long series of invocations, readings of family trees and titles, meles and prayers, the kahunas brought a large square of white tapa. During the ceremony Kamehameha was bare to the waist in deference to the Niau-pio rank of Keopuolani. The kahunas then draped the tapa cloth over the couple. In this partial privacy, they rubbed noses. Then the kahunas chanted in unison: "The Chiefs are wed! Hoao na'lii e!" and the dancing and feasting began and went on well beyond the middle of the night.

But Kameha's courtiers, and particularly his favorite queen Kaahumanu, sharply observed that the giant king was not in any hurry to carry his diminutive and frail new wife to the bridal hale. Kaahumanu was pleased with the courtiers' gossip that the big king did not spend the night with his bride. Instead he talked at length with Ke-e-au-moku. And the fact was that the first child of this sacred wife was not born for two years. That was his eventual heir, Liholiho.

In short order, Kamehameha ploughed ahead with his ambitious plans to secure and expand his holdings. He made the vast preparations to invade Kauai, with a fleet of 600 war canoes and more than 15,000 men.

And to secure his hold on Maui, he sent Ke-e-au-moku as regent there, with the admonition to be prudent in his administration of justice.

Ke-e-au-moku had no trouble as Kamehameha's governor in Maui. But Kameha, despite all proper spiritual preparations with the kahunas, encountered sheer disaster with his great amphibious assault on Kauai. It was in the spring of 1796.

That disaster, easily read as intervention of the gods, was violent, stormy weather which blew up without warning as the fleet got underway.

In the tumultuous Kauai Channel, where some of the biggest breakers in the world build up to crash on Oahu's north shore, the canoe fleet was wrecked. Hundreds of the warriors were drowned, out of sight of land in the violent storm. Even the flagship *Britannia*, carrying Kameha, had a hard time beating back to Waikiki.

And back in Waikiki with the wreckage of his fleet and his army, Kamehameha was stricken with further bad news from the Big Island. This was that Kaiana's brother Nama-keha had staged a coup and seized control of much of the island.

Kameha sought the advice of his kahunas, and decided that only a major effort would drive out Nama-keha. He surmised the struggle might be a long one, so he left his old counselors (not the younger, more revolutionary types) in command in Waikiki. At the head of that government seat were Kameeiamoku, Kamanawa and Kalani-moku.

Kamehameha headed for Hilo, where Nama-keha had made his inroads. The mighty Kamehameha army engaged the rebels, killed some and dispersed the others, and Nama-keha's plot fell apart at the seams. Nama-keha himself was captured and sacrificed at the great heiau for Ku-kaili-moku at Kawaihae.

Kamehameha was glad to be back in his home island, and he saw many problems to be attended to there. Kawaihae and Keala-kekua Bay and Kailua, the white surf at Hapuna and Anaehumalu, the ti slides of the Kona coast and the waterfalls of Kona—all these looked good to him.

He decided he would stay awhile at Kona and Hilo and patch up the troubles he could see on the Big Island. Above all, he wanted to stabilize the dissident elements left in Hilo and in the provinces of Puna and Ka'u on Hilo's southern border.

Meanwhile he would once more construct another armada. This would be the largest ever, to finish off Kaumu-alii. It would be a vast army and a fleet of larger, deeper-draft war canoes, the kind the Hawaiians called "waa peleleu," literally "wide, long canoes." These would be built with a wide platform between two long, wide and deep hulls.

Some of these peleleu canoes would have the conventional, Polynesian rigs, derived from the lateen sails of the Middle East. But many would be modeled on the Haole sloop or cat rigs, which could sail far closer to the wind than the Hawaiian sort.

He also had started work, both at Kealakekua Bay and at

Waikiki, on two more large conventional sailing craft on the order of the *Britannia*. The one at Waikiki was forty tons displacement, about fifty feet long.

These were being constructed by his large staff of Haole shipwrights and carpenters. Now there were a dozen such foreign experts at his three major ports. And the great chief was accumulating stores of rifles, cannon, powder, ball and shot from trading ships at both Kealakekua and Waikiki. He was still going to teach Kaumu-alii his lesson in servility.

Meanwhile, Kameha constructed a capital, complete with a small heiau, at Kailua, Kona, and chose to live most of the time there.

With him, he had his womenfolk, including Kaahumanu, the new sacred bride Keopuolani, and the seven others who so far could claim the official title of wife to the moi, or king.

Soon he had installed most of his court—including his kahunas, his kahili and spitoon bearers, and his leading chiefs and advisors. Among those who came over to join his Kona court was Kalanimoku, who soon became his leading executive. He was a kind of combination prime minister and treasurer. Accordingly, Kalanimoku (literally "fixture of heaven") adopted the name which visiting sea captains told him was that of his British counterpart, William Pitt. Visiting British and American skippers shortened the name to the good-natured Billy Pitt. And Billy, feeling the affection behind it, liked the name.

Besides the building of another invasion fleet and army, Kameha and Billy Pitt fashioned a new regime of peace in the Big Island, Oahu, Maui, Molokai and Lanai. They made sure that they collected ample annual levies at the tax-collecting season, the Maka-hiki time of the New Year. And they continued to build an army and the expanding fleet of peleleu canoes and schooner-rigged Haole vessels constructed by Haole carpenters. A former sailor, James Boyd, was the principal boss of the shipwrights. Kamehameha was now a multiisland monarch who commuted from Kona to Lahaina (Maui) to Waikiki and coaxed along his new maximum effort.

And up until 1802, he kept his capital—as established by the presence of his womenfolk—at Kona. When he traveled, in the *Britannia* or one of the James Boyd schooners, he left the weather-beaten but durable Olohana, John Young, in command at Kona. Ke-e-au-moku remained his regent in Maui, assisted by the venerable Kameeiamoku. Billy Pitt, the former Kalani-moku, was a commuting prime minister, following in the watery canoe tracks of his monarch, from Kona, to Lahaina, to Kanakakai, to Waikiki.

In 1797, Keopuolani, the sacred wife, gave birth to the first of her Niau-pio children for Kamehameha. He was Liholiho, full name Kalani-nui-kua-liholiho—ke-kapa, meaning "From-heaven-great-back-burning-now-tapa (cloth)." Mainly, the name indicated that the highborn chief had the back-burning kapu, the most exalted of social castes, meaning of course that anyone treading on any of Liholiho's kapus would be killed and burned completely.

From Liholiho on, Keopuolani was to have ten more children for Kamehameha. But of these ten, only two others survived. The others died of childhood diseases, viruses which were much more virulent in the islands since the coming of the White Man.

The three who survived into adulthood were Liholiho, Kau-ike-aouli (born 1814) and Nahi-ena-ena (born 1815).

When Kameha shoved off for his great venture with the peleleu canoe fleet in 1802, 800 vessels strong, Liholiho, his first born and heir apparent, was only five years old.

As usual, Kamehameha concentrated all his energies in the peleleu armada, calculated to be his last campaign. And as usual, his fascinating and favorite wife, Kaahumanu, insisted on going with the expedition.

The fleet, 800 vessels and 16,000 men, sailed first to Lahaina, and paused there. A sudden emergency in Kameha's life had arisen: Kameeiamoku, one of Kameha's closest associates for a lifetime and half-brother of Kahekili, was mortally ill at Lahaina.

In a regal hale on the beach at Hana-ka-oo, where lines of the small Lahaina surf beat, he found the fallen warrior. Now Kameeiamoku, he of the tempestuous temper and predilections toward violence, was like Kalola on her deathbed, only a shell of a major human entity.

Kameeiamoku was not struggling for air as Kalola had been. He did not seem to be as close to death as she was then. But as she was a husk remaining of one of the most fascinating, charming and warmhearted of Polynesian women, so he was a sunken shadow of a formidable, fierce warrior. He had been once as strong, supple and sure of himself as a tiger, or as a chief should be. In fact, his boldness, as in the case of his seizure of the ship *Fair American* and the killing of her crew (except for the valiant Isaac Davis), had frequently verged on the vainglorious or braggadocio.

Now, he seemed incongruously small under his wide tapa sheet —oceans away from the big-chested giant he had been when he moved with the grace and power of a supersized cat. Now, as he and Kameha rubbed noses and embraced, Kameha felt how frightfully thin his friend's shoulders had become.

Kameha had left his kahili bearers and his array of pahu beaters outside. He brought with him Pinao, one of his favorite kahunas. Kameeiamoku was attended by one of his kahunas, I-i. Kameeiamoku had ordered all the others of his courtiers to leave. Very evidently, he wanted to be nearly alone with Kameha, with only a few trusted pairs of ears to hear what he wanted to communicate. Outside the hale, the modulated, low verbal genuflections of a solemn mele were being chanted in a mournful dirge. The courtiers were fully prepared for the death which the kahunas had warned them was imminent. They had been administering herbs and teas, but Kameeiamoku was growing weaker. He was troubled with pains across the chest and back which left him struggling for strength, and sick in his stomach.

Now, however, he seemed to have some of his old vigor in his voice. He spoke about his lands in Kohala and Hilo, how he wanted them disposed of. Then he looked out the door toward the low, undulating sound of the chanters and their mele.

He spoke to I-i. "Tell them to go away—as far as a stone's

throw. Until awa-kea." That was noon and it was only a short time till that station of the day when the sun was straight overhead.

Kameeiamoku waited until he heard them moving away, outside, and their mournful chant growing fainter as they kept on singing. Then he reached under his tapa mat and pulled out a carved bone object which he extended to Kamehameha.

It was a lei niho palaoa, a walrus-tooth carving with its characteristic ski-jump upswept ivory prong supported on a necklace of black human hair. He extended it to Kameha, who examined it curiously.

For long minutes he held it up at arm's length (he was growing farsighted in middle age) so that he could examine it in the light.

Kameeiamoku watched and waited until Kameha was ready to speak. "Kahekili," he said. "I recognize the carving of his own lei niho palaoa. That pattern of half-black, half-white was his warrior's mark. Why do you show it to me?"

"I knew you would recognize it. But what I am to tell you, you would not know, Pai'ea."

Kameha waited. Kameeiamoku was far from finished. Next, he pulled out from under his tapa another item, a gleaming white boar's tusk wrist bracelet, or ku-pe-e.

"This," he said, "belonged to Kekui-apo-iwa. I am sure you have seen her wearing it."

Kameha nodded. Kameeiamoku went on: "What you did not know is that the ku-pe-e was the gift of Kahekili to your mother. And that the lei niho palaoa was his favorite lei niho, his favorite mark of his nobility. It was given him by your mother. He gave me this, your mother gave me the other—as tokens to prove to you that they were your parents."

Kameha was stunned. Kameeiamoku went on. "So Kahekili was your father, not Keoua."

Kameha got up, walked to the doorway, and stood looking out. Then he came back and sat beside Kameeiamoku again. His face was saddened, but not without a flush of anger.

"Why did you wait till now to tell me? I might have avoided killing my brothers."

Kameeiamoku was not at all dismayed by this. There was a ring of the old bravado in his voice as he answered.

"Pai'ea! Do not speak hoo-mali-mali! You would have quarreled with them anyhow, and they with you."

Kameha's tenseness melted. If he had been a smiling man instead of a lonely and thoughtful one, he would have laughed. "You are right, Kameeiamoku. Still, I wish I had known earlier. I would have treated him differently. I always did respect him as an enemy. He was clever, he never quit, he kept on with new ideas for winning."

"I know you thought that, Pai'ea. He knew it too."

"Then I am glad he knew I respected him." Kameeiamoku suddenly looked ill and I-i fed him sips of herb tea. Kameha went on. "But why did he try to have me killed when I was a newly-born baby? In the cave in Kohala. When Kekui-apo-iwa was hiding me from him?"

Kameeiamoku struggled wtih his stomach resurgence. Then, in his illness, he was able to laugh. "You knew Kahekili, Pai'ea. He had a fierce temper. As you do. And I do—did."

"But why was he angry with *me*?"

"You know, as I do. Because when your mother was with child, she had a dream that she craved to eat the eye of a chief."

"This has been told to me. And that the kahunas said it meant that I would overthrow all the other chiefs, and rule all the islands."

"And still you wonder why he wanted to have you killed? Would not you have done as he did?"

Kameha's wide lips curved, in a shadow of a smile. "Yes. I probably would have."

He looked away pensively. "But now I am not so sure about grinding Kaumu-alii into the earth. He would be the last of Kahekili's line—except for you and your brother."

Kameeiamoku smiled again. "You are only mellowing like a banana in your middle age."

Kameha's temper flared. "No. I will bring Kauai, and Kau-mu-alii, under my hand." He got up and looked out the door toward the lines of surf. Then, just as suddenly, his hard, scarred face seemed to soften. "But this time I will send messengers to him to try to arrange a peaceful way."

"And what about your fleet, and your army? Will they sit and wait?"

"Yes. Even if arranging peace will take months."

Kameeiamoku's long life lasted only a few hours after this. His stomach sickness suddenly grew worse, he began to regurgitate as if his insides were determined to find their way out. And the gagging did not relieve him. It went on endlessly. He sank steadily and his will to fight disappeared. It was as if Fate or Kane or Lono or Ku had kept him alive long enough to give Kameha his last message. Now he had fulfilled his mission and he no longer seemed to want to live. Like a good and devoted courtier, he lived for his chief, and quit when the last of his utility left him.

But despite the "tokens" (Kamakau's word) which Kameeia-moku showed him, and Kameeiamoku's position of authority, Kameha still did not totally believe that Kahekili was his father, or wanted to. It was true that Kameeiamoku had been at Wailuku when Kameha's mother had been there. And it was long-standing court gossip that the two had been through an affair.

But in the wake of Kameeiamoku's death, three of Kameha's closest associates counseled him against accepting the story. One was Ke-e-au-moku, the others his sacred wife Keopuolani—and Kaahumanu too. They agreed that too much was at stake if he let it be known he was the son of Kahekili.

Keopuolani naturally opposed it, for she also had everything to lose. If Liholiho were to be the sacred child, to be born with Niau-pio caste, to inherit the divine rank of the "burning kapu," Keopuolani and Kameha had to be half-brother and sister. If Kahekili was Kameha's father, then Liholiho was not divine at all. And all of the ceremonies, all of the honors and all the divine respect which had been paid to him—even his name, meaning

"very hot," an obvious reference to his burning kapu caste—
were suddenly invalid.

Kaahumanu had become the principal guardian and companion
of Liholiho—at her own insistence. She was well aware of the
king's fondness for the sacred child. She had fought not only to
go along with Kameha on his ponderous expedition to beat Kaumu-alii and conquer Kauai; but she also insisted on taking the
five-year-old Liholiho along too.

So he was at Lahaina at the time of the death of Kameeiamoku.
Now Kamehameha laid on the most elaborate ceremonies in a
heiau in Lahaina, and there he gave the boy custody of his gods,
except for the war god, Ku-kaili-moku, which temporarily at
least he still kept for himself.

Giving his gods to Liholiho was like an official act of desig-
nating his successor. Then, with a party of kahunas, he sent the
boy on a tour of the main heiaus in the Big Island and Oahu.

It seemed now that Kameha might pause with his fleet for
some time at Lahaina. His new doubts induced a slower course
of attack.

He kept his armada at Maui while his peace ambassadors were
dispatched to Kauai. Several were sent. But after a polite hearing,
Kaumu-alii sent word each time that he could not come to meet
with Kamehameha. He was clearly still distrustful.

While he was waiting, Kameha swam and surfed with Kaahumanu at Kekaa and Kaanapali. They made love in the surf at
the long, wild strand of Kaanapali. With their surfboards, they
played in the small breakers at Kekaa. They rode the bigger,
longer rollers of Honolua, north of Kaanapali. And they tried
the ti-leaf slides and bathed in the pools of Kihel. And most of
the time, they were alone, each content with the akamai and
sympathetic presence of the other.

They were close together in the way in which they thought.
She listened with fascination to his stories of court intrigue, his
long sagas of battles in the past, the negotiations with Kaumu-
alii, his plans to invade Kauai if in the upshot Kaumu-alii would

not make peace. She, probably the successor to Kameha's power if he should die while Liholiho was a child, was eager to learn all she could about the workings of the machinery of state. And besides, she was close to him, she had respect for his hard warrior's heart (coupled with a finally soft fondness for her). As the Bard wrote of Othello and Desdemona, "She loved me for the dangers I had passed, and I loved her that she did pity them."

There was no doubt that Kamehameha loved his imperial-sized queen more than the others. But he loved a dozen and a half others also. As he orbited among his chores in Lahaina and Waikiki, he accumulated more wives and lovers. This, by Polynesian standards (and the standards of many other parts of Asia), was something he could brag about, quite definitely an accomplishment. By the time he died, seventeen years later, he had accumulated twenty-one wives. And his children, in and out of wedlock, had totaled more than fifty. Most of them, as in the case of Keopuolani's children, died in infancy. Of the wives and children, more later.

But Kaahumanu was his true love—if this can be said of such a peripatetic Polynesian lover. He and she were closer to each other, they saw more of each other, they spent more time together, made more love and had more fun (and anguish) together than he had with any other of his lady loves. And Kaahumanu generally had a tolerant view of his amorous meanderings, just as he ended by forgiving her when his jealousy was raging. For she, too, was lusty, amorous, Polynesian, and accordingly had a free devotion to enjoying the sensations of life.

He and she continued to have their quarrels, like the contumely which Vancouver had settled with ingenious diplomatic maneuvering in 1794. And in her hot temper, she several times threatened and tried to commit suicide by jumping among the sharks of the Lanai Channel, or into the swift currents when they were running their worst off Kaanapali Point, Maui. But she always arranged that Kamehameha should know her intentions, before she tried. And though she was often thoroughly mauled by Kameha in his anger, he dutifully rescued her from her suicide attempts and their violent quarrels repeated the Vancouver pattern: They usually ended in tearful embraces.

In this period of interregnum in which he attempted to arrange a peace without further war against Kauai and Kaumu-alii, Kameha began to organize a regime of peace and prosperity which he hoped would continue everywhere once all the islands were under his control.

Now that the flame of war was finished with its scorching path in Maui, Hawaii, Oahu, Lanai and Molokai, he encouraged the farmers toward record crops. One great assist he gave was to proclaim the Law of the Splintered Paddle as an inviolable statute. This provided that no soldier or group of soldiers could appropriate anything from any farmer or other civilian without proper governmental authority. "Let the old men, the old women, and the children sleep in safety by the roadside."

And centering his trade efforts in Lahaina, Honolulu and Kealakekua, he did everything he could to encourage British and American sea captains to bid for Hawaiian items like sugar, whale oil, forest wood, and yams, coconuts, pineapples and sandalwood. In return he received more rifles, pistols, ammunition and cows and, in 1802, the "long-eared and oversized dogs" which the Haoles called "horses."

So the time went, until in exasperation, in 1803, he decided to go ahead with his plans to invade Kauai and conquer Kaumu-alii. By this time, besides the peleleu canoes, he had twenty smaller Haole-type vessels of twenty to forty tons. His armaments included forty swivel guns, fourteen smaller cannons and 600 muskets.

He moved his invasion fleet and army to Waikiki and prepared to start his attack from there. But as the mammoth logistics preparations for the largest military attack in Hawaiian history mounted, a dreadful catastrophe struck Kamehameha and his armies.

Like an avenging bolt from his polytheistic pantheon, a plague struck into Honolulu, Waikiki and the invasion fleet. It was called mai okuu; it smashed down Hawaiians by the hundreds, and they died in the same quantities. Mai okuu, literally "It comes in squatting," refers to the fact that the disease starts with dysentery, with diarrhea.

It was a lethal epidemic, and a dreadful one. The corpses frequently turned black, and it was likely that the disease was black plague with cholera mixed in. Certainly, the curse had been brought in by Haole sailors from one of the disease-ridden port cities of Asia, most likely Canton. Starting as a sizable epidemic, the black death soon raged into the worst disaster which had ever struck the Hawaiian Islands. It grew rapidly into the most soul-searing agony Kamehameha and his countrymen had ever endured. In the ghastly wake of this murderous disease, Kameha lost all of his close counselors on Oahu except his prime minister, Billy Pitt. Half of the population of Oahu was wiped out, and despite the natural isolation which the islands enjoyed from each other, the plague of mai okuu spread in lesser quantities to the Big Island, Maui and Molokai. And amid a disaster of such size, the massive invasion armada aimed at Kauai fell apart. About half of the solders died. The shores of Waikiki and Honolulu harbor were strewn with the untended hulks of the supersized canoes—as the families carried out their dead.

Convinced the gods were violently displeased with him, Kamehameha consulted with his kahunas, and followed their advice on the way to win again the favor of the gods. Hundreds of hogs, thousands of coconuts and bananas were offered on the altars of the Oahu heiaus. Three warriors who had broken an eating kapu by feasting on coconuts with Queen Keopuolani were blinded and their arms and legs broken. After a while they were killed and sacrificed at a heiau in Waikiki. But these barbaric religious measures did not work. The epidemic continued to run its course.

Keopuolani had already been punished by the gods. She had fallen violently ill with one of the lesser viri of the epidemic. She was one of the extremely lucky ones who survived.

And the saddest blow of all to Kamehameha was the loss of his long-time friend, fiery companion-at-arms and father-in-law, Ke-e-au-moku.

Ke-e-au-moku was dying in the Koko district, near Diamond Head. Kameha and his leading chiefs came to weep over him. The epidemic killed rapidly and the host of Kamehameha crowded around the dying man. In accordance with the Hawaiian custom, they wanted to hear his last words, to catch his dying advice.

Kameha especially was deeply moved and asked the question closest to his heart.

"When you are gone—will plotters take the kingdom from me?"

Ke-e-au-moku managed to say: "No, Pai'ea." With his usual forthrightness, in front of his leading courtiers, he said: "None of your chiefs is strong enough to try."

He went on, still his amazingly frank self: "Only my daughter could depose you—if she wanted to." The courtiers reacted with a gasp.

"So—my advice, Pai'ea: Keep her away from lovers who might plot with her."

"But Ke-e-au—she did not plot with Kaiana."

A kind of chuckle came from the sick man; it creased his gaunt face. "No. She has never plotted against you. But if any man sleeps with her, you must watch him."

Kameha's face grew dark. "I will have him killed." And later, Kameha did proclaim such a penalty. Sometimes it was enforced, sometimes not. For the sensuous Kaahumanu continued to have lovers—and her handmaidens were generally fond of her and wanted to protect her, and her lovers, from Kamehameha's wrath. Both Kameha and Kaahumanu still had long spans of vigorous life before them.

CHAPTER 15
The Victories of Peace

BUT IN 1804, as the plague gradually subsided, the scars ran deep and were slow to heal. The plague, like most dreadful illnesses, left in those who survived a craving for constructive works. Kameha was no exception.

He vigorously encouraged farmers by himself tending crops in some of his lands on Oahu. But he also, being an irresistible force in his will toward conquest, continued to negotiate with Kaumu-alii to bring Kauai into his domain—and the domain of Liholiho.

Where he could salvage them and had the military manpower, he kept his peleleu fleet in commission. And he continued to enhance his strength (and strain his finances) by purchasing small schooners and sloops (and cannon and muskets) from the Haoles. Yet close associates observed that his will to conquer Kauai was not quite so irresistible as before. The news about his being a son of Kahekili, and the knockout blows of the plague, had given him a greater inclination toward diplomatic methods of settling quarrels (with, of course, the underlying threat of force to make it stick). And his appetite for the productive development of his society also was increasing, in trading agricultural and forest wealth for the treasures of European and American civilization.

In 1805, in a deal with an American trader, Captain William Shaler, he secured the *Leila Byrd*, a brig of 175 tons. This ship was to be the new flagship of his navy and the pillar of his first venture into creating a Hawaiian merchant marine for the China trade.

He kept a large force of Haole shipwrights at work with ample forces of Hawaiian assistants and apprentices: sailmakers, carpenters, smiths, riggers and ropemakers. His fleet of small, Western-style vessels, with Haole sailing rigs, he maintained and slowly increased in number. He knew that his strength in the magic weapons of the Haoles, especially ships with cannons, was the best persuader in his efforts to bring Kaumu-alii to terms.

So he continued to send presents and emissaries to his only remaining rival, this king of Kauai. One of the most persistent ambassadors was an American trader, Captain Nathan Winship. Through Winship and other sea captains he eventually managed to convey to Kaumu-alii that he could be the lord of Kauai—provided that he came to Oahu and offered his fealty to Kamehameha as his overall sovereign. But Kaumu-alii, no doubt remembering well what had happened to another rival, Keoua, when he tried to meet with Kameha to arrange peace in 1790 at Kawaihae, kept finding excuses for failing to appear in Waikiki.

Kameha continued to rebuild his strength, military and otherwise. Sagely, he granted lands to his remaining leaders in various parts of his insular empire—but he managed to keep their holdings spread out among the islands. In that way, no one (except Kaumu-alii) had a large and cohesive body of territory and too many followers in any one focus of power.

And knowing that the Haoles—despite their obvious fondness for wine and distilled spirits—still held the key to his strength in their guns and ships, he continued to build the Haole colony of advisors. Now in his fifties, he still had enough mental elasticity to struggle for more Haole knowledge. He knew that the Haoles were far advanced not only in weapons, manufacturing techniques and science, literature and art, but also in governmental science.

He still believed that he had some governmental links with King George III and the Kingdom of Beretania, though he had never heard another word from the agreement he had signed with Vancouver. Nor had he seen hide nor hair of the ship of war which, Vancouver had promised, King George would send him. He heard from several of the British sea captains that Vancouver had died after his return to England. But he still expected that his very own man-of-war from Britain would be sailing into Honolulu or Waikiki, as a symbol of the recognition and protection to which Vancouver had agreed.

On Oahu, Kameha kept one of his two oldest advisors, Isaac Davis, shortened to the Hawaiian Aikake, as his "Supreme." Davis was his trade chief, and principal interpreter too. John Young, or Olohana, the old bosun, was his governor and deputy on the Big Island, at Kailua. Both men had large acreage in several islands, and retinues of 400 or 500 servants or tenants.

And another Haole, Don Francisco de Paula Marin, a Spaniard, was rising high in the Kamehameha hegemony. A Renaissance man with a wide spectrum of talents, he dabbled in botany and horticulture and established wineries and breweries in his wide holdings. The Hawaiians called him "Manini." He too served as a trade advisor and interpreter.

Kamehameha was much attracted to the trade in sandalwood, a tropical tree, *santalum album*, which grew in quantity in the islands. It was laau ala, or "fragrant tree," in Hawaiian. And Hawaiians soon learned that the wood was in demand both in the European world and in China for perfume and furniture.

Nathan Winship, the captain who became the principal negotiator between Kamehameha and Kaumu-alii, was active in the sandalwood trade. And sandalwood became the source of most of Kamehameha's growing wealth from trading. The method of payment for some of the Haole-type ships he bought was to dig a hole in the ground, the same size as the ship, and fill the hole with sandalwood logs. By 1816, the cash value of the sandalwood trade had grown to $400,000 per year.

Another brisk trade continued to be in feminine favors. To sailors at sea for months on hard-tack diet, the Sandwich Islands women were a glimpse of paradise. The trading ships pulling into Honolulu, Lahaina, Kealakekua Bay or Kawaihae were prime sources of this shore-to-ship trading intercourse, and the drain on the manufactured items aboard the ships was always heavy. Those items were clothing, mirrors, scissors, nails or any other iron objects from which fishhooks, daggers and crude tools could be made.

Since the Hawaiians had a more liberal attitude about love-making than the European world, husbands or fathers would take their beauties to the ships by canoe, or the girls would swim out by themselves. Love-making, of course, was a legitimate and enjoyable sport to the Hawaiians, and if it was also profitable, that was only a bonus.

Kamehameha, ever watchful for ways to fill his tax coffers, soon began to levy a tax on the love trade. Another restriction was imposed at the request of the sea captains. When the amorous hugger-mugger continued to interfere with regular work-a-day duties, the custom of the sunset gun began. A cannon was fired at sunset to begin the period of revelry, and another at dawn, to end it. The libidinous ladies were eager to go to the ships each night when the sun was over the yardarm.

In 1809, when Archibald Campbell, a British sailor and sail-maker, began a year's stay at Waikiki and Honolulu, it was a bustling trading community. In his journal, *A Voyage Round the World*, Campbell noted that a staff of workmen were building a house for Kameha "in the European style, for his residence at Hanaroora. When I came away [a year later, in 1810], the walls were as high as the top of the first story."

Campbell writes vividly of Kamehameha, with the parenthetical editorial note that "Captain King has spelt it Maiha Maiha, Mr.

Samwell, the surgeon of the *Discovery*, who published an account of Captain Cook's death, Cameamea; Portlock, Comaamaa; Mears, Tomyhomyhaw; Vancouver and Broughton, Tamaahmaah; Lisianski, Hameamea; Langsdorf, Tomooma; and Turnbull, Tamahama."

On the great chief's appearance and deportment: "In 1809 the king seemed about 50 years of age; he is a stout, well-made man, rather darker in the complexion than the natives usually are, and wants two of his front teeth."

Campbell found Kamehameha "mild and affable in his manners, and possesses great warmth of feeling. . . . Although a conqueror, he is extremely popular among his subjects; and not without reason, for since he attained the supreme power, they have enjoyed repose and prosperity."

The sailmaker also noted that Kameha had warehouses full of "European articles of every description, particularly arms and ammunition—war, not commerce, seems to be his principal motive in forming so extensive a navy."

And Campbell's analysis was soon confirmed. While he did not have to use the large amphibious force he was building, Kamehameha's threat soon bore fruit with Kaumu-alii. In the spring of 1810, Nathan Winship managed to bring Kaumu-alii from Kauai to Honolulu. (First, he had to leave his first mate at Kaumu-alii's court as evidence of good faith.)

Kamehameha rolled out all the pomp and circumstance he could muster for the occasion. As the *O'Cain* sailed into Honolulu harbor, a wide array of canoes, the flagship *Leila Byrd* and several of her brood of smaller sloops and schooners spread across the bay. Along the muddy shore and in the lee of the village of thatch-roof hales, several thousand brown kanaka onlookers waited.

By the Honolulu landing, a rickety lumber structure put up by Kamehameha's carpenter crews, a throng of nearly 500 Alii, like a bouquet of bright, particolored fresh flowers, stood by. And on the usual fleet of imposing, double-hulled war canoes, the top-flight VIPs, with an impressive complement of warriors, were moving out to meet the *O'Cain* as she came to anchor.

The peleleu canoes maneuvered smartly around the *O'Cain*. The leading canoe, carrying Kamehameha and his principal courtiers, came alongside. While the deep-toned pahus rumbled, the kahili bearers with their flowery staffs of authority preceded the king to the quarter-deck. Following them, a tall herald with an ihe spear, and the kapu-stick bearer.

On the quarter-deck with Kaumu-alii stood a selection of his courtiers, including two of his favorite wives—lush, café-au-lait colored, buxom beauties in the seminude loveliness of the usual malo, or pareu loincloth.

With this regal party stood Captain Nathan Winship, skipper of the *O'Cain*, trader *par excellence* and now the amateur diplomat who had brought the two feuding chiefs together. In the course of years' experience, Winship and his brother Jonathan had both become fond of Kaumu-alii.

They had been attracted at first by his youth, his handsomeness, his mental alertness and his eagerness to speak English. Like the other traders with a humanitarian streak, the Winships were more interested in trade for articles of peace, like sandalwood, than selling guns to warring chiefs. They had the vision to see that a united and prosperous kingdom of Hawaii would be a much fatter treasure for them than a feuding island archipelago constantly devastated by war.

They had carried personal messengers and reciprocated parades of gifts, the customary ho-o-kupu, in vain, in previous efforts to make peace. On an earlier trip, they had brought a wife and a nephew of Kaumu-alii, Kama-halo-lani, as peace envoys. Kameha had sent them back with the explanation that only Kaumu-alii himself could make the necessary pledges of fealty, in person.

Now, in March of 1810, the day had come. Following the kahili bearers came the spitoon bearers, with their tooth-edged calabash.

Next came the Great Chief himself and a group of courtiers.

Included in the group was the Premier, Billy Pitt; also present was Aikake, Isaac Davis, who was Kameha's "Supreme" on Oahu. And, with the red-bannered god images on poles, the kahunas.

Behind this group came Kameha's wahines and their female attendants. Leading the wahines was the favorite queen Kaahumanu, now grown portly but still feminine and delicate, with finely chiselled features and perfect smooth skin, and small hands and feet. The much smaller figure of the sacred wife, Keopuolani, seemed peaked and sickly beside Kaahumanu. And with them, the sacred prince Liholiho, now thirteen years old, was in magnificent small-sized European uniform with a plumed hat.

Kamehameha wore his traditional Hawaii warrior-chief costume, his gleaming gold mamo cloak and towering yellow helmet to match. He carried his intricately carved ceremonial short spear.

Kaumu-alii was also dressed in regal garb, but his was mostly on the European model. He wore a large, red, gold-braided cloak which Vancouver had given him as a gift from King George III of England. However, he covered both sides of the fence by wearing a Hawaiian warrior's helmet. And he was barefoot. Despite the incongruous costume, he was a tall, imposing and handsome figure. Kaahumanu, who was always attracted to handsome men, took much note of him. After Kamehameha died, she married him.

Now the heralds of the two chiefs faced each other, and declaimed the pedigrees of the two heavenly (Kalani) lines. The kahunas of both sides took turns with lengthy chants. Then the two tall leaders greeted each other. In this time, undoubtedly, many of Kaumu-alii's courtiers were apprehensively reflecting on the meeting of Keoua and Kamehameha on the beach at Kawaihae ten years before, when Kamehameha had cold-heartedly stood by while Keoua and almost all of his close associates were killed.

But by this time, Kamehameha had changed and mellowed somewhat. According to Kamakau, the historic dialogue at this big moment in Hawaiian history was as follows:

Kaumu-alii: "I am here; is it face up or face down?"
Kamehameha said nothing.

Kaumu-alii: "This is my gift at our meeting: the land of Kauai, its chiefs, its men, great and small, from mountain to sea, all above and below, and myself—to be yours."

Kamehameha: "I shall not accept your land, not the least portion of your domain. Return and rule over it."

Then indicating his heir, Liholiho: "But if our young chief makes you a visit, be pleased to receive him."

Kaumu-alii (bowing): "We have met, and now I am returning."

Kamehameha (jovially): "Let us land. We have food, and fish and wealth. Better come ashore." They rubbed noses as a gesture of affection and solidarity.

Before that evening's festivities—marking at long last the formation of a united Hawaiian kingdom—could be begun, a dire event had developed. Aikake heard that some of Kameha's chiefs were planning to poison Kaumu-alii at the luau. So did Kamehameha.

Kameha was told of the plot by a kahuna named Ka-umi-umi. The plan was evidently to pass to the Kauai chief a sea-lion's tusk formed into a drinking cup. It would contain a lethal drink. Possibly it was popo au-huhu, which causes quick death with unpleasant convulsions.

Kameha rebuked the priest and refused to sanction the plan. Isaac Davis told Kaumu-alii directly about it, and the Kauai chief and Nathan Winship announced that they had to remove the *O'Cain* from the harbor for an undisclosed emergency. They left, but the chiefs plotting Kaumu-alii's demise were enraged. They blamed Isaac Davis, and managed to slip the poison to him instead.

Thus died Aikake, one of Kamehameha's oldest and most trusted friends and companions-in-arms. They had been close for twenty years, except for a brief alienation in 1807. Possibly the cause of the friction at that time had been that Kameha, remembering Ke-e-au-moku's dying advice about Kaahumanu's lovers, had then executed his nephew and ward, who was the exceedingly handsome and well-formed nineteen-year-old Ka-niho-nui, the darling of the court. He had also become the almost-adopted son of Kaahumanu and Kameha.

When Kameha announced that this favored ward would be

executed, there were protests not only from a tearful Kaahumanu but also from Aikake. However, the effects of that quarrel with Aikake wore off rapidly, and had been nearly forgotten by the time of his death.

Kamehameha was deeply disturbed by the loss of Aikake. The king gave the Haole the kind of funeral rites he wanted, and interment in a grave with a marker.

But besides losing a trusted friend, Kamehameha was now happily busy with the establishment of his united kingdom of islands. He still had his other trusted Haole, John Young, as governor and his chief deputy on the Big Island. And with him on Oahu, of course, was the redoubtable Billy Pitt, or Kalani-moku.

When Archibald Campbell, the sailmaker, was about to head back to England in 1810, Kameha insisted on sending with him gifts for King George III and a letter. Kameha assumed that England was a small kingdom like his and that a sailoring man like Campbell would have access to the monarch. Campbell tried to disabuse him of the idea, but rather quickly agreed to be Kameha's messenger and envoy. Curiously enough, he did manage to reach the British Foreign Minister's office and convey both the letter and the gifts. And still more amazing, the Foreign Minister sent a letter saying that the British monarch was at that time mentally disturbed and incapable of carrying out his duties. And there was no word about the man-of-war or about the alliance between Britain and Hawaii to which Kameha had agreed.

Kameha's principal gift to George was his own splendid, war-scarred golden feather cloak. And the letter, probably written by John Young, read:

His Most Sacred Majesty, George III of the United Kingdom of Great Britain and the Sandwich Islands King, Defender of the Faith, etc, etc.

Brother

We Kamaahmaah King of the Sandwich Islands, wishing to render every assistance to the ships of His Most Sacred Majesty's subjects who visit these seas, have sent a letter by Captain Spence, Ship Duke of Portland, to his Majesty, since which Timoree (Ka-umu-alii), King

*of Atooi (Kauai), has delivered his island up, and we are now in pos-
session of the whole of the Sandwich Islands. We as subject of His
Most Gracious Majesty, wish to have a seal and arms sent from Britain,
so as there may be no molestation to our ships or vessels, or any
hindrance what so ever.*

*Wishing Your Majesty a long, prosperous and happy reign, I am
Brother*

Kamaahamaah

Ooahoo, Oahu, August 6th, 1810

The seal of Britain, and the shipment of arms (he could have
meant coat of arms) did not arrive. But one of the British traders
brought two large packing cases, a gift from the English Crown.
Inside were an abundance of bright-colored dress uniforms, a
selection of carpenter's tools, and two ornamented brass speaking trumpets.

Despite the failure of Britain to send the man-of-war, or the
seal or the arms which Kameha had most recently requested, the
new Hawaiian united kingdom was prospering.

Kameha adopted a new national flag, a British-type Union
Jack in a box in the upper left hand quarter, with eight long
parallel bars in the main body of the flag. The idea of the bars, one
for each state, the designer of the flag had borrowed from the
American stars in the American flag. The bars alternated in color,
red, white and blue.

The flag had been designed by a former sea captain, George
Beckley, who had settled on Oahu in 1806. From 1812 onward,
the Jack-and-Bars of Hawaii flew over the islands.

Kamehameha kept his capital at Honolulu until 1812, then
moved it to Kailua, on the Kona or sunny side of the Big Island.
Meanwhile, the trade of the new kingdom grew apace. Accordingly, the capital showed the signs of a new affluence.

Kamehameha's palace at Honolulu was an odd combination of
Polynesian and European civilizations. There were substantial
European-type eating, sleeping and living houses, but most of the
structures inside the protecting, rustic, palisade wall of young
tree trunks and branches were thatch-roof grass shacks. There

were a guardhouse for the king's garrison, a powder magazine, and two large warehouses full of European and Chinese luxury items.

Near the palace sat several cannon, most of them from the king's flagship, the *Leila Byrd*. That ship, and a dozen smaller schooners and sloops, floated at anchor in the harbor. So did a host of trading ships from all over the world.

On the muddy Honolulu beach, near the cluster of more than 500 grass hales, the hulls of a score of other small Haole vessels had been hauled up. These, Kameha's navy, were carefully guarded and tended, for they were his strength in the event of a revolt anywhere in his kingdom. But the sails and much of the rigging had been removed, and were kept in the warehouses. Along the shores around Honolulu, the rotting hulks of much of his peleleu fleet still lay.

Considering the large store of Oriental luxuries which crammed his warehouses, Kameha lived a rather spartan and athletic life. Although he was busy with the sandalwood commerce, and the bustling business with the other traders, he seemed to have considerably more leisure time, now that his wars were over.

He missed the dreadful excitement of conquest and mortal combat, the challenge of a formidable, powerful opponent. He missed the drama of the most dangerous, extensive and demanding of chess games, war.

With amazing vigor for a man of what we would call "retirement age," he attacked the problems of agriculture and large-scale fishery as if they were enemies. In his wide Puu-loa acreage, he cultivated record crops of taro, working in the fields like a Kauwa. In the same area, he pitched in to build the walls of large fish traps. Again like a serf, he carried rocks to help with the work. The labor he did was calculated to set an example: an example to the people of the united islands that now, protected by the Law of the Splintered Paddle, they could go about the work of building for comfort and wealth for their families in the blessed (if often selfish) environment of peace.

He worked hard, he bargained with all the unscrupulous cleverness and unprincipled histrionics of a Connecticut Yankee horse trader or a goldsmith in a Mideast Medina. And yet he had plenty of time for games, and for the most fascinating game of the peaceful orbit, love. He still surfed in the long and short, high and low, easy and strenuous wave-sets of Waikiki—with his favorite partner in the white walls of water, Kaahumanu. His queen was plump now, but in the jewellike clarity of that bay shading from pale emerald to aquamarine to sapphire, he and she rode the waves and swam with all the joy and grace of Polynesian giants reared to live in this often hostile element as if it were their own.

Kamehameha's vigor burned with amazing youth, and his warrior's heart had not ended its youthful quest for excitement. He chose more wives to add to his female garden of loveliness as if he still had fifty years to live.

With the astounding Polynesian ambivalence, when it comes to matters of libido and the enjoyment of the sensuous in life, he had already married Kaahumanu's younger sisters Kala-kua and Namahana.

Not as brainy or aggressive as Kaahumanu, though equally beautiful (and slimmer), Kala-kua became the mother of two later Hawaiian kings, who ruled as Kamehameha IV and Kamehameha V. She was also the mother of a princess named Kamamalu who married her half-brother, the heir-apparent Liholiho (Kamehameha II), so that they too could have children of the Niau-pio, or very sacred caste.

Kamehameha also married another of Ke-e-au-moku's daughters, Namahana. Greatly different in character from her two sisters, who were fiery and hot-tempered like their father, Namahana was a hale-lady-well-met. She was fatter even than Kaahumanu, jolly and always inclined to stop and pass a word of conversation or a joke with anyone going by. She was known to the people as Pi-ia (child mountain); she was loved by them because she was always smiling. She loved to be carried in her regal cart among large crowds of people, and she had a typically Hawaiian fondness for eating; that sport, like surfing, swimming, the ti-leaf slides and the delightful sport of making love, being a main reason for wanting to go on fighting life's battles in this worldly paradise.

Kameha continued to take more wives in his golden autumn days. Kamakau noted that even at the very end of his life, he "took as wives two young chiefesses to warm his old age." They were Manono and Keke-ulu-ohi.

But Kamakau also noted that Kameha's so-called old age was different from the usual pattern. In *Ruling Chiefs of Hawaii* he wrote that he was "an old man well on in years, white-haired but with the erect body of a soldier, without the flabbiness of age, and with the features of a young man."

His subjects were delighted to see that their king was still a productive practitioner of the arts of love. In 1814 and 1815 his sacred wife Keopuolani gave birth to two royal children who survived. At that time, Kameha must have been well over sixty. And in the year he died, 1819, when he was probably a good sixty-eight or sixty-nine, he had his last child. She was Ka-papa, daughter of Manono.

Through his last years, Kameha kept up a rigorous campaign of physical exercise. Since Captain William Shaler had brought him Hawaii's first horses at Lahaina in 1803, he had added riding to his catalogue of sports. While he had his capital on Oahu, he liked to take out one of the large "long-eared dogs" early in the morning, for a gallop along the beach.

And to his last days, he had warriors assigned to the job of surprising him by throwing spears at him when he did not expect it. When he lived at Kailua, Kona, where he died, he took brisk walks up and down the hills in the afternoon, and warriors were still detailed to lie in wait for him somewhere along the way, and throw spears at him. He continued, right up to his last year, to be able to dodge or catch them. When a visiting sea captain commented that this was very dangerous to the monarch, Kameha said: "There is no danger. There is no man in Hawaii who can throw the spear that I cannot catch."

Of course up to his final illness, this Napoleon of the Pacific considered swimming and surfing to be his native birthright and the sports which kept him in the best of condition—keeping him flexible and strong in all his musculature.

He followed a few less active sports as the years of peace flew by. One was konane, a Hawaiian game like checkers. He taught his Haole visitors konane—and astounded them with his brilliance in the Haole game of draughts. Hawaiians in general were quick to pick up the Haole customs and games, and soon excelled. The European and American colony complained that the Hawaiians were rapid learners. When Archibald Campbell, the sailmaker at Waikiki, asked another shipbuilder-sailor named Boyd for a loom so that the Hawaiians could learn how to use it, Boyd refused. He said the Hawaiians, being so quick, would soon know how to do everything and there would be no more need of Haole advisors.

The Hawaiians rapidly learned a smattering of English and American ways and language. In 1812, a Haole sailor-visitor to Oahu saw a weird mixture of Hawaiian and Haole costume and customs. He saw Kamehameha sometimes wearing a striped British shirt with collar, and trousers. But in the heat of the day he generally discarded these civilized vestments in favor of the more comfortable malo—or still more comfortable, no costume at all when he went swimming or surfing. The classic South Sea costume bastardizing European and Polynesian garb, a frock coat on top of a malo and bare feet, originated here. So did the insouciant and appealing feminine ensemble of malo, bare breasts and a beaver hat.

Visitors also saw that many of the Hawaiians had adopted Haole names: Thomas Jefferson, James Madison, Bonaparte, Tom Paine, Charley Fox—and of course Kamehameha's prime minister, Billy Pitt. Some of the Hawaiians, used to a costume of nearly nothing, had their adopted Haole names tattooed on their arms, legs or middles.

Then, the new Hawaiian nation with its beautiful new flag became involved, peripherally at least, in a violent extension of foreign affairs. The American-British War of 1812 broke out and raged across the seas. Several American ships sought refuge in Kamehameha's harbors while British men-of-war patrolled outside, waiting for them to venture forth.

Kamehameha, since he had not yet been accepted into the British Empire, nor received the ship-of-war promised by Vancouver, the arms, or even the seal which he requested, was friendly with both sides. And both sides respected his neutrality, especially when they saw his battery of sixteen guns on the ground in Honolulu, and the seventeen Haole-type small ships of his navy riding at anchor in Honolulu harbor. He was never to forget the value of the steel hand in the velvet glove. And his brush with another European power trying to expand an empire across the Pacific was proof enough that the amnesia of peace from the hard realities of international relations had not yet seeped into his consciousness.

CHAPTER 16
End of a Comet

I N 1812, the ever vigorous Kamehameha again moved his capital
to the Big Island, which was home to him. He set up a new
palace in Kailua, Kona, about midway on the west coast. There,
close to his old stamping (and swimming and surfing) grounds of
Kealakekua, Kawaihae and Hapuna, he built a new heiau and
moved some of his ships to Kailua Bay and Kealakekua.

His court of about 1,000 followed him: wives and children and
Kau-kau Alii, his leading chiefs and wives whom he liked to
have with him so that they could be under his watchful eye. With
all this, of course, came the usual train of followers adhering to
royalty anywhere.

Here, the types were quite different from a European court.
In both scenes, of course, there were ample staffs of priests and
soldiers. But the others were different: canoe and surfboard
makers, dancers, Lomi-Lomi massage artists, feather workers,

soothsayers, athletes, wood-carvers. Also, there was the important segment of Haole advisors needed for instruction and guidance. And the inevitable "Kau-kau" followers came seeking sustenance, awa and, nowadays, Haole-type firewater.

A new adaptation of Haole civilization, by the way, was okole hau. It was brandy made from a brew of the root of the ti plant. The name meant "iron-bottom." This might have indicated that it was brewed in an iron pot (which it was) or that an iron stomach was required to ingest it. Or perhaps it had a sexual connotation, that okole hau made the drinker amorous. Anyhow, a group of Haole beachcombers invented it and it flourished.

At any rate, such was the court at Kamehameha's headquarters in Kailua when he met the last military challenge. The challenge was the advent of Russian imperialism in the Hawaiian Islands and he met it with ample remembrance of his lifetime lesson of the value of plenty of threatened force as a prerequisite to peace.

The trouble began in November, 1815, with the arrival of Anton Schäffer (rhymes with wafer), who proclaimed himself a representative of the Russian government and a medical doctor and naturalist. He also had the mission of recovering (or getting indemnity for) a Russian ship which had been lost on a reef off Kauai.

The Russian Empire had expanded from Siberia across the Bering Straits to Alaska. Russian traders were ranging across the Pacific, and had appeared in the Sandwich Islands as early as 1804. Now Schäffer, a German, was working for the Russian-American (Trading) Company. Reaching Kailua with his two ships, the *Ilmena* and the *Kadiak*, he made friends with Kameha and Kaahumanu. He could see that Kaahumanu was closest to, and had the greatest influence upon, Kamehameha.

He bent his maximum efforts and a good share of time to persuading Kameha that both of his objectives were just and promising. And Kameha soon expressed agreement. Kaahumanu saw to it that Schäffer was granted extensive lands in Oahu. The mission of salvage, however, still had to be accomplished in Kauai.

When he got to Kauai, he found fertile ground for conspiracy in the personable and ambitious Kaumu-alii. Schäffer began to conspire with Kaumu-alii, who still had great dreams of deposing Kameha. Kaumu had been through a dispute with Kameha over the sandalwood trade. The Winships had long since lost their monopoly—and plenty of money, too.

Before he left Kauai, Schäffer made another pact, this time with Kaumu-alii. Now, together, they were going to overthrow Kameha—with promised military help from the Russian government. And in return, when he had thrown out Kameha and taken over all the islands, Russia would have "half the island of Oahu, and all of the sandalwood forever, and also whatever provinces I might want to select on the other islands."

Kaumu-alii gave Schäffer grants of land on Kauai, and the German began to build a fort at Hanauma Bay, and fly the Russian flag there. He then sailed to Oahu and encountered a deeply hostile group of American traders (who had heard about his flying the Russian flag in Kauai) and a suspicious John Young.

The American traders harassed Schäffer as he built a waterfront stockade. They encouraged the Oahuans to set fire to his structures and followed him to Kauai. (John Young later completed the fort at Honolulu.) They tried to haul down one of his Russian flags at Fort Alexander (Hanalei, Kauai). They were finally driven off by the bayonets of Kaumu-alii's troops.

Schäffer stayed on Kauai, building fortifications and waiting for a message of approval from his boss Baranov. But it never came. Instead, word of Schäffer's conspiracy against him reached Kamehameha at Kailua-Kona. In late 1816 a Russian exploring expedition, commanded by Lieutenant Otto von Kotzubue, reached Kailua.

Von Kotzubue told Kameha that the Russian government did *not* back Schäffer's grandiose plan. Kameha, stimulated by reports from the American traders, sent word to Kaumu-alii that if Schäffer were not immediately ousted, the Americans would send eight ships to drive him out. Kaumu evidently decided that an order from Kameha had a lot more authority than one from Schäffer. And perhaps also that it was more unpleasant to take orders from Schäffer than Kamehameha.

So in May, 1817, Schäffer was driven out of Waimea by a mob of irate Kauaians. And the menace of a larger, international involvement faded from Kamehameha's horizon.

Kameha gave thanks to his gods. He had remained devoutly religious through all his years. When Lieutenant Kotzubue stopped with him, in 1816, Kamehameha embraced a god image in a heiau. Then, Kotzubue reports, the King explained:

"These are our gods, whom I worship. Whether I do right or wrong, I do not know. But I will continue to follow my faith, which cannot be wicked as it commands me never to do evil."

Years earlier, in 1794, when Vancouver had offered to send a missionary to instruct him in the Christian religion, Vancouver says that Kamehameha answered: "These are my gods. They are gods with mana. Through them, I gained control of the government and became supreme chief."

In the last years at Kailua, a devout Yankee skipper asked why Kameha did not follow the only true God, that of the Christians. Kameha told the Yankee that if he would jump off a cliff, then he would stand by to see if his God saved him. Naturally, the zealot did not have enough zeal for the experiment.

In 1818, still venturesome about trade, Kameha decided that he would send his own ship to Canton with a load of sandalwood. He bought a new ship, renamed her the *Kaahumanu*, loaded her with sandalwood, and sent her forth under Captain Alexander Adams.

But the venture turned out to be a complete bust. Adams came back with an empty ship, without profit or the load of Chinese luxuries which Kameha expected. The captain had a complete hard-luck story, starting with the refusal of the Chinese authorities to recognize the Hawaiian flag.

One benefit came to Hawaii from the trip. Hearing of the heavy fees demanded by the Canton authorities, Kamehameha im-

mediately imposed a tax of $60 on every vessel entering the Hono-
lulu outer harbor, and $8 more for entrance to the inner.

In 1818, another Russian explorer, Captain Golovnin, visited
Kailua, and wrote of Kamehameha: "He is still strong, active,
temperate and sober. He does not use liquor or eat to excess."

But the next year, despite his vaunted good health and strength,
Kameha slipped into a nagging illness. No one knows what it was.
We know that it lasted at least a month, possibly a good deal more
than that.

At first, the king seemed only slightly ill. He was attended by
his kahunas, bathed in the kahunas' first panacea, seawater, and
fed herbs and a diet free of certain often-contaminated seafoods.
The usual chants and meles were sung. It is more than possible
that it was a common cold that started the trouble. For ordinary
colds, little more than an annoyance to Europeans, could be fatal
to Pacific islanders. The Polynesians, Melanesians and Micronesians
had never built up immunities to the ordinary minor maladies of
the Europeans.

Kameha called for his sacred son, Liholiho, who was now
twenty-one years old, and Queen Kaahumanu. In accordance with
Liholiho's burning kapu, Liholiho's head had to be above Kameha's
at all times, and the king had to remove any clothing above the
waist so that his upper body was bare in the presence of the
Heavenly One.

Kameha, not suffering any diminishment of his superior mental
acuity, was thoroughly aware by now that Liholiho's cerebral
ability was little more than average, perhaps not even that. But the
king's beloved and fiery Kaahumanu would serve as regent if
Kameha died, and bring along like a mother the handsome, if
slow, Heavenly One so that eventually he would learn something
of statecraft. Kamehameha had several times discussed this with
Kaahumanu. If Kameha died, Liholiho was to be king. But Kaahumanu would be the kahina-nui, a kind of co-ruler.

Kameha had been much aware of Liholiho's fondness for wine
and intoxicating spirits. The Sacred Son had of course learned the

addiction, and many other European customs, from the Haoles. By this time, many of the Alii had also found it in many ways more pleasant (and certainly easier to arrange) than chewing the awa. Kameha too had gone through a slight bout with the Haole firewater in the early 1790s. But his most loyal and closest Haole friend, John Young (who was a devout Christian and did not drink), had counseled him against imbibing that extra glass of rum or okole hau. Since that time, Kameha had been very temperate about his use of the fermented grape or distilled grain.

Liholiho, however, enjoyed endless parties well lubricated with the Haoles' favorite oil. And Kaahumanu had a similar fondness for the magic water that makes the knees weak. In fact, when Kaahumanu's love affair with her ward, the nineteen-year-old Ka-niho-nui, had come to light, Kaahumanu blamed the Haole firewater for her involvement. And Kameha had observed that her fondness had continued. So she could hardly be counted on to correct Liholiho's addiction. Kameha would have to count on the young man's kahu, or his leading "Foreigner," the same John Young who had eliminated his own interest in the magic water. He had already talked to Young, Olohana, about Liholiho's problem.

It seems likely that this early in his illness, Kameha had a presentiment that it might be his last. He summoned his sacred wife Keopuolani and asked her to bring along his second sacred heir, Kau-ike-aouli (later Kamehameha III). This child was now five years old. Like Liholiho he was exceedingly well-formed and physically attractive, and he seemed even at the age of five to be a brighter, more responsive child than his brother.

Kameha again removed his upper clothing, and keeping his head low, lay on his back so that in accordance with the kapus, the Third Kamehameha could sit on his chest and play with him.

Kamehameha was always content to be visited by his children, especially the sacred ones. He called them his grandchildren because they seemed so much younger than he. Now he was cheered and his illness temporarily seemed to recede. He called for John Young, his Foreigner, and Hoa-pili, his closest Hawaiian counselor, to consult with him. At this time, Hoa-pili was the closest of the Hawaiian chiefs to him—a massive muscular young man who looked like his father, Kameeiamoku, the late, hot-tempered half-brother of Kahekili.

The name Hoa-pili, meaning "closest friend," was Kameha's designation of this son of Kameeiamoku. Hoa-pili's birth name was Ulu-mahe-ihe (Ooloo-mahay-eehay). If Kahekili had been Kameha's father (a possibility which he probably no longer admitted even to himself), then Kameeiamoku was Kamehameha's uncle and Hoa-pili his first cousin.

Now, Kameha had a long discussion with both of these "closest friends," and with his usual single-minded mental vigor, he attacked the problems closest to his heart: the upbringing of Kamehameha III, the drinking problem of Kameha II, the mechanism needed so that Kaahumanu could function as a regent with ample authority but with some check on her impetuosity.

Hoa-pili brought up a problem of which Kameha had been tolerantly aware. It was much better that a Hawaiian close to Kameha should mention it, rather than "Kamehameha's Foreigner," Olohana. Hoa-pili said: "You know, Sire, that your soaring, turning, twisting bird [the meaning of the name Kaahumanu] has not always followed the letter of the kapus."

Kameha snapped dead alert, his silver-crowned, clear-cut head turned, his still near-black eyes focused sharply on Hoa-pili. "Yes? I know this, Hoa-pili. But are you speaking of more than one kapu?"

Hoa-pili knew that the searchlight of Kameha's maximum concentration was upon him and that he must be exact and explicit. Close friend or not, he was now subject to the demanding scrutiny of this absolute monarch. Kameha's whim could end his life in a moment.

"No, Pai'ea. I mean only the eating kapus."

Kameha seemed relieved, suddenly almost benign again. "I have known about several times when she has transgressed the kapus, especially the kapu against eating with men."

He turned to Olohana and again the faint suggestion of a smile crossed his lips. "From the first visit of the Haoles, there has been a strain on many of the customs of our ancestors."

Olohana's wedge-shaped brown face creased in a smile. "A strain on many of ours, as well, Sire."

"You are right, Olohana. We must—what is your word?—compromise."

He turned to Hoa-pili. "That is true, except among our own people. With us, kapus must be observed. For our own good."

For a second, a look almost of softness lit his battered warrior's face. He turned back to Hoa-pili.

"But with my soaring, twisting bird, of course we must be patient. She will always come back to being sensible, after she has made her flight."

Hoa-pili smiled in good nature, but not without a flash of that warrior's temper for which his father and grandfather were famous.

"Yes, Sire. Provided that her flight of fancy does not carry her too far from sense."

Kameha's temper flared in response. His face darkened. "Remember, you are speaking of the Queen!"

Kamehameha's Haole, Olohana, who had seen many previous combustions of the temper in both Kamehameha and Kameeiamoku, smiled again.

"Comrades! You must stop speaking as if the King were gone to the shades and Kaahumanu were already regent. This is only a slight sickness."

That intervention removed the tension of the moment. Both Hawaiian faces lightened. And Hoa-pili's temper had totally subsided.

"Of course," he said. "And in the future, in the time when Liloliho is Kamehameha II and Kaahumanu is regent, I will do as you say, Pai'ea."

But the optimism of Olohana was not justified by fact. Kameha became feverish, his unnamed malady grew worse, his breathing grew congested. The kahunas became alarmed, and insisted that he be carried to the expanded Kailua Heiau for Kane, the god of long life, to absorb some of the temple's mana.

Meanwhile another priest, Kua-ka-mauna, voiced the demand that human sacrifices were required. A new heiau of ohia wood, the tree which was particolored red and brown like the mountain apple, was put up for Ku-kaili-moku. In the usual ceremony of seeking favorable omens from Ku, pig sacrifices were made, and meles and specific prayers for Kameha beseeched Ku's intercession. But the feathers on the head of the god image did not stand out as if electrically shocked, to indicate that he wanted a human sacrifice.

The kahunas waited for further signs from Ku. He might still fly to a kahuna's shoulder as a final sign that he wanted the sacrifice.

The people of Kameha's capital town of Kailua, Kona, heard the stories of proposed human sacrifice. They left town in large numbers.

And Kameha, with his usual decisiveness, forbade the whole procedure of the human offering. He said cryptically, indicating Liholiho, "Men are sacred to the Chief."

This not only canceled the move to make the highest sacrifices in a move of desperation to save Kameha; it also indicated quite clearly that Kameha had already resigned himself to dying and that he already thought of Liholiho as the king.

From then on, Kamehameha went steadily downhill. Hoa-pili summoned Billy Pitt and Marin (Manini) from a visit to Oahu. Manini knew a little of medicine as he did of a broad spectrum of other skills. He had several other times cured ailments of the king.

But Manini's services did not help. Neither did the best efforts of all the kahunas. Kameha grew weaker and weaker and he was having trouble sometimes with breathing.

The chiefs and kahunas (and Liholiho) had moved him to two new houses specially built to represent the Pua (male) and Kapo (female) principles. There was a belief among several kahunas and family members that mana which would heal the sick would be generated in large quantities if these two divinities were assuaged. Kameha did not resist being carried to the new dwelling, but the treatment did not help. In fact, he grew worse. After three days in the new venue, the kahunas took him back to his old sleeping house.

By this time, early May, 1819, Kamehameha's officialdom and his friends had come from all over the islands. The word had gone out everywhere that the Old Man was dying.

On the afternoon of May 7, according to Marin, the tide rose to a freakish high, six feet above normal, and the water was an odd red color. This Red Tide, caused by the presence of millions of aweo-weo, a small red fish, was popularly supposed to portend the impending death of a chief. Kameha, weak as he was, saw it too, and prepared for his death. So did his Alii. That day, a messenger sent to Molokai to consult with a famed kahuna on Kamehameha's prospects for life or death, had returned with the message:

"When the night of Hoku [full moon] comes, the Spirit will return to the gods of his ancestors." And that very night, May 7–8, was to be the night of the Hoku.

All day long on the 7, the Alii, the kahunas, all the court followers clustered around Kameha's home buildings. The pahus beat all afternoon, and the chanting of the meles was unending. All of the regular workaday life of the area had halted. That night, beside the never-ending sound of the sea at Kailua, the chanting of meles and the distant beat of the pahus, and in the flickering light of koa-lamps and the ever-attendant stars, Kameha's foremost courtiers and family gathered by the side of his couch to hear his final words of counsel.

Kameha, however, was laboring for life and breath. He managed no words at all and one of the courtiers, Kai-iki-o-ewa, finally dared to speak: "We are all here. Your younger brothers, your chiefs, your Foreigner [John Young]. Give us a word."

Kameha managed an answer: "Why?"

"As a saying for us," said Kai-iki-o-ewa.

Kameha thought and struggled for strength and air, then he said: "I have given you—the greatest good: peace. And a kingdom which—is all one—a kingdom of all the islands."

John Young bent over, embraced him and rubbed noses with the dying chief. Hoa-pili came to him and whispered in his ear that he would carry out his promises and hide his bones well so that only the stars would know. Kamehameha spoke to all the courtiers, relatives and friends, and motioned impatiently with his arm to indicate they should go. He said: "That is all. Pau." And they shuffled out of the room. Only Kaahumanu stayed, waiting beside his couch.

But death did not come for hours. Kaahumanu held his hand and talked to him. Yet he was barely conscious.

At midnight, under the mellow disk of the Hoku moon, the kahunas took him again to the eating house. But once he had reached it, he began to pant for breath.

They took him back to the sleeping house, but from then on he was unconscious. His heart was beating still, but he reacted to nothing. And at two in the morning, May 8, 1819, he breathed his last.

The crowds, as usual with the death of a great chief or chiefess, ran wild in the vicinity. Some beat out their grief by knocking out their teeth. Some burned houses, and made unrestrained, frantic love to any women they could see. None, as far as is known, killed himself in his attempt to make a memorial to the death agony of the king. The old extravagance of mo-epu-u, suicide for a master or husband, had been fading away as the impact of the Haole culture grew.

His chief courtier, Hoa-pili, after Kamehameha's body had been reduced to bones in the kahunas' earthern oven, took the remains and hid them by night in a cave along the Kona coast.

Liholiho went away for about a week while the kahunas purified the king's capital of the defilement of death. Then he came back and donned his most splendid British uniform, a red coat

trimmed with gold lace. But over this he wore his Hawaiian warrior's cloak of golden feathers, and golden helmet to match. Thus
he was, like Kaumu-alii of Kauai on his peace mission to Kameha
in 1810, a living symbol of the blending of European and
Polynesian cultures.

Taking two chiefs with him to carry his kahili, his kapu sticks
and the other badges of his rank, he went to the rocky Kailua
coast where a throng of thousands were gathered for the unique
coronation ceremonies. There, Queen Kaahumanu was to make
the investiture.

Kaahumanu was waiting in her most splendid European costume, surrounded by a bright bouquet of royal women in their
best finery.

She said: "O Divine One, hear me and I will make known
the will of your father. Before you are the chiefs of your father,
this is your land, these are your guns. But you and I share the
rule of the land."

To this, Liholiho bowed assent, and he assumed the title of
Kamehameha II. Kaahumanu became kahina-nui. With her taking
of the role, the post was vastly enlarged from the appointment
which Billy Pitt had held. Now the kahina-nui, or Prime Minister's
post, assumed the status of regent, by far the dominant one of the
two roles invested with the supreme authority in the Hawaiian
kingdom.

And within six months, the strong-willed Kaahumanu had
managed a drastic, revolutionary measure which remedied one of
her chronic complaints against the Old Order; the Order, that is,
before the coming of the Haoles. Many of her Haole friends had
argued that a good many of the kapus were senseless. She began
a brave campaign to abolish some of the kapus, especially those
most annoying to Hawaiian women, prescribing that women
must never eat with men and that several delightful foods—pork,
coconuts, bananas, shark meat—were forever kapu.

Kaahumanu remembered well that when her nineteen-year-old
ward Ka-niho-nui was sacrificed for kapu infringement, it was
officially for eating with Kaahumanu, not for being abed with

her. Now she was making a heroic move which would have given her great prominence in the Women's Liberation movement of today.

She had often mentioned to Haole friends that the kapus on women's eating were especially galling. As soon as she gained her position of supreme power, she began planning to abolish the whole kapu system.

She had a staunch supporter in Keopuolani, the Sacred Wife of the late Kamehameha the Great. When Kaahumanu tried to enlist Kamehameha II (Liholiho) in the movement, he hesitated. Finally he said he could not support her. This was a surprise to Kaahumanu. Generally, he had been sympathetic to the heretical beliefs of the Haoles, who were impatient with the pantheistic, idol-worshipping and kapu-ridden Hawaiian religion. On the other hand, through much of his life he had been schooled by his Hawaiian elders that the kapu system was necessary for the smooth functioning of the Hawaiian society and the Alii system. Now he was torn between two opposite schools of thought.

Immediately, to lend her strength to Kaahumanu's suggestion, Keopuolani summoned her second sacred son, the five-year-old Kau-ike-aouli (later Kamehameha III), and ate with him. Liholiho knew of this and did not punish either woman.

Kaahumanu and Keopuolani both kept up their pressure on Liholiho to abolish the kapus. So did his latest kahu, Hewa-hewa nui, and his Haole friends. Hewa-hewa was young and he tried to maintain an open mind about the vast new world of ideas and materialistic inventions in the vast Haole domain so far beyond the seas. Many of the Haoles were devout practitioners of the religion of Christ. Most had ill-concealed disdain for the paganism of the Hawaiians. They even talked about bringing missionaries to preach their religion. It was odd that almost all of the Haoles were vehement in their condemnation of the Hawaiian religion. The devout ones naturally opposed it as an abomination. But curiously enough, the most determined sots and reprobates generally agreed. This friendly agreement of the two moral extremes was understandable, but thoroughly hypocritical.

Hewa-hewa did not know that already a Protestant missionary group was being prepared to sail from Boston in the brig *Thaddeus* to convert the Hawaiian heathens. At any rate, Hewa-hewa, spurred by Kaahumanu and her Haole friends, urged Liholiho that all kapus should be abolished.

Word of all this became known and a conservative group under an Alii named Kekua-o-kalani began to organize an army to resist. They also planned to kill all the Haoles, for the Haoles had been responsible for this wave of sacrilege, and the loss of many of the old Hawaiian ways. And by this time, the Haole group and even Hewa-hewa had counseled him that not only the kapus, but the heiaus too should be destroyed.

By November, 1819, the two queens had persuaded Kamehameha II to make a public demonstration of violating the eating kapus. At a Kailua banquet, Kamehameha II left his table and went to dine with the women. The guests were astonished, many shocked, and they clapped their hands and cried "Ai noa! Free eating!" The eating kapu was broken.

After the meal, the king proclaimed that all kapus were abolished and most startling of all, that all heiaus and the god images should be destroyed. A wave of desecration and looting of the temples swept through the islands. Often priceless god images were used for firewood.

It should be parenthetically noted that most of the kahunas and the heiaus escaped destruction. Most Hawaiians kept to their old faith, but the eating kapus, at least, were demolished so that women could eat with men. Ai noa, free eating, was a fact.

And the Hawaiian religion and the kapu system had been dealt a severe body blow. When the American missionaries arrived four months later, in April, 1820, they found a ready ground for their preachments. The recent collapse of the Hawaiian religion they attributed to divine intercession in their behalf. Years later when Kaahumanu became a convert, the missionaries saw in this another sign that God was helping them directly.

Now, in early November, 1819, in the wake of Kamehameha II's (and Kaahumanu's) proclamations, no dire supernatural consequences ensued, as some conservative Hawaiians had predicted. Kamehameha II and Kaahumanu were not struck dead by thunderbolts. And even the goddess Pele was quiet. Not a single volcanic eruption occurred.

But the dissident, conservative element under Kekua-o-kalani broke into open revolt. They had massed a sizable force near Kailua and at Hamakua.

So Kamehameha II (advised and directed by Kaahumanu) sent a large army, well equipped with fresh cannons and rifles, against the rebels. They were soundly defeated at Kua-mo-o, half way between Kailua and Kaa-waloa. Both Kekua-o-kalani and his favorite wife were killed in the battle. The rest of the rebels were finished off in Hamakua.

And so, despite the new unity and peace which Kamehameha the Great had achieved, change, radical change, continued to be the order of the day, month and year for that new nation of Hawaii. The train of successive, decisive alterations started by the great conqueror and unifier continued in this odd combination of paradisiacal environment and fast-moving dynamism. This fortunately has remained her fate in the world's most unique and successful meeting place of East and West. Kamehameha the Great, the Polynesian giant and Napoleon of the Pacific, was the man who set it all in motion. He was a naturally selected Napoleon of the handsome Polynesian people of the Pacific, gifted also with the brainpower and will to put it all together in a state which is in many ways still oceans and generations ahead of the times.

⚎⚎ Bibliography

Adler, Jacob, *The Kamehameha Statue. Hawaiian Journal of History*, vol. III, 1969. Cathay Press, Hong Kong, 1969.

Ai'a, Kamaka Paea Kealii, *Kamehameha the Great*. Published by the author, Kamuela, 1966.

Anderson, Bern, *The Life and Voyages of Captain George Vancouver: Surveyor of the Sea*. University of Washington Press, Seattle, 1960.

Apple, Russell A., *Hawaiian Archeology Trails—From Steppingstones to Kerbstones*. Special Publication #53, Bishop Museum Press, Honolulu, 1965.

Beaglehole, J. C., *Cook the Navigator*. The Royal Society, Great Britain, 1969.

———, *Some Problems of Cook's Biographer. The Mariner's Mirror*, vol. 55, no. 4, Great Britain, 1969.

Bell, E., *Journal*. Ms. Alexander Turnbull Library, Wellington, New Zealand. Library, University of Hawaii.

Boom, Robert, *Colorful Hawaiian Fish*. Published by the author, Honolulu, 1971.

———, & Christensen, J. S., *Important Hawaiian Place Names*. Boom, Honolulu, 1969.

Buck, Peter H. (Te Rangi Hiroa), *Arts and Crafts of Hawaii*. Special Publication No. 45, Bishop Museum Press, Honolulu, 1957.

————, *Explorers of the Pacific: European and American Discoveries in Polynesia*. Special Publication #43, Bishop Museum Press, Honolulu, 1953.

Bushnell, O. A., *The Return of Lono*. University of Hawaii Press, Honolulu, 1971.

Butterfield, Alfred, *The Coral Reef*. Odyssey Press, New York, 1964.

Campbell, Archibald, *A Voyage Round the World: From 1806 to 1812*. University of Hawaii Press, Honolulu, 1967.

Cook, Captain, James, *Captain Cook's Voyages of Discovery*, ed. by John Barrow, F.R.S. Everyman, London, 1906.

————, *Journals of Captain James Cook on His Voyages of Discovery*. Cambridge University Press, New York, 1965.

————, *Journals of Captain James Cook*. 3 vols. Cambridge University Press, New York, 1955, 1967.

————, & King, J., *Voyage to the Pacific Ocean, 1776–1780*. 3 vols. London, 1784.

Cox, J. Halley, & Stasack, Edward, *Hawaiian Petroglyphs*. Special Publication #60, Bishop Museum Press, Honolulu, 1970.

Damon, Gertrude MacKinnon, *Moanalua Valley*. Moanalua Gardens Foundation, Honolulu, 1971.

Daws, Gavan, *Shoal of Time: A History of the Hawaiian Islands*. Macmillan, New York, 1968.

————, *Illustrated Atlas of Hawaii*, ed. by O. A. Bushnell. Island Heritage, Honolulu, 1970.

Department of Land & Natural Resources, *Historic Preservation*. 1969–70 Annual Report, State of Hawaii, 1971.

Dibble S., *History of the Sandwich Islands*. Lahainaluna, 1853.

Dixon, G., *Voyage around the World, 1785–1788*. London, 1789.

Elbert, Samuel H., *Spoken Hawaiian*. University of Hawaii Press, Honolulu, 1970.

Ellis, William, *Authentic Narrative of a Voyage, 1776–1780*. 2 vols. London, 1782.

————, *Polynesian Researches: Hawaii*. Tuttle, Tokyo, Rutland, Vt., 1969.

Emerson, Nathaniel B., *Unwritten Literature of Hawaii: The Sacred Songs of the Hula*. Tuttle, Tokyo, 1965.

Fornander, Abraham, *An Account of the Polynesian Race: Its Origin and Migrations* (three volumes in one). Tuttle, Tokyo, 1969.

Freund, Gordon, *Skin Diver's Guide to Hawaii*, ed. by R. "Bob" Collins, Honolulu.

Garanger, Jose, *Sacred Stones & Rites*. Société des Oceanistes Dossier, Paris, 1969.

Gosline, William A., & Brock, Vernon E., *Handbook of Hawaiian Fishes*. University of Hawaii Press, Honolulu, 1960.

Gwyther, John, *Captain Cook and the South Pacific: The Voyage of the Endeavor, 1768–1771*. Houghton Mifflin, Boston, 1954.

Hargreaves, Dorothy and Bob, *Tropical Trees of Hawaii*. Hargreaves Co., Kailua, Hawaii, 1964.

Hawaii Audubon Society, *Hawaii's Birds*. Audubon Society, Honolulu, 1967.

Holt, John Dominis, *Monarchy in Hawaii*. Bishop Estate, Honolulu, 1963.

Hubbard, Douglass H., & Bender, Vernon R., Jr., *Trailside Plants of Hawaii National Park*. Hawaii Natural History Association, Honolulu, 1960.

Ii, John Papa, *Fragments of Hawaiian History*. Bishop Museum Press, Honolulu, 1963.

Jourdain, P., Commandant, *Ancient Tahitian Canoes*. Société des Oceanistes Dossier, Paris, 1970.

Judd, Gerrit P., *Hawaii: A Students' Guide to Localized History*, ed. by Clifford L. Lord. Teachers College Press, Columbia University, New York, 1966.

Kamakau, S. M., *Ka Po'e Kahiko: The People of Old*. Special Publication #51, Bishop Museum Press, Honolulu, 1964.

———, *Ruling Chiefs of Hawaii*. The Kamehameha Schools Press, Honolulu, 1961.

Kamehameha Schools, *Ancient Hawaiian Civilization*. Tuttle, Tokyo, 1965.

King, James, *Journal*. Ms. Adm. 55/116. PRO, State of Hawaii Archives.

———, *Voyage to the Pacific Ocean*. London, 1784.

King Kamehameha I & Father Damien. U.S. Government Printing Office, 1970.

Kitson, Arthur, *Captain James Cook.* London, 1907.

Kotzubue, O. Von, *Voyage of Discovery, 1815–1818.* 3 vols. London, 1821.

Kuykendall, Ralph S., *The Hawaiian Kingdom*, vol. 1, *1778–1854: Foundation and Transformation.* University of Hawaii Press, Honolulu, 1938.

Kyselka, Will, *The Hawaiian Sky.* Pacific Books, Honolulu, 1971.

Law, J., *Journal.* Ms. Add Ms. 37327. Library, University of Hawaii.

Macdonald, Gordon A., & Kyselka, Will, *Anatomy of an Island.* Special Publication #55, Bishop Museum Press, Honolulu, 1967.

McAllister, J., *Archeology of Oahu.* Honolulu, 1933.

Malo, David, *Hawaiian Antiquities*, trans. from the Hawaiian by Dr. N. B. Emerson. Honolulu Gazette Co., Honolulu, 1903.

Mead, Margaret, & McClanahan, Preston, eds., "Peoples of the Pacific." *Journal of the American Museum of Natural History*, vol. 5, 1971. New York, 1971.

Meares, J., *Voyages Made in 1788–1789.* London, 1790.

Mellen, Kathleen D., *The Lonely Warrior: The Life and Times of Kamehameha the Great of Hawaii.* Hastings House, New York, 1949.

Mitchell, Donald D., *The King Kamehameha Memorial Statue.* Statuary Hall Commission, Honolulu, 1969.

Munro, George C., *Birds of Hawaii.* Tuttle, Tokyo, 1960.

Murdoch, Clare G., & Gotanda, Masae, eds. *Basic Hawaiiana.* Hawaii State Library, Honolulu, 1969.

Pacific Islands Year Book, 11th ed., Pacific Publications Pty., Ltd. Sydney, 1972.

Pole, James T., *Hawaii's First King.* Bobbs-Merrill, New York, 1959.

Portlock, N., *Voyage Around the World, 1785–1788.* London, 1789.

Pukui, Mary Kawena, & Elbert, Samuel H., *Hawaiian Dictionary: Hawaiian-English; English-Hawaiian.* University of Hawaii Press, Honolulu, 1971.

———. *Place Names of Hawaii.* University of Hawaii Press, Honolulu, 1966.

Roberts, Helen H., *Ancient Hawaiian Music*. Dover Publications, New York, 1967.

Rotar, Peter P., *Grasses of Hawaii*. University of Hawaii Press, Honolulu, 1968.

Samwell, D., *Journal*. Ms. Egerton 2592. State of Hawaii Archives.

Sinclair, Marjorie, "The Sacred Wife of Kamehameha I." *Hawaiian Journal of History*, vol. V, 1971. Cathay Press Ltd., Hong Kong, 1971.

Skelton, R. A., *Captain James Cook: After Two Hundred Years*. The British Museum, London, 1969.

St. Lawrence, Sister Mary, O.P., *Exploring Nature in Hawaii*. Books I, II, III, IV, VI, VII. Roman Catholic Diocese of Honolulu, 1955, 1958, 1959, 1961, 1962.

Sterns, Harold T., *Points of Geologic Interest in the Hawaiian Islands*. Pacific Books, Palo Alto, Calif., 1966.

Stewart, C. S., *Journal of a Residence in the Sandwich Islands*. University of Hawaii Press, Honolulu, 1970.

Suggs, Robert C., *The Island Civilizations of Polynesia*. New American Library, New York, 1960.

U.S. Department of the Interior, *Hawaii Volcanoes*. U.S. Government Printing Office, 1968.

Vancouver, G., *Voyage of Discovery to the North Pacific Ocean, 1790–1795*. 3 vols. London, 1798.

Villiers, Alan, *Captain Cook, the Seamen's Seaman*. Hodder & Stoughton, Great Britain, 1967.

Wyndette, Olive, *Islands of Destiny*. Tuttle, Tokyo, 1968.

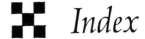

Index

THE WARRIOR KING

Glorious in war, powerful in peace, prodigious in love, and the most monumental figure in Hawaiian history, Kamehameha was the first Polynesian ruler to unite and rule *all* of the Hawaiian Islands. Swathed in ambiguous legends about his parentage, he displayed his future eminence early in adolescence by dislodging the massive and intractable black lava Naha Stone which, according to fable, could be lifted only by the man who was to become Hawaii's greatest king. As he grew to the massive height of six feet, six inches, his natural athletic and amorous prowess became more clearly marked, and Kamehameha came to epitomize the highest Hawaiian values of pure beauty, freedom and power. He alone had the vision, military skill and administrative acumen to triumph over the deadly rivalries that simmered upon these lush, fragrant islands.

With consummate skill, Richard Tregaskis again demonstrates his unique ability to transport the reader to another time and place. Colorful and expressive, his broad canvas accurately reflects the Hawaiian paradise that produced the heroic Kamehameha and formed the magnificent backdrop of his long and multidimensional life—his exciting career as leader and warrior, his tempestuous romances, his twenty-two wives and fifty children and his torrid, long-lasting marriage to the six-foot giantess Kaahumanu, his most beloved queen.

In cinematic detail, the author tells of the first European explorers—who were thought to be gods by the natives—and describes the vicious battles that erupted among neighboring chieftains: the fleets of canoes and hostile amphibious assaults attacks on cliffs, beaches and rock trimmed caves; hordes of malo-clad warriors locked in deadly hand-to-hand struggles in the midst of flying stones, daggers spears and the fire of European arms—all of which reaped a deadly toll in human blood. It was Kamehameha the Great—so called for his innovative use of the British cannon in the decisive Battle of Kepaniwa in the Iao Valley—who emerged as the supreme leader. Remaining faithful to the mores of Hawaiian culture and religion, he nevertheless united and reformed his homeland and brought about the adoption of many of the white man's customs.

Here is Kamehameha's story . . . the first full-length adult biography of Hawaii's greatest king.

RICHARD TREGASKIS, a renowned novelist and war correspondent, was the author of many highly successful books including *Guadalcanal Diary,* a Book-of-the-Month Club selection that was made into a movie; *Seven Leagues to Paradise,* a Literary Guild selection; *Vietnam Diary,* winner of the George Polk Award for Hazardous Reporting; *X-15 Diary;* and *John F Kennedy and PT-109,* a selection of both the Book-of-the-Month Club and the Landmark Series. Like Kamehameha, the six-foot, six-inch Tregaskis was a devotee of water sports, an ardent student of the military arts and a lover of Hawaii. He died in August 1973.

Falmouth Press